COLD TEA
AND TEARS

COLD TEA
AND TEARS

IT DID HAPPEN TO A DIETITIAN!

MARY FARMER

Matador
9 Priory Business Park
Kibworth Beauchamp
Leicester LE8 0RX, UK
Tel: (+44) 116 279 2299
Fax: (+44) 116 279 2277
Email: books@troubador.co.uk
Web: www.troubador.co.uk/matador

ISBN 978 1848766 549

British Library Cataloguing in Publication Data.
A catalogue record for this book is available from the British Library.

Cover illustration by John Rose

Typeset in 10.5pt Book Antiqua by Troubador Publishing Ltd, Leicester, UK
Printed and bound in the UK by TJ International, Padstow, Cornwall

Matador is an imprint of Troubador Publishing Ltd

DEDICATIONS

To the memory of my beloved Mother, who from the tender age of 70 was embarrassed at the amount of money that "us dratted olds" cost the country. She was my best friend. At 90 years old, she kept her dignity, her wonderful sense of humour and her marbles to the very end.
I miss her greatly.

To my dear husband who came up with the title, whose patience was sorely tried by my agonising over this whole project and who confessed that he "would be amazed" to see me in print.

And to my good friend, Alex, who has made his meteoric rise as a well respected medical journalist and author with the speed of a high velocity bullet, at the same time as working as a junior doctor in the NHS and training in Psychiatry. You unwittingly inspired me to write.

DISCLAIMER

Mary Farmer is a pseudonym.

All the scenarios are based on true facts but characters, names and geographical locations are fictitious to protect anonymity.

This book is not in any way endorsed or authorised by the NHS, by The Health Professions Council or the author's former professional body, The British Dietetic Association. Nor are any of the views and opinions expressed here reflected by these august bodies. They are entirely based on personal experiences.

CONTENTS

INTRODUCTION

If you are idle, be not solitary; if you are solitary, be not idle

Samuel Johnson, "Letter to Boswell"

"So what did you do before you retired?" asked James, a fellow guest at a friend's ruby anniversary party. He lovingly twirled his wine glass in his hands, admiring the velvety, plum-coloured, mini vortex. We were soaking up wine and sun in equal measure and had admired the prettiest garden in Surrey, our senses equally stimulated and soothed by the warm still air, clear blue sky, freshly mown grass, exquisite floral perfumes, merry chatter, laughter and the gentle tinkling of wine glasses. Tomatoes in the greenhouse blushed gently towards their eponymous red. It was a perfect English summer afternoon. We had exchanged pleasantries and jokes and were feeling suitably replete from the exquisite buffet, enjoying the companionship and camaraderie around us. The conversation moved on to more serious, sobering topics.

I mulled it over. It's a funny thing – retirement. One day, you are a professional person. You have a badge with a logo and your name and status on it to remind you and your colleagues who you are: "Mary Farmer, Senior Dietitian". You are "Somebody". You are respected. People take you seriously. They do what you advise – well, mostly – and best of all, you get a monthly salary.

Then, the next day, you are simply a grey-haired, invisible little old lady or gent, melting into the background of that misty, silver cloud of humanity labelled "The Over-60s".

1

"Well..." I ventured, "I used to work in the NHS as a community dietitian."

"Ah...I *see*..." with great emphasis on the "see". He focused closely on me. The wine glass twirled more vigorously, as he reflected on this revelation.

I had been finding out about James' "previous". He had been an official tea-taster in Kenya but now worked as a practice manager in a GP surgery. I could see him mentally deciding in which box to place me. His expression changed from puzzlement to enlightenment. He had found it.

"So you advise people how to lose weight then?"

"Umm...not exactly...well...not all the time..."

His eyebrows shot up to the quizzical position. He rested his wine glass on the table, tilted his Panama hat and turned his head towards me so that his spectacles glinted in the sun.

"OK then – tell me..."

So James, this is it. Peek between the pages of a very ordinary and 'umble dietitian's diary and all will be revealed! And I hope it shows that dietitians do a lot more than just help people get thinner!

It is also a potted and very personal history of a particular branch of dietetics. Not every dietitian would tell the same story. They are used to "multi-tasking" and their many skills allow them to work in a wide variety of settings. This story is just about one of them.

DID I HAVE LUNCH?

Sometimes I just sits and thinks. Sometimes I just sits.

Attributed to "Punch"

It is a hot summer's day. Unusually and REALLY hot. The sun beats through the many windows of our new office in the centre of Calmershire, which our team of dietitians share with district nurses, speech and language and occupational therapists and physiotherapists.

I am sitting at my desk – well, I like to think it is mine, although recently, now that we are in a new building, the Powers-That-Be have decreed that we should "hot desk" – a scenario that we all just as hotly resist. It is relatively rare that we actually manage to sit down after having made visits, been to care homes to train staff, or attended meetings, training events or promotions for the latest nutritional supplements, tube-feeds or thickening agents. To snatch a few minutes time for paper work but then find that there is nowhere to sit and that one's filing cabinets are out of reach is decidedly frustrating.

The chair is of synthetic material and although I have cotton underwear, I can feel myself sticking to the squab. Oh God! I hope there isn't a little damp patch when I leave – gross! There is enough of that in the care homes that we visit – and there, it's not condensation or sweat (See: "'Elf and Safety"). There are no blinds (too expensive) and I can barely see the screen of my laptop, as it is so bright. My sweaty finger sticks on the touch-pad as I try to write a report, having observed lunch being

3

served at one of the care homes – that was an eye-opener (see more under "Age Shall Not Wither Them") – and then catch up with letters to the GPs of patients I have seen. I give up the challenge and leave, not daring to glance back at my chair. It is time to make some visits.

It is cool in the end-of-terrace cottage, where Queenie sits in her chair in the little sitting room, gazing out of the window into the garden with a faraway look in her eyes, or with them closed, lost in her own world. The quote, "*Sometimes I just sits and thinks. Sometimes I just sits*", comes to mind. Her arms are folded defensively across her body, her head is bent forwards and her bare legs are crossed. She is wearing a loose top and a crumpled, knee-length black skirt, which fits badly round her oh-so-thin little body. Her short, straight, grey hair has been combed and would hang limply round her face but she intermittently runs her hands through it, causing it to stick out in all directions. My hands twitch, as I fight the urge to comb it gently back into place. Occasionally there is a flicker in her eyes when she sees the birds at the feeder in the garden or when the budgie twitters in his cage, but this is fleeting. More often, there is puzzlement and bewilderment when spoken to, and she looks to her husband for reassurance.

Queenie is in her late 70s and has advanced dementia. She has "forgotten" how to look after herself, how to chew, how to speak, how to walk or to wash, or to take herself to the lavatory. Occasionally, she does try to walk without assistance, only to tumble and fall. Her bare legs, which end in a pair of battered black slippers, are covered with scars and bruises. Sometimes she sports a jaunty sticking plaster on her forehead. She takes only liquid food, which has to be offered frequently. Her husband, Johnny, is her main carer and is a true saint. He has time and eyes only for her. He is constantly at her side, always cheerful, chatting away and telling jokes. Occasionally, Queenie mumbles unintelligibly in response. To him, she is still his childhood sweetheart whom he married, when the ship on which he was serving during the war sprang a leak, and the crew were given extra leave. He saw his advantage and took it! Looking after her is no chore to him, even though by the time that I met them, he had just turned 80. With a little bit of help from their daughter, he also looks after the house, washing, cooking, cleaning and gardening.

I am one of a team of community dietitians working in Calmershire. We have a large area to patrol and Queenie is on my list of home visits.

"We manage," says Johnny cheerfully, in response to my question as to how they are doing. "We manage…"

When I 'phone to make my routine appointments, he never sounds rushed, just always welcoming. "Come whenever you like, my dear," he says. "Any time to suit you."

I pass through the kitchen to the living room. There are the remains of a meal on the table. I worry that Johnny may not be eating enough. Half a cup of cold tea sits with it. It has slopped onto the table. Did Johnny have to put it down quickly to attend to Queenie? The washing patiently awaits its turn for the machine in a wicker basket. An upright hoover stands to attention near the door, ready to burst into action. Occasionally, I bring my dog to work and today is one of those days. She would normally stay in the car.

"Do bring her in," says Johnny. Queenie likes that and there is a little spark as she bends forward to stroke her, murmuring and mumbling gently as she does so.

I visit once a month in order to monitor Queenie's weight and to ensure that she at least doesn't lose any more than she already has. Hovering at around seven stone (44.5kg), this is marginal. Together, her husband and I help her into the portable "sit-on" weighing scales that I bring with me.

"Come on Queenie, love," urges Johnny, as he puts his arms around her. "I'm just going to help you sit in this chair."

There is no resistance on Queenie's part – just a general helplessness and a residual wish to please her husband and to do as he asks. Her puzzled expression reminds me of a dog in training, which wants to please his master but cannot comprehend the command.

Keeping her weight and general nutrition stable, means offering Queenie highly nutritious liquids every hour, as she takes only a few sips at a time. This requires absolute dedication on the part of her husband, as she refuses them from anyone else, even her daughter. We have been through all the usual attempts to help her eat and drink and she is now totally dependent on the special drinks that are prescribed by her doctor. Johnny tells me that the pharmacist inadvertently sent the wrong flavour, which Queenie doesn't like any more. I agree to write to the GP and change the prescription.

Queenie's weight is steady. A good day! I congratulate them both. We chat a little more, trying to include Queenie in the conversation. Johnny is originally from Lincolnshire and worked with the railways, as an engineer. He tells me about his job but Queenie makes no effort to appear to listen or join in. The dog leans against her quietly and comforts her. Eventually, we make another date and say "Goodbye". There are more home visits on my list for that afternoon.

At last, I go back to the office, where I write my report for Queenie's kindly GP and request more special drinks of the right flavour. We both know these are extremely costly. I argue that they are good value for calories. They are keeping Queenie in her own home and out of hospital. That's about as good as it gets.

I finally drive home, reflecting on the day: Queenie is often in my thoughts. Over the many visits I have made, I have become fond of them both and am lost in admiration of Johnny's patience. "There by the grace of God, go I," I mutter to myself. Makes you sit and think, doesn't it?

Caring for someone who has advanced dementia, watching the pitiful, gradual deterioration of someone you love, seeing the very essence of that person fade, is one of the hardest things to do, especially if this is a close member of the family.

As the author, Terry Pratchett, says of Alzheimer's disease: *"It sweeps you away from yourself."*

"We face a tsunami of Alzheimer's," he warns, after revelations are made that the labour government spent less on Alzheimer's research than the cost of building one mile of motorway.[1]

British experts estimate that there will be 65.7 million cases with diseases of dementia in 2030 and that this could nearly double again 20 years after this. Many people believe that dementia is an inevitable part of ageing, rather than a disease, which can be reasonably managed with early diagnosis and treatment. Early diagnosis seems to be key and it has been recently reported that a simple eye test might just do that. NICE guidelines originally ruled that doctors were unable to prescribe the necessary medication early enough. Their hands were tied. The reason given was cost but at around £2.80 a day, was this too much to extend quality of life and keep people out of hospital or care homes? Luckily, active and energetic campaigning, together with the results of new research, resulted in a recent *volte fäs* by NICE: those in the early stages and with mild symptoms of the disease will now be able to have the medication they need.

Many residents in care homes have dementia or Alzheimer's disease to a greater or lesser degree. Shocking reports have emerged that many of these "lost people" are subjected to physical abuse and, unbelievably, these "serious untoward incidents" have

[1] Smith, R. 2009. Terry Pratchett: Britain facing tsunami of Alzheimer's disease. *The Daily Telegraph Online.* September 22nd Available at:
http://www.telegraph.co.uk/health/healthnews/6214019/Terry-Pratchett-Britain-facing-tsunami-of-Alzheimers-disease.html

risen sharply. These include residents being tied to their chairs to stop them wandering; being left on the floor if they fall; not being fed or hydrated adequately; not being kept clean and dry or worse, being administered "chemical coshes" – anti-psychotic drugs – to keep them quiet. Many of them die as a result of the overuse of these, the numbers being estimated at around 2,000 a year. It is reckoned that four out of five such residents are given anti-psychotics inappropriately, which, the Alzheimer's Society estimates to total around 100,000 dementia residents in care homes. Apart from the ethics of forcing dangerous drugs on vulnerable people, one side effect of these is to triple the risk of having a stroke. John Burstow, the minister for care services, has been campaigning for years against such misuse of drugs and now plans are unveiled to improve all aspects of dementia care, which include further training for doctors and nurses, as well as restricting the use of unjustified anti-psychotic medicines.

Some residents whom I have visited in care homes are so drugged up that they are too sleepy to eat or drink. No wonder then, that many of them are very poorly nourished, which in turn paradoxically "feeds" their addled and tangled brains. A text from my trusty college tome pops into my head: *"The three D's – dementia, diarrhoea and dermatitis – are significant indications of Niacin (vitamin B3) deficiency ..."* and, I would suggest, probably a lot more.[2]

A typical scene in residential and nursing homes is one in which all the residents sit around the edges of the day room, staring vacantly into space, with nothing better to do than wait for their number to be called from above.

The BBC's revealing programme about dementia featuring Sir Gerry Robinson, showed that there are alternatives.[3] A key to

[2] Passmore, R. and Eastwood, M.A. 1986, *Human Nutrition and Dietetics, 8th Edition.* Churchill Livingstone

[3] BBC2. 2009. *Can Gerry Robinson Fix Dementia Care Homes?* Broadcast December 8th and 15th. Available at: www.bbc.co.uk/programmes/b00pf0s2/episodes/2009

changing such a scene is the qualitative observation audit, as pioneered by David Sheard of Dementia Care Matters. A member of staff masquerades as one of the residents, sitting with them just as they do, noting requests and activities (or not!) of both the residents and staff. A pattern emerges that can then be discussed and acted upon.

Adequate feeding of dementia patients is beset with riddles and detective work. One patient I met would only eat red food – food colouring is a useful asset here! Some may steal from others. The gentleman in question had been a prisoner of war – his food had been stolen. Now he was getting his "retaliation in first", albeit somewhat belatedly! Some eat sweet food only. Sugar on minced beef or scrambled eggs sounds bizarre but if it is enjoyed and eaten, does it really matter? Others won't sit still and need finger foods to nibble as they pace constantly up and down. Because of this, weight loss is a constant worry but it also seems that the very dementia itself is a calorie-demanding condition. Many refuse food altogether. Is this their last bastion of some kind of control over their own lives? Have they forgotten how to eat? Or is this their way of giving up altogether?

Force-feeding, in any shape or form, is not the answer. Like many others, I was shocked to read recently of the discovery that thousands of old people were having feeding-tubes inserted if they want to be cared for in a home, "because it is easier for the staff". Insertion of a feeding-tube is a decision that is not taken lightly (see "Tubes and Twiddly Bits") and in such circumstances is beset with ethical problems.

In their own homes, dementia patients do not always get the treatment they need. The case of one Harry Denton comes to mind. It was reported that he was ignored by his carers for five days and had no food or water.[4] When he failed to open the

---

[4] Unnamed reporter. 2009. Pensioner with dementia died after carers failed to visit. "News in Brief", *The Daily Telegraph*. August 12th

door, political correctness took over. No one tried to gain access or alert relatives. He had collapsed. Eventually he was taken to hospital but died soon afterwards.

We hear, all too often, that dementia patients are "being failed by the NHS", even when they are in hospital. Not only this, but some patients are said to be discharged in a worse state, both physically and mentally, than when they were admitted. In his investigation into care homes, Sir Gerry Robinson described some of the care as "downright appalling". Much of this has been attributed to lack of specialist training and knowledge amongst nursing staff.

Allowing others to enter into that shadowy world, where Alzheimer's dominates, is heart-breakingly detailed by John Bayley, husband of Iris Murdoch, the author, in his book, *Iris*.[5] Their apparent separate lives made for a good marriage but, once Iris became unwell, it was *"designed into a new marriage"*, which necessitated them becoming much closer. *"We could not do otherwise"*, he wrote, and described it as a *"certain comic irony"* that, after more than 40 years together, their marriage had morphed into something different. He did not cherish it: it just happened, *"like the Alzheimer's"*.

His patience, like Johnny's, was unbounded. Except on one occasion: something that Iris was doing was caused him to snap. He described his rage as *"instant and total, seeming to come out of nowhere"*. He was astonished and ashamed at himself how that rage produced *"another person"*, which repelled him, even though he recognised it as himself but speaking with another voice.

Anger seems to be a way of continuing to deny that there is anything wrong. But it is rage and anger, not at the patient but at the *"demon"*, as Terry Pratchett names it, of Alzheimer's itself.

---

[5] Bayley, J. 1999. *Iris: A Memoir of Iris Murdoch*. Abacus.

The reaction of bewilderment, consternation and fear that such a rage produces is too much. Misery, self-loathing, remorse, contrition and the need to return to the strange but now habitual "normality" overloads the carer. The patient's dementia can be a living hell, not just for the individual but for the partner and family too.

The good thing is that more people are "coming out" about caring for spouses and family members who have this crippling and cruel condition. John Suchet (journalist, broadcaster and brother of David, the actor) has recently told his story about his wife, Bonnie, while Andrea Gillies, an award-winning writer, details how she thought she could care for her mother. Both have bravely and honestly set down their experiences in their recent publications.[6] [7] Other authors have used their imagination, intelligence and empathy to craft stories, which make for grim reading, such as Samantha Harvey's *The Wilderness Years* (Vintage, 2009). Such heroic and unflinching accounts not only tug at the heartstrings and elicit compassion but also help us to understand what it's *really* like, living with Alzheimer's.

The previous labour government, under Gordon Brown, initiated a campaign to encourage greater awareness of dementia.[8] Let's hope that this reached staff in those NHS hospitals that failed badly in their care. This is a five-year plan, which was launched in February 2009 and is the first of its kind for dementia. £150 million had been put aside for it. But will dementia patients (or "pre-dementia" individuals, which

---

[6] Suchet, J. 2010. *My Bonnie: How Dementia Stole the Love of My Life.* Harper Collins
[7] Gillies, A. 2010. *Keeper: Living with Nancy. A Journey into Alzheimer's.* Short Books.
[8] Department of Health, 2009. *Living well with dementia: A National Dementia Strategy.* February 3rd. Available online at:
http://www.dh.gov.uk/en/Publicationsandstatistics/Publications/ PublicationsPolicyAndStatistics/PublicationsPolicyandGuidance/DH_094058

possibly means most of us) actually benefit from this? Apparently, none of it is to be spent on research: rather, it is to be for "training" nurses and other healthcare workers to do...what exactly? Or is it just another "cosh" to delude us into thinking everything will be fine now, thank you? A recent report from the Public Accounts Committee suggests that this particular pledge has been broken.[9] Poor care continues. Worse, the report found that around £60 million given to Primary Care Trusts for dementia care has "gone missing".

Currently, around 700,000 people in Britain suffer from dementia.The most common form of this is Alzheimer's, which claims 400,000 people. 1.4 million within a generation are likely to join the club.

Funding for further research into dementia and its prevention needs to triple say 31 medical experts in a letter to *The Daily Telegraph*.[10] They state: *"For every pound spent on dementia care, a fraction of a penny is spent on research"*. Heart disease and cancer research race ahead: dementia is the poor relation. Without further research into its prevention, dementia could cost the NHS £50 million a year. These are dire warnings. It is frightening.

Why-oh-why I wonder, did governments separate "Health" from "Social"? When I first worked in the NHS, the overall governing body was the DHSS, the Department of Health and Social Services. This was created in 1968, following the dissolution of the Ministry of Health and its counterpart, the Ministry for Social Security. 20 years later, in 1988, the DHSS was dissolved and reverted back to two departments. In my view, "health" and "social" are interdependent and symbiotic. Living

[9] The Alzheimer's Society, 2010. *Public Accounts Committee criticises lack of dementia priority*. March 16th. Available at:
http://alzheimers.org.uk/site/scripts/news_article.php?newsID=640
[10] Smith, R. 2010. Triple dementia funding or face a devastated NHS, say 31 experts. "Letters to the Editor". *The Daily Telegraph*. July 21st

conditions, working environments, housing and so on all have a direct effect on health and vice versa.

Recently, we have had spectacular examples of where this has fallen down. Thousands of Alzheimer patients have been wrongly forced to pay for their care as they have been deemed to have a "social problem" not a health issue. How Alzheimer's can be deemed to be solely a social issue beats me. We even call it Alzheimer's *disease*. There is a clue in the title!

The "personal care", which is often what these patients need, slips through the loop-hole which has been created between medical needs and social needs. To date, three families have been successful in reclaiming care fees. These are just the tip of the iceberg. The floodgates will open and Primary Care Trusts (PCT's) should gird themselves against a torrent of claims.

So what can we do to prevent Alzheimer's disease? The Alzheimer's Society is quoted as saying: *"What is good for the heart is also good for the brain."* In practice, this means eating what is currently considered to be "a healthy diet" which is aimed at keeping the cholesterol within recommended levels: small amounts of meat (too much protein may be linked to onset of the disease); lots of fruit and vegetables; wholegrain cereals; nuts; omega-3 oils from oily fish; virgin olive oil and even curry. Low fat dairy products; reduced salt and sugar; drinking alcohol and coffee in moderation are also recommended. And taking regular exercise – and this means "everyday" – not three times a year! *And* it means more than just a wander round the shops!

The actual beneficial ingredients of the Mediterranean diet have been identified as fruit, vegetables, olive oil and, joy oh joy! Wine! Albeit, in "moderate amounts". It appears that those who follow such a diet not only live longer and healthier lives, but they do not develop Alzheimer's so readily. Other lines of research suggest that wine can keep weight gain and heart attacks at bay and that beer can beat brittle bones. In the light of this, perhaps GPs could prescribe wine, until further research shows that it kills

COLD TEA AND TEARS

you outright! (Just kidding!) We all know that excesses of the fermented grape can cause memory problems and other serious illnesses and that binge-drinking amongst the younger generations has led to a trebling of alcohol-related deaths in the past 25 years in this age group. Further, according to Professor Nutt, the disgraced chair to the Labour government's Advisory Council on the Misuse of Drugs, alcohol should have a higher danger rating than cannabis. Oh dear…What a tangled web we weave!

Very recently, an exciting British study from Oxford University suggests that cheap and cheerful vitamin B supplements could slow or even halt the progress of Alzheimer's disease.[11] The emphasis is on vitamin B12 (cyanocobalmin) in amounts far in excess of the recommended daily quota. At this level, it is likely that the effect is pharmacological.

Taking herbal supplements such as ginkgo biloba, munching on acai berries and crunching peppers and celery (which contain luteolin); using the spice curcumin in our cooking (found in curries); sipping blueberry smoothies and green tea have all had a lot of attention lately as preventative strategies, partly due to their antioxidant properties but also due to the fact that they encourage increased blood flow to the brain.

Add to that, keeping the brain active with puzzles and crosswords, card games, reading and writing, using the Internet, socialising with friends and family, giving ourselves a sense of purpose, or even learning to juggle, and we are doing the best we can until the new research, which has uncovered hitherto unknown genes, can halt the progression of Alzheimer's. This tantalising, terrifying and debilitating disease, can tear families apart and impacts on so many around the victim.

There are indeed many ripples from this particular heavy stone, when thrown into the pond of someone's life.

---

[11] Alleyne, R. 2010. Vitamins B pill could halt Alzheimer's. *The Daily Telegraph.* September 9th.

THE BIRTH OF A DIETITIAN

There's a sucker born every minute.

Attributed to Phineas T. Barnum

My generation has been lucky enough to be brought up post-war on good, decent, honest, trustworthy, simple, seasonal and tasty food. I was fortunate to have a mother who could cook well with whatever ingredients she was presented. We weren't fussy. We had enough to eat. We didn't over-eat.

I had my appendix out when I was eight years old at a children's hospital in Sussex. Visitors were allowed each afternoon, happily at the same time that the evening meal was served. A staff nurse would be at the door as parents filed in. "Any food for the children?" she would call out sternly. My mother kept her head held high and her basket containing forbidden foods well covered. We knew that these goodies would never be distributed to us: it was highly likely that the nurses supplemented their own diets with the fraudulently extracted contents!

Mum and I discreetly swapped. I gave her the "bread-and-scrape" with the two to three tiny cubes of "mouse-trap" Cheddar cheese on the metal plate that was our supper. She took this "evidence" home to show her friends. I wolfed down the banana sandwiches and quite likely would not have recuperated as well without them. She was brilliant at making these: thinly-cut, fresh white bread, the crusts removed, buttered and filled with mashed banana, a little lemon juice (to stop it going brown), sprinkled with sugar and cut into bite-size dainty

15

portions. After being unwell, these were always the first food to tempt my return to normal eating. Another nursery favourite was sugar-sandwiches – or, for special treats, bread and butter with Nestlé's sweetened condensed milk. Yummy!

After minor abdominal surgery, not long after I was married, my husband attempted to emulate my mother's skills – but the bread was brown, thickly cut and the banana was sliced, not mashed. It was the thought that counted – but they weren't the same!

When she wasn't well, my mother's tastes varied wildly from normal: one of her cravings was bread and milk. Cubes of white bread, soaked in hot milk and sprinkled with sugar. Sounds disgusting? But it wasn't to her! My friend's parents used to make chocolate blancmange to help them recover from 'flu; others live on porridge or breakfast cereals until their appetites return. "Nursery foods" are easy to eat and bring comfort, not least because of their reminiscent value of being cosseted as a child.

Getting it right when appetites are low and need to be tempted back to normality is absolutely crucial to recovery. Patients may not be able to make suggestions themselves and so knowing some background of favourite foods is essential.

When I was four years old, I decided on my future: I was going to be a nurse. Family photographs show me at that age, standing solemnly and proudly by my newborn cousin, with a starched, double-damask napkin, nun-like round my head, masquerading in my new role. Whether this "calling" was due to some kind of "imprinting" from my birth, as I was very ill for the first six weeks of my life and spent them all in hospital, we will never know! If I managed to get my way, games with my older cousin always included "Doctors and Nurses". Teddy Bears and dolls were our patients. "Doctor! Doctor! One of the patients has been sick," I would clamour to Rory.

"Well – it's the nurse's job to clear it up!" he would respond laconically and as gruffly as he could muster.

"You won't like nursing, dear," said Mother. "You'll be permanently tired." Nothing would sway me from this decision. I already had a load of books on the subject. I was going to be a fabulous and highly skilled nurse; my cool hand would soothe fevered brows; my very presence would ease tensions, fears and worries. I would make people better, marry a handsome, kind and clever doctor and live happily ever after.

At 18, I joined the "pupil nurses" of a top-notch London hospital, being one of the lucky ones to achieve a place – there were 2,000 applicants for 200 places. I was excited and thrilled. It wasn't quite as I imagined. My romantic notions crashed. Puzzlement and the shock of reality hit me in equal measures. It didn't work out. I wasn't a bad nurse: I simply wasn't strong enough nor had the necessary physical, mental or emotional stamina. Night duty was a killer! Mother was right. I didn't really mind the idea of "working" exactly – it was what one did – but I hoped that it wouldn't be for very long and then I would find that Mr Wonderful who was going to look after me for the rest of my life. Ah! The stuff of dreams!

I gave it up after a year and went to a technical college to catch up on the necessary A-Levels for a Nutrition degree and then went to university – something I had never even considered in my late teens – only really clever people did that! And it was something that was never encouraged by the convent I went to. Popular careers were nursing, posh secretarial courses – or, of course, marriage, hopefully to a rich and kind Catholic! Or… horror of horrors – become a nun!

"A degree is all very well, dear," philosophised my mother. "You need a training as well."

When I was seven, my Auntie Phyllis gave me my first cookery book. I was hooked! It contained a small section on "Invalid Cookery". What a splendid opportunity to try out some of the recipes and practise my combined skills when my mother had 'flu! She was subjected to beef tea; scrambled egg; lemon barley, egg custard and sago cream. Luckily she liked all these things and they still remain a useful basis for invalid cookery today.

I learned to cook at an early age. My father ran a small preparatory school for boys and my mother cooked the lunch. The boys' mothers had a love-hate relationship with her. Too often they would tell her, "My son says you cook much better than I do!" When it was his birthday, each boy was allowed to choose a pudding – of which there was always a choice of two. "Stodge" and "Stink-Puff" were great favourites (translated as steamed pudding and "Pink Stuff"/pink blancmange)! My mother always saved me a portion of pudding from the boys' lunch, which I gulped down immediately on returning home from my own school.

My father died when I was eight and my mother attempted to keep the school going on her own, with outside teaching assistance. When she decided that the classrooms needed a coat of paint, she said, "Well…you'll have to make lunch, while I do this."

Scrambled egg and jam tarts were my first attempt – edible but perhaps not quite Cordon Bleu or "Master Chef". (We don't need to guess what Gordon Ramsay's comment might have been). Even so, the seeds of a dietetic career were sown.

HOW IT ALL STARTED
BSc SRD

"My salad days, when I was green in judgement"

William Shakespeare, "Anthony and Cleopatra"

"Well! At least you can't kill anyone! Well done everybody!"
We all blinked in surprise and goggled at each other, horrified. Our mouths made a collective silent "Whaaaa…t…?" The bubble of our shared excitement and having passed our final exams burst. Hopes and dreams were shattered. That heady feeling dissipated. The balloon popped – loudly!

"Death by dietetics?" "Dietitian deals death blow?" Surely not!

We were six students who had just qualified as dietitians from a top London hospital. These immortal words, cheerfully imparted with a toothy grin, were from our chief dietitian, Miss Emily Newcombe.

Miss Newcombe was in her 50s, a clever woman but sadly not blessed with attractive physical attributes. She had an imposing presence, was tall, had iron-grey hair, severely cut and an Edwardian-style bust. Her impressive stature was marred by very poor teeth – a challenge for any dentist. We all noticeably straightened our spines whenever she approached. She was held in very high regard within the profession and by the medics. Certainly, we were all in awe of her and more than once had experienced the sharpness of her tongue, as she honed and trained us to her inimitable professional skills.

We could now put BSc, Dip Diet (Bachelor of Science,

Diploma in Dietetics) after our names and once we had registered with our professional body, we could then add SRD (State Registered Dietitian). Nowadays, this is replaced by the simpler "Registered Dietitian"/RD. The Americans have always insisted on spelling "dietitian" with a "c" (dietician) while the Brits have always insisted on the two "t'"s. After arguments back and forth across the pond, it would seem that both spellings are now uniformly acceptable, though the Brits still have a tenacious preference for two "t'"s.

The fact that we had all passed was one surprise: the other was that we were to be let loose upon the unsuspecting public. This was tremendously exciting and nerve-wracking at the same time!

St. James' Street
Hammersmith
December 3rd 1970

Dearest Mum

Thank you so much for your letters: it was so nice to have them. I've not been too happy about the exams, I must say, so I hope it is possible to redeem myself at the oral.

You mentioned the possibility of visiting Auntie Phyllis next week: would you like to come on the Tuesday and then I could come over after the oral and we could go home together?

The flat is shaping up and I like living here very much: you must come over soon!

Lots of love, Mary xx

Our maverick Professor of Medicine had assisted me, and possibly others, at the oral examination. During our training, we went to his London teaching hospital once a week for medical lectures and, if we were lucky, he would throw in a ward-round as a bonus. We could meet real patients! I loved these sessions. Prof. Thomas had a wicked sense of humour (as do many medics) and could be quite sarcastic at times, not suffering fools gladly. One of the more dour and pedantic examiners who was presiding over our oral exam (there were about four or five of them, if my memory serves me correctly) had asked me some obscure question, the answer to which I had no idea. Out of the corner of my eye, I was aware of some vigorous movement: Prof. Thomas was nodding in the affirmative.

"Yes," I answered the examiner firmly. Prof. nonchalantly scratched his ear and winked. The examiner looked satisfied and in due course I received my certificate and quickly got a job.

As dietetics developed, and as dietitians were given more responsibility for diagnoses and treatment plans, Miss Newcombe's words came back to haunt me. A dietitian probably could at least contribute to the death of a patient, if some gross error occurred. I would fantasise about a detective thriller based on this!

Part of our training was in outpatient clinics and on the wards, where we developed a more than healthy respect for ward sisters and doctors. It would be some years before we would develop the confidence to realise that we were specialists in our own fields. Times have changed. Doctors used to prescribe a diet for a patient – not always very accurately, it has to be said, sometimes hilariously getting calories and carbohydrate balance totally out of kilter! It was the dietitian's job to "translate" this "prescription" into food and meal patterns. Nowadays, doctors ask the dietitian to "help" a patient, given a diagnosis or a set of symptoms.

One of the younger consultants specialised in renal disease. He was good looking (of course! Think, George Clooney), had great charisma, charm and a lovely sense of humour. He and Miss Newcombe would enter into earnest discussions about shared patients. How we envied her! And how interesting it was that so many of us wide-eyed, naïve students suddenly decided that we had an unlimited interest in kidneys, even attending out-of-hours lectures on the subject!

One of the outpatient clinics was held in an open-plan format: "patient confidentiality" had not been invented. It was a large sunny room that got uncomfortably hot in the summer. A row of desks with one or two chairs strategically placed, stretched the width of the room. Another lonely chair sat at the other side of each desk and this was where, as students, we had to take diet-histories of our ingenuous patients. Not only that, but as each food item was listed, we had to make an educated guess as to the portion size and then convert it straight away into calories and grams (g) of protein, fat and carbohydrate, tabulating them as we went. This meant memorising basic nutritional analyses of most common foods and then multiplying these up with the portion size. This was just not My Thing. How we sweated! Especially when Miss Newcombe hovered behind us and told us to hurry up. A glance upwards and there was the next patient, waiting and getting – er- IMpatient! Later, when I did freelance work, which included devising slimming diets for magazines, this skill allowed me to do this relatively quickly. After that, there were calculators to help us and nowadays, of course, there are sophisticated software programmes that make these assessments much easier.

"So how do you become a dietitian?" asked my elderly maiden Aunt, never having heard of this profession. Auntie Phyllis was a force to be reckoned with, especially when she drew herself up to her full height of four feet, eight inches. Having been brought up with three brothers, my father being one of them, she was a suffragette under the skin, adamant that women should receive a proper education, training and earn their own living. She did not tolerate insubordination or childish mischief and became irritated with indecision and lack of clarity. She had worked all her life as a translator in five European languages for companies with international connections. I always felt intimidated by her and it wasn't until I was in my 20s, that we became friends. As a child I used to stay with her and, on more than one occasion, probably made her very glad that she had never married or had children! Developing mumps and being sick on her best pink eiderdown was one of them. Added to that, when I was well enough my mother came to take me home and our Sealyham Terrier found something exotic to roll in, stunk the house out and had to be bathed. My poor Aunt's single orderly world turned upside down!

"Well…there are various routes to the ultimate qualification. My friends and I did a degree course first and then followed this up with a diploma in dietetics. First, we studied biochemistry, physiology, microbiology, food technology, food preparation – cooking to you and me – and nutrition. Lots of it takes place as practical sessions. Other routes can be an 'all-in-one' degree, or via nursing, catering, institutional management, human biology or even some arts subjects. It was initially suggested that I joined a nutrition survey team in Ethiopia after my degree but then someone mentioned bed-bugs – a post-graduate diploma in dietetics suddenly seemed a preferable option!"

I loved physiology! Especially when we were told that the level to which we aspired was equivalent to a second year medical degree. Most of the experiments in the final year were done on ourselves. (Dare I say that many of the other investigations, such as muscle and heart functions, were done on frogs? We had to sign a Home Office certificate to be able to do these horrible things to anaesthetised or "pithed" animals. I hasten to add that it was the Home Office-approved lecturer who anaesthetised the laboratory animals).

One experiment on ourselves involved being loaded up with a sort of rucksack (Benedict Roth), that measured the amount of oxygen that we used when exercising and compared with that used at rest. We had to run several times round the quadrangle.

A fellow student would then take our pulse at timed intervals and read changes in oxygen consumption off the machine.

One of my favourite moments was being the girl in our class to win the step-test for fitness: one of the rugby-playing boys was top and I came second! It was just stubborn determination that kept me going plus the fact that I was actually taking ballet lessons, starting as a very mature, 21-year old, aspiring ballet student! My flat mates gave me my one and only leotard – which I still have and can still get into, more than 40 years on!

Investigating stomach acidity and digestion meant swallowing a Ryle's tube and manfully keeping it down. Ryle's tubes, made of rubber, are rarely used these days, technology having advanced so that gastric tubes are made of smoother polyurethane and are much narrower and easier to pass. Imagining that it was an overlong piece of spaghetti helped the swallowing process but it was impossible not to gag. Once it was safely in the stomach, checked with litmus paper, we all giggled nervously, which made it vibrate in the back of the throat, making us even more uncomfortably aware of its presence. Changes in gastric acidity were calibrated at varying intervals by drawing up measured samples of gastric contents and seeing the effect over time of having swallowed some gruel (like thin porridge).

Ryle's tubes were initially used in tube-feeds (more about those later in "Tubes and Twiddly Bits") but also to pump out the stomach contents of patients, who had overdosed, taken excess alcohol or other dangerous substances. Nowadays, if taken to A and E Departments, inebriated patients are simply hydrated and everyone waits till they sober up.

To investigate kidney function, we had to drink a measured amount of water every 15 minutes and then go to the loo with a "suitable container". Part of this study also involved a 24-hour urine collection, which meant that at the queue for the loo, all one's fellow students would be clutching their "suitable

containers" – usually a Winchester bottle, such
wine-making – with varying degrees of embarı
amazing what one can learn from urine! One's mos
secrets are laid bare. We goggled openly at fellow   ..ıs'
offerings: the quantity produced; colour range – from deep
amber to pale honey to straw; clarity and cloudiness.

"And then there are medical lectures," I continued, "learning
about different diseases and how diet can cure or influence
these and then…" I drew a deep breath. "Dietitians advise
people on how they can change their diets so as to treat or
prevent diseases."

"So how do you do that?" she demanded.

A good question! There were many times in my work when
I wished that I had done a further degree – in psychology. As it
happens, a psychology module is now included in the training.
So much of a dietitian's work is in encouraging people to change
their lifestyles. Not an easy task! None of us likes change and
unless we can see a good reason for it, it is only human to desist,
or at least to find some short cuts.

"And is it all to do with getting people to lose weight?"
Auntie Phyllis continued.

"Lord no! A lot of the work does hinge on helping people to
do that but there is much more to dietetics than just making up
slimming diets."

And, when attempting to guide overweight patients on how
best to modify their diets and lifestyles, it was extraordinary to
me then how their problems went much deeper than just
choosing unsuitable foods. One became privy to their
relationships and sex problems; difficulties at work;
complications with accommodation, with their families and so
on. As a young, inexperienced, newly qualified dietitian,
working in the hospital setting and seeing patients in outpatient
clinics, I felt utterly incompetent at dealing with these and, as a
result, made very good friends with the clinical psychologist, to

whom I referred quite a number. Further, the approach to dietetic advice then was quite didactic and prescriptive. No "softly, softly" in those days!

I was put in my place severely by Mrs Bond, who had been referred by her GP to lose weight. She was mutinous and not impressed.

"I don't eat that – and I NEVER eat those," she informed me, as we went through the diet-sheet.

"Well…" I tried to be placatory but firm, "the less foods you try that are on the diet-sheet means less choice overall."

She tried another tack.

"Well…I can't afford those things. And anyway, I don't see why I should lose weight and who do you think you are to tell me how to spend my money? If I want to spend it on cigarettes and the food I like, then I will."

We reached an *impasse*. I got on my high horse and went into "hoity-toity" mode, with all the arrogance and hubris that only the newly qualified, in their crisp, starched, white coats, can do.

"Well, if that's how you feel, I shall simply write to Dr Ford and tell him."

"You can't do that…!" My face indicated that I could and would, if pushed. She capitulated.

"Oh! I don't want you to do that. All right then, show me that diet-sheet again."

Afterwards, I reflected. She was absolutely right. Who was I to tell her – or anyone else for that matter – how to spend her hard-earned money? Who was this prissy young upstart, who talked posh and wore a white coat? What did *she* know about life and its trials and tribulations?

Encouraging someone to make changes to a lifestyle is quite complicated. Luckily, two researchers from the minefield of addictive behaviour, such as smoking and drinking, came up with a model. Prochaska and DiClemente proposed that before the actual change (in lifestyle behaviour) can take place, there are various stages that one needs to go through first.[1]

In brief : *Pre-contemplation* is the stage in which the possibility of changing a habit is not seriously considered. This may be because the individual does not recognise that there is a problem, or they refuse to acknowledge it. This is probably the most difficult stage to go through.

Patients may be told that they have to lose weight, for example, but can't see what medical impact their overweight has on their lives or just think their doctor is having a go at them.

Contemplation describes acknowledgement and/or awareness but the patient dithers between the advantages that he or she would achieve and the hard work that these entail. You will often hear – and I've said this many times myself – "I know I ought to, but..." And it's amazing how inventive one can become in making excuses!

Preparation describes the decision to commit. Eventually, one moves into *Action*. Perhaps this is where health professionals try to rush their patients: we want results too. And so do our managers!

Research suggests that making small changes to start with is more successful than "going for gold" immediately. A staggered, or step-wise approach works well. Even so, during this time patients need lots of reassurance and praise and this is why dietitians' outpatient clinics are filled with follow-up appointments.

Maintenance can be an anxious time, because patients are worried about relapsing. The model describes a circular series of states of mind but one does not necessarily lead straight to

---

[1] Prochaska, J.O. and DiClemente, C.C. 1983. Stages and processes of self-change of smoking: toward an integrative model of change. *Journal of Consulting And Clinical Psychology*. 51, 390-395

the next. It is possible to lapse or re-join at any stage. Rather like a hamster's wheel, one can fall off but clamber on again! There are some who never make it past the first stage and those who paddle along merrily.

Counselling skills are now added to the dietitian's armoury: the authoritarian, didactic approach didn't work. Getting patients on board by motivating them to do something positive for themselves is paramount. Final objectives and goals are set together in small steps. For the very obese, the ideal healthy weight might seem an unattainable goal but it is worth remembering that a loss of even ten per cent helps to normalise the things one can't see – blood pressure, cholesterol and glucose levels. Dietitians are taught to recognise the patient's emotions and address them. Active and reflective listening needs practice: one needs to be fully engaged, empathic, non-judgemental and genuine.

A busy clinic requires determination and resolution. At the end, when one has repeated oneself several times for different patients one is gasping for a cuppa! If patients fail, it is natural to feel let down, cross, annoyed and the feeling that a lot of time has been wasted. But this is selfish and one's *raison d'être* is simply to be there, give out helpful and accurate advice, encourage and gently cajole. Only once did I lose my composure.

By this time, I was in Woodlandshire, employed by the County Health Department as a community dietitian. It was decided to start groups for those patients who needed to lose weight. There was much to be said for this. Research suggested that people with similar problems supported each other; that they felt they understood their problems better than the professionals. After all, *Weight Watchers* was a runaway success: why couldn't we do the same? It was also a much more economic use of dietitians' time. It wasn't so wearing. And the tea didn't get cold!

We did our own research and found out that "closed groups", where there are definite starting and finishing dates, worked better than "open groups". Ideal numbers for each group were between eight and ten. Many of these were started by the community dietitian and then taken on by keen health visitors.

I ran one of these myself. Twisting the arms of colleagues, I persuaded them to take the occasional session, so that the group had a different speaker each week – the consultant, the psychologist, the physiotherapist, the occupational therapist, the counsellor – all took a turn and, as this was summer, I also encouraged a group walk (more of an amble!) round the nearby park on alternate weeks. Results were impressive. I did a graph for my boss. He was dazzled. So was I! Ten weeks in and it was the summer holidays. It was agreed to have a break. Returning afterwards, the results were totally disheartening. Nearly everyone had returned to the pre-group weight. I was stunned. How *could* they have let me down so? I laid into them saying how really disappointed I was, how much time and NHS money they had wasted and so on.

They went very, very quiet! And apologised, promising to do better next week. Which they did, but the trust that had built up between us was shaky and I had to ask myself what was more important: their enthusiasm or my results?

"So what is biochemistry?" my Aunt persisted. "And why do you need to study that?" My Aunt was never one to let go lightly; she was highly intelligent but found new concepts hard to embrace and patience was not one of her virtues.

"It's studying all the minute chemical reactions that take place in cells in the body; their impact on health and how they are influenced by diet, lifestyles, medicines and drugs."

"Hmm…" pursing her lips, she digested this and then another thought occurred to her.

"Then…what's the difference between nutrition and dietetics?"

"Oh…we study nutrition too – and that's to do with all the

nutrients that we need for optimum health. Nutritionists *per se* aren't specifically trained to advise individual patients on changing their diets when they are ill. To make it confusing, nutritionists are often doubly qualified as dietitians too. These people most likely will have studied for a degree in nutrition and then followed that with a diploma in dietetics like my friends and I did, or have taken an "all-in-one" degree in both. Nowadays, the term 'dietitian' is a 'protected species' – no one can use that title, unless they are registered with the Health Professions Council (formerly this was the Council for Professions Supplementary to Medicine) and can prove that they've undergone appropriate training and Continued Professional Development (CPD)." She nodded.

"Dare I say," I added, "*Anyone* can call themselves a 'nutritionist' and this has lead to confusion as to whether his or her qualifications are *bona fide*. Ideally, such people should have official academic training. You won't find a nutritionist in the National Health Service as such. Many of them work in health promotion; research; lecturing; the media; the food and/or health supplements industry, or overseas with nutrition surveys and services. But then, quite a number of dietitians can do that too. You *will* find dietitians working both in private and NHS hospitals and in the NHS community services. Those employed by the latter link up with GPs and other caring professions, as well as education and social services."

"OK," she concurred, "So, as a fairly 'new' profession, how did it start?"

"Actually, that's quite interesting," I replied. "From the late 19th century, the profile of proper nutrition for hospitalised patients was raised. Don't forget that Florence Nightingale realised its importance in the Crimean War. Nurses who took on the role of 'housekeeping' (purchasing and preparation of food), 'hospital stewardship', or who showed a particular interest in catering, merged into the role. As physiology and biochemical research uncovered the body's mysteries and its requirements for so many nutrients developed, so dietetics, as a specific paramedical entity, evolved."

We were sitting in her "brown" sitting room – carpet and furniture were all shades of brown or dark oak – a remnant of her Victorian upbringing. It was a sunny summer's day, which meant that every 30 seconds another aeroplane from Heathrow, filled with eager holidaymakers, droned over her bungalow, which seemed to be directly under a popular flight path.

She refilled my teacup and offered me another of her inimitable watercress and salad cream sandwiches.

"And we have cooking lessons too, though it's rather grandly called 'Food Preparation,'" I continued. "Most of us can cook reasonably well and enjoy it, so I'm afraid we tend to muck about a bit. The worst part is we are all starving at the end of the lesson and just want to eat the fruits of our labours but we have to wait, impatience and hunger pangs mounting, while Mrs Robertson analyses our efforts!"

I regaled my Aunt with stories of how we decorated a lemon meringue pie with sprigs of parsley to see if the lecturer noticed and, to show how well I had tied up a steamed syrup pudding, I swung it round my head. At the crucial moment, it left my grasp and, like a pro at the Highland Games, my "shot-put" crashed across the pristine kitchen quarry tiles with dramatic effect and with all the extra syrup I had put in being highly visible. I told her how, when we were testing packet steam puddings against the homemade versions, we had to stand by our exhibits, while the tutor came round.

"Well," said Mrs Robertson, viewing my offerings, "You can easily tell which is which…" I tried to keep my face impassive and failed. I started giggling.

"You're not telling me that…*that*…is the one that *you* made?" She pointed to the shrivelled, diminutive, shrunken, solid object in front of me.

31

"I think we need to practise these," she concluded, shaking her head and trying not to laugh.

When I was more experienced and students joined our dietetic department for the practical part of their training, I discovered that one in particular really didn't like cooking at all and wasn't in the least interested.

"So how do you think you are going to advise patients to change their cooking methods and types of foods?" I challenged her. "Give them different suggestions? Or devise a diet for a coeliac patient who also has diabetes, for example? Or tempt an older patient after major surgery?"

She shrugged. I cajoled her and advised her to invite friends round for a meal, look at different ways of cooking her favourite foods, collect recipes and so on. It transpired there was more to this than met the eye: Lisa was overshadowed by another student, who was pretty, vivacious and clever. Lisa took refuge by shrinking into the background. With encouragement and nurturing, she started to blossom and I learned later that she had even started to enjoy cooking! Enjoying and being enthusiastic about food can be infectious: patients need to know that dietitians are practical as well as able to give advice.

"So, er…why have you chosen to do this exactly?" my Aunt continued.

"Well…" I felt embarrassed now. "Remember when I left school, I had always wanted to do nursing?" She nodded.

"It just didn't suit me…night-duty wiped me out! And you know what? We had to cook the breakfasts every morning! I used to do trays of sausages and bacon in the oven and sometimes the boiled eggs were rather hit and miss! The ones at the top of the pan were barely cooked and all watery, while the ones at the bottom were rock hard! The patients were so kind and uncomplaining about that! The men on the medical ward used to call me either 'Smiler' or 'Apple Cheeks' because of my rosy complexion!" Auntie Phyllis chuckled.

"Then I got pneumonia and had to spend Christmas in Sick Bay."

The sister in charge was a real dragon and wouldn't believe me when I said that the antibiotics didn't suit me. She had to agree when I showed her the rash all over my front and kept asking for the vomit bowl. I was beginning to think that maybe my mother was right after all – mothers usually are! – that nursing wasn't the right choice for me. I felt bad. It was the only thing that I ever wanted to do since I was four years old. I was permanently tired. Day shifts were 12 hours, with a break of two in the middle. Night duty, which was ten nights "on" and five "off", was tough. The shifts were from 8.00pm – 8.00am and then we had to travel to and from the night nurses' home, which meant the precious time in bed was less than it could have been.

I found it difficult to make friends. All the others in my set had enough energy to go to parties after work and chase likely medical students and junior doctors. I romanticised and dreamed about it. That was as far as I got!

I had considered physiotherapy as a career too. It was still helping people and I liked sport and was pretty fit but then I read a career book that mentioned having to give talks and lessons to groups. What me? Standing up and addressing groups? No fear! Oddly enough, in subsequent jobs as a dietitian, I had to do exactly that!

Auntie Phyllis laughed with me at my pathetic memories of flirting with nursing.

"Anyway, Mum suggested dietetics," I continued. "She told me it was important to have a training of some kind. She thought that it might combine the caring bit and she knew I liked cooking. I thought it sounded OK and there wasn't any night duty!"

"Yes, your mother was right about the training," she agreed. "It was hard for her without one, especially after your father died."

One of my brother's girlfriends had a sister who was a dietitian. We went to visit her – a formidable, inspiring and highly energetic lady! She gave us a wonderful lunch, talked about her work and clinched my decision.

"Now..." Auntie Phyllis leant forward with a twinkly gleam in her eyes, "What about boys? Do they do this course too?"

"Yeees...there are a few but most of them seem to be frustrated medics!" Actually, one of the students I trained with was a gorgeous Greek chap, who matched this description. It is still largely a female profession, though, as it becomes more scientific, more men are attracted to it, preferring research posts rather than practical dietetics. Having said that, when I returned to work in the NHS after several years freelancing, I was quite surprised (and pleased!) to see male dietitians walking the hospital wards.

Unlike doctors and nurses, dietitians are not front-line, all-action men and women in the hospital or community health care, dealing with medical or surgical dramas. Rather, they beaver away in the background, actively promoting healthy eating campaigns; writing dietary advice leaflets; liaising with other staff within and outside the NHS, such as health visitors, practice nurses, district nurses, midwives, care staff, school health and so on. They advise patients how they can treat their conditions, using food as the major, sometimes the sole part of their treatment. In spite of being told what foods are advised – or not, many patients are actually quite grateful for the changes that the dietitian has helped them to make and to give them a better understanding of food and diet. Occasionally, the dietitian can score a small triumph by picking up a missed diagnosis, which makes the day very exciting!

An Asian lady had been referred from the rheumatology clinic to our outpatient department in Borderland. Apparently, she needed to lose weight. This was obvious but as I watched her walk down the passage to our clinic room, a sentence from our trusty textbook jumped out of my memory bank:

"Waddling gait is indicative of osteomalacia." [2]

Osteomalacia is an adult form of rickets and is usually due to deficiency of vitamin D, either due to a shortage of the vitamin in the diet or lack of sunshine exposure, or both. Vitamin D is essential for allowing calcium to be absorbed from the gut and be assimilated into bone.

Mrs Patel definitely waddled. Like Jemima Puddleduck.

We chatted through her diet and her life. She had spent many years in Glasgow – not known for its sunny climes! – before moving to Borderland. Her traditional diet, as is the case with many Asians, was decidedly short on vitamin D and what sunshine is available in the UK does not always reach the people it should. Traditional Asian dress ensures that there is very little skin exposed. Skin colour also forms another barrier to vitamin D absorption from sun. Asian diets can sometimes compromise calcium absorption too by the nature of chapatti flour and a high fibre diet. In this respect, the odds are stacked against these people.

Somewhat diffidently, I wrote to the referring consultant suggesting that maybe her joint pain had a different origin and that her vitamin D status might be further investigated. He replied courteously and generously and confessed that he hadn't thought of that aspect. Later, I found out that she did indeed have osteomalacia.

Latterly, I worked with "Elderly Care" in the county of Calmershire. Mrs Clarke had had an amputation and it wasn't healing. She was being looked after in the rehabilitation ward at the community hospital. We chatted and Mrs Clarke's diet seemed to be reasonable enough. As she spoke, I could see that her tongue looked remarkably red – like a strawberry!

[2] Passmore, R. and Eastwood, M.A. 1986, *Human Nutrition and Dietetics, 8th Edition.* Churchill Livingstone

"Excuse me asking, Mrs Clarke, but is your tongue sore?"

"Oh yes," she said, "And they give me some fizzy stuff to drink (vitamin C and zinc supplement to promote wound healing) and it makes it worse!"

I looked at her nails. All the signs pointed to iron-deficiency anaemia.

"Do you mind if I ask them to do a blood test for you, Mrs Clarke? I think you may be anaemic."

"No that's fine, dear, you go ahead.

Back at the nurses' station, I made the request.

"Oh, you'll be in trouble," laughed the sister on duty. Raised eyebrows. "Making more work for the doctors," she added.

"Well...I would like it done please," I said firmly, writing my request in the doctors' book, Mrs Clarke's notes and the nurses' care plan, trying to remember the hints we had had on our assertiveness course. A few days later, the results came back.

Mrs Clarke's haemoglobin clocked in at 80.0g/litre. It should have been well over 120.0g/litre. Iron supplements were started. In due course, all went well. Her leg healed and she could go home.

In the community hospital outpatient dietetic clinic, a delightful, middle-aged lady was a regular patient and had been struggling with her weight for a long time. Mrs Stock was Finnish and had the characteristic high cheekbones and almond shaped eyes, typical of the Scandinavian races. She was hypothyroid, meaning that her thyroid gland wasn't putting out enough of the thyroid hormone, thyroxin. One of the consequences of this is a slower metabolism and weight gain. That afternoon, she attended for a follow-up visit and her weight had disappointingly stabilised. I looked at her. Her eyes looked more prominent than usual and her skin looked dry.

"When did you last have a blood test for the thyroid function?" I asked, after going through the usual routine of weighing her and catching up with her progress, or lack of it.

"Not that long ago and they told me it was all right," she replied.

"Do you mind if we ask them to do it again?" I was still suspicious.

"No – actually, I think the levels must have dropped again myself." Sure enough, on a return visit she looked much better, as a result of increased thyroid medication. AND…had lost some weight. A happy patient!

Of course, sometimes patients just tell you what they think you want to hear.

Newly qualified and I was at a big London hospital taking an outpatient clinic all on my own. A large Caribbean lady was sitting opposite me and I was taking a diet history.

"Well, Mrs Graines, can you tell me what you have for breakfast?"

"Weeelll," she responded with her attractive soft, West Indian voice. "I 'ave a lit'l bit o' caabbage…" I forgot my manners.

"What??? At breakfast..?"

Going to work and wearing a white coat felt great. My little notebook was jammed into my pocket, giving me a lop-sided appearance. It was full of useful cribs like how many millimoles of sodium there were in a milligram of salt, and other useful minutiae. There was a sense of freedom from student days but also a sense of "being Someone." I was a DIETITIAN – I answered the 'phone in the office, "Mary Farmer, dietitian speaking." That felt so good, until the caller flummoxed me by rattling off some blood results of a patient and I had to ask them to repeat them! Or it was to do with an order for the kitchen that I didn't understand. Or one of the wards had requested some highly complicated diet for a patient.

Before this, I had taken a locum post. I had taken my finals but was waiting for the results and hadn't actually qualified.

The chief dietitian, Mrs Collins, was a very kind woman who offered me the interim job.

"Well...you're *nearly* a dietitian!" she assured me.

She took great care of her students and at weekends was determined to make us appreciate the local fens, canals and cathedrals. She had a little campervan into which we would all cram, stopping along the way for a brew of tea. We loved her! Everyone called her Mrs C.

She had been widowed for some years. Her husband had been a GP and so she was well-known in those circles. It was her suggestion that GPs send their referrals directly to the dietetic departments, rather than going via consultants in the hospitals. How proud she would be to learn how this service has grown now!

As part of my continuing education, and knowing that I liked things medical, she thought it would be "A Good Idea" that I be present and observe a cataract operation. The patient was an elderly diabetic lady and she was having the procedure done under a local anaesthetic. I was told to position myself near her head, so that I could talk to her. The surgeon inserted the syringe around her eye. It was very warm in theatre and I began to feel queasy. The surgeon continued. He probed around and the eyeball was resting gently on the patient's cheek.

"Excuse me...I'll have to go," I muttered. I began to feel better after some air and returned.

"Hold her hand and talk to her," advised one of the nurses. "It'll take your mind off things." It didn't.

I tried. I really, really tried but had to leave again for fear of embarrassing myself.

The next patient was having exactly the same procedure. He was an elderly gentleman but was having a general anaesthetic (GA). This time, I had no trouble at all, taking a keen interest in all that was going on.

Staying in the nurses' home meant that I was invited to the

nurses' parties. One Saturday, they persuaded me on the basis that there would be a number of airmen from the nearby RAF base. Rather reluctantly, I joined them. It was in their recreation hall and I soon got chatting to a young and dashing pilot officer. He invited me over to the base a week or so later to a party in the Mess. He fetched me in his Ford Anglia.

"I drive rather fast," he warned.

"Doesn't worry me." I laughed. I liked driving fast too – although in my A35, known affectionately as "The Egg", due to its ovoid shape, "fast" was comparably pedestrian. This was fun!

After a great evening meeting his friends in the Mess and after lots of laughing, it was time to take me back. Thick, thick fog enveloped the area.

"I'm sorry," said Dirk. "I'm not prepared to drive in this – it's too dangerous. You'll have to stay here. You can have my bed and I'll bunk down with my mate."

He was a gentleman to the last! I undressed to my petticoat and climbed into his bed. In the morning, his batman brought me a cup of tea. A real "Jeeves"! His demeanour suggested that he was not fazed at all and that finding a woman in his young boss' bed was a frequent occurrence! It probably was!

"Good Morning Ma'am. The gentleman will be ready to take you back to the hospital in 15 minutes. He will be waiting for you in the hall." And so he was. Somehow Mrs C. heard the story and thought it was hilarious!

Nurses' Home
October 27th 1970

Dearest Mum

Thank you so much for sending on my letters.

One of them was from Ricki (friend of a school friend). He has got me a car!!! It sounds very nice: an A35 – (with the big back window!); light blue; 1959; new tyres; new battery; only three owners in ten years; MOT for one year and taxed until December. Ricki is doing some work on it for me. All for £60.00 Not bad, eh?

I think I'll be able to collect it in a fortnight and see Shelia at the same time. She is having a baby! Isn't that thrilling! It is due April 22nd.

Thank you so much for your cheque. What with that and the money Mrs. C. gave me for writing some abstracts, I shall be nearly there! I am very excited and it will be marvellous to have it while I am here and Sue (another dietetic student) and I can go out together.

I am at Honeysuckle Wing this week and am all on my own. It's a bit chaotic but fortunately there aren't too many patients and the cooks are very quietly efficient and really know what they are doing! More than I do! But at least I feel needed!

Sue and I went to a Slimming Club on Wednesday night! It's a local organisation along the lines of "Weight Watchers". They had enlisted Mrs. C's help, so we were given the job of designing their diet-sheet!

They now are keen to have a dietitian at all their meetings, which at first, seemed a good idea but now they want to start different branches all over the place – a lot of time out for the dietitians.

I quite enjoyed it though. It seems to be something which only a certain type of person would go to (mainly women). I think you or I would be acutely embarrassed if we had to have our weight read out loud to all and sundry – especially if it was more than it should be!! They were a friendly bunch and asked lots of questions. But some weird ideas! One lady told me that eating lots of fish burnt up more calories! And nearly all of them had problems with constipation, since they started the diet. This made them very worried!

After a talk by the "Queen Bee" and a little chat from Sue and me, some of them were awarded ribbons – different colours according to amount of weight lost – all claps and cheers!

THEN we had to join in with an Eileen Fowler musical movement session – all leaping about and throwing their arms around!!

I have to go to a convalescent home tomorrow for the day – AND *give my little talk! I haven't managed to wriggle out of it!*

Mrs C. has given me a flannel graph – that might fill in a few pauses, while I scratch my head!

Lots of love, Mary xxx

How quaint using a flannel-graph as a visual aid sounds now in the world of sophisticated power-point presentations. I doubt that many current students would even know what it was!

Nurses' Home
November 2nd 1970

Dearest Mum

Have just done a really stupid thing! I got in a muddle last night with my clocks and have got up an HOUR too early!!! Well – it's given me time to write to you but I did wonder vaguely why it was so dark and simply decided it was the rain!

I had a lovely weekend with Shelia- as always! She looks well but says she does get very tired. The baby is due towards the end of April – 22nd/23rd.

Ricki took us all out to dinner on Saturday evening, which was great! I ate far too much and was quite glad to have plain old Ryvita and cheese the next day!

AND…I've got my little car! It's absolutely fabulous! It makes me realise that John's car (my brother's) is beginning to crack up! I can really accelerate in this one and the steering wheel is easier to turn. Ricki drove it round to Sheila's and we all went out to dinner in it! I then took it to Church in the morning – a suitable "maiden voyage", I thought! Then I had a little "tootle" round before driving back here.

Shelia and Tom put me in touch with another friend of theirs who was able to insure it for me.

What a pleasant change from the journey down here: I had to get the train but just missed one, so had to wait 40 mins – AND change at Surbiton – and then had to get a bus, which didn't move for AGES!

COLD TEA AND TEARS

I have an interview at The Brompton Hospital!! That's the chesty place! What a surprise! What shall I wear??

Haven't heard from North West yet ..

Do you mind sending me my road maps?

Lots of love, Mary xx

Nurses' Home

November 5th 1970

Dearest Mum

Thank you so much for your letters and the little parcel.

I was offered the job at The Brompton!!

I think it will be OK – quite a small hospital, which I think would be a good thing to start with – I would be assistant to the group dietitian – nice old bird! No Sundays and alternate Saturdays, 9.00am-6.00pm. Dietitians don't go on ward rounds with the doctors but maybe once I get there, and show interest, I could join in. It's not very "high powered" as Miss Newcombe put it, so I think it would be a good place to find my feet. The building is rather ancient – but in a nice part of London.

My friend Sue has left now but there are two other students so I am not alone. I have been busy today making gluten-free bread, biscuits and cakes etc, as well as tube-feeds.

Will write again soon.

Lots of love, Mary xxx

Although I was offered a job at The Brompton Hospital in London I didn't take it, but accepted a post at a large general hospital in North West London instead. It was 1970. There were only three of us in the department and I was the "baby". Julia, the chief dietitian, was a lovely woman. She was a dead-ringer for Jane Asher in her hey-day and was the daughter of an eminent medical professor, who had actually written a definitive tome on nutrition. She was a pretty and slim redhead and always wore a long skirt with either a fetching blouse or polo neck sweater, over which her white coat draped seductively. Her knee-high boots and wide belt, which emphasised her tiny waist, set off the whole ensemble. A history of chest infections and frequent bouts of bronchitis gave her voice a permanent husky, sexy timbre. Julia would be seen swanning off down the long corridor in earnest conversation with one of the consultants. I yearned to be able to do that and to be able to chat professionally on the same level.

White coats are not worn by dietitians or other hospital health professions now but when we were students, they were standard uniform. Apart from the doctors, who wore unbelted white coats over shirt and trousers, and the nurses, who had their own uniform, others were identified by the colour of their belt and the relevant professional association buckle. The dietitians favoured pale blue and the buckle was a metal facsimile of the British Dietetic Association logo – an ornate ibex mounting a shield in blue and gold. Association badges were worn on the lapel as further identification of who and what you were. Later, ordinary clothes were worn under an open white coat and then the white coat gradually disappeared altogether. Some hospitals now insist on uniform for their dietitians, which complements that worn by other therapists: dark blue for physiotherapists (physios or PTs), bottle green for occupational therapists (OTs) and so on. Even so, some community-based staff wear "mufti" (normal clothes) all the time and trousers are now commonly worn, being considered more practical. In the 1970s, this was unheard of, being considered far too casual!

My humble tasks included liaising with the kitchen staff – the kitchen was right next door to our tiny office – and visiting the "elderly wards". I also took some outpatient clinics, all on my own, without Miss Newcombe breathing down my neck!

St James' Street, Hammersmith
December 16th 1970

Dearest Mum

Thanks so much for your letters and for forwarding the Christmas cards.

I am just loving the job! This hospital is part of a group – there are several hospitals involved and I go to one of them all on my own!

It is very friendly and everyone knows everyone else but, unlike Suffolk, the doctors keep their distance from us!

The only thing is that a lot of the patients are immigrants in this area and vegetarian to boot! It makes life very difficult as they are not used to English food.

There is quite a lot of outpatient work too, which is nice: I like that!

It's so nice to be on one's own and muddle along – it's good too, to be giving, rather than receiving.

I like our chief dietitian, Julia, very much. She and Miss Newcombe were at The Middlesex together, so she is pleased I have gone to the North West.

The personnel people have said I might be able to have some of my salary before Christmas! Wouldn't that be nice!

We went to a drinks do after work today in the Gastroenterology Dept and met Dr K – he is on the BDA Committee and another consultant, who used to examine our college students!

Tomorrow, I have been invited to the Christmas Dinner at Williams Hospital, so that should be fun.

Look forward to seeing you soon.

Lots of love, Mary xx

The Williams Hospital
January 11th 1971

Darling Mum

This is very naughty – I am using some headed hospital paper, so you can see what it looks like! Very official!

I am actually in the outpatient clinic, waiting for some "customers" to appear: I've only had two this morning so far – usually, they pile in one after the other! Probably they'll all be sent by the doctor, just when I want to go to lunch!.

I hope your arthritis isn't acting up too much – I've checked out the medicines you're on – funnily enough, there is a patient on the a ward here with arthritis and she is on a low protein diet – but that was because the drugs she was taking interfered with her protein metabolism. I haven't found out yet what they were …Must be tricky socialising with those kind of restrictions.

The diet cook is showing a bit more interest in her work now! The catering officer gave her a "talking to"!!!

Must go now…

Love always, Mary xxx

Kitchen staff were always difficult to recruit. Many of ours at the North West came from the African continent but we knew little then about warring tribes, such as Hutus and Tutsis. On one occasion, Julia came into the kitchen to find a serious fight in progress, in protest against the new cook. There was lots of shouting and the knives were out – literally! It turned out that, inadvertently, we had employed a lady from a hostile clan. Quite how it started, no one was sure, but it obviously had to be nipped in the bud and quickly, before someone was seriously hurt.

All the food, for both patients and staff, was cooked in a central kitchen and taken to the wards in hot trolleys, with the "colds" precariously balanced underneath, where they ended up being slightly warmed! At midday, there would be a queue of porters outside our office waiting for the lunchtime trolleys to be loaded, with last minute additions and changes being made. This performance would then be repeated in the afternoon for the patients' suppers at five o'clock.

The hospital was very near a brewery and many of our patients worked there. A number of them were alcoholic (an occupational hazard!) and obesity and diabetes were common. Many of them were of Caribbean origin and I had to get used to their popular green banana (plantain), yam and sweet potato, which in those days did not feature in our trusty *Composition of Foods* – an essential guide to the nutritional analysis of hundreds of foods.[3] Luckily, at the time, I lived near a Saturday market, which had huge displays of these exotic and colourful vegetables, so my flatmates and I tried them for ourselves. Many of these patients would use condensed (evaporated) milk – sometimes sweetened – in their tea, which made rather a difference to their calorie intake! In my naivety, I found this very odd.

Racism or discrimination of any kind in its more modern sense did not enter our vocabulary, nor our daily lives. We never had to think about it. Walking down the hospital corridor one sunny afternoon, one of my patients, met me.

"Hey Miss Farmer! You going out in the sun today?"

"Well, I hope so, later…"

"You be careful, Miss! You could end up black as me!" And the very tall, dark-skinned Ethiopian ambled away, chuckling with his high-pitched and infectious giggle.

In time, I was allocated my own wards and then, my own little hospital!

In those days, larger general hospitals had smaller satellite ones which were managed and staffed from the main hospital teams. I visited Williams Hospital several days a week. I loved it. It was run on the old-fashioned cottage hospital principles and was small and friendly. I had my own office. It was about the size of a broom cupboard but it was all mine! Next-door was Charlie, the store manager. He was a true little cockney cock sparrow! Always chirpy, dapper in appearance and a real diamond, he took me under his wing, popping his head round the open door each day and making sure that I was always all

---

[3] Paul, A.A. and Southgate, D.A.T. 1978. *The Composition of Foods. 4th Edition.* H.M.S.O.

right. His build was slight with Charlie Chaplin bendy legs. His kindly, crumpled face, which was always smiling, was framed by well-combed and neat but sparse white hair.

Most days, he would poke his head round the door, combing his hair with one hand, following it with the other, smoothing it down.

"OK Mary? I'm just going to wash my boat, put on my peckham, comb my barnet and go off down the frog in my jam for my lily with my trouble… see you la'er." He turned to go.

"Er…?"

"Gor' blimey!" he grinned over his shoulder. "Would you Adam and Eve it! Boat race – *face*; Peckham Rye – *tie*; Barnet Fair – *hair*; frog and toad – *road*; jam jar – *car*; Lily and Skinner – *dinner*; trouble and strife – *wife*! And then I need to get on the dog to put that order in – dog and bone – *phone*! Come on Mary, I'll have to teach you rhyming slang!" And so dear Charlie helped me to complete my somewhat limited education. But I could never grasp that elite language of speaking backwards!

The Williams Hospital
July 26th 1971

Darling Mum

This is bad – I am using a sheet of headed paper from the hospital – again!

Guess what! Julia is ill again – she really seems to have a horrid problem with her asthma – and Valerie (my senior colleague) has the morning off again tomorrow – so I shall be on my own! Funny how everything happens at once!

I am writing to Susie to fix a date for her to come round and I will pump her about the Flour Advisory Bureau!

I am working this Saturday but hope to come and see you when I finish, if that's OK.

Lots of love, Mary xx

One of my patients on the wards at Williams was diabetic; so far so good, I could deal with that. But then, he developed kidney disease. Not so good. Nephropathy can be a common complication of diabetes.

In those days, in the absence of readily available kidney dialysis, treatment was largely by diet. As the kidneys fail, so the by-products of protein metabolism – mostly urea, rise in the blood. This makes the patient feel rough as hell – and it makes the skin very itchy too.

The basis of diet treatment then was to reduce the amount of protein, the principle being to give the kidneys less work to do. The Giovanetti diet, which allowed only 20 grams (g) of protein per day, was the one in vogue. It was important to ensure that this precious protein was supplied by rich sources, such as egg, meat and milk, rather than the little bits and pieces that one gets from cereals and vegetables.

If I tell you that one egg, one ounce (30g) of cooked meat and one-third of a pint of milk (190mls) each contain seven grams of protein, you can see that this meagre allowance is soon used up. In an attempt to safeguard the body protein, it is essential to try and increase the calorie intake, otherwise the body starts to use its own protein as a source of energy and bang! Up goes the urea again!

In view of the diabetes, there was a limit to the amount of carbohydrate foods one could allow and, as fat is twice the amount of calories, I tried to encourage this poor man to eat cream and butter, cream cheese and fried foods to ensure the high calorie intake. Imagine grappling with this, when you don't feel well! In addition to this, there were restrictions on sodium (salt) and potassium intakes – a dietitian's nightmare to work all this out to the nearest millimole – and a patient's too!

Because of the high number of immigrants in the area, occasionally there were language barriers. No interpreters were available then. I was asked to see an Asian lady to find out what she would like to eat. Mrs Kapur spoke no English and I hadn't even heard of Urdu, Gujarati or Punjabi at that time. Through mime, we managed to establish that she did not eat meat or fish (art is not my thing but my sketch of the Christian sign of a fish helped!). Eggs were something else: I drew an egg – she looked puzzled. I started clucking, flapping my arms...and then mimed laying an egg. She started laughing. We both laughed. We giggled. Helplessly. Then...an ominous silence. She shook her head: "No!" More giggling.

Once I had moved to Calmershire, interpreters could be available – but at a cost to the department. I had been asked to visit a shelter for Vietnamese refugees. None of them could speak English at all and there were concerns that they were not eating well, owing to the unfamiliarity of local foods. What a fascinating place it was! They grew their own vegetables and had developed a "little corner of Vietnam" in the middle of a busy city centre! An oasis of tranquillity!

Later in my career, I was asked to give a talk on "healthy eating" to a group who were hard of hearing. It was slightly unnerving to have to concentrate on using relatively simple words and phrases, so that they could be quickly interpreted into sign language. I was amazed at the speed at which the interpreter's hands and fingers moved. I have a friend who is an actress and was in the play, *Children of a Lesser God*, which starred Trevor Eve and the deaf actress, Elizabeth Quinn. After the show, we were invited to a party at Joan's house. One of the rooms was filled with people and there was a total and strange silence. Then, every so often, peals of laughter and giggling would erupt. It was infectious! Signing was obviously no barrier to telling jokes and having fun.

Back at Williams Hospital, kosher meals were no problem: we could buy them from a reputable source ready-made. But feeding an Asian vegetarian was a tricky thing. In the end, my patient's family was able to bring meals in for her and I would buy odd extras. At that hospital, there was no specialised diet cook, as there was at the North West Hospital, so the diet menus had to be relatively simple.

Pests in these old hospital kitchens were a common problem. Cockroaches found the lagging round the steam pipes an irresistible place to hide during the day, coming out at night to scavenge once the kitchen staff had gone home. Quite often, working late, I would go into the kitchen after hours and there would be an ominous scuttling and scratching on the tiled floors, as the light snapped on.

On my last night at that hospital, my flatmate, whom I had known from college, came to help me finish up. I let Lisbeth in through the back door. Tom, her boyfriend had come too. He had offered to replace the springs on my dear little old A35 (The Egg). There had been a sinister creaking. Tom stayed in the car park, got out his toolbox, put on his overalls and dived underneath The Egg. Lisbeth and I went into the kitchen.

"OK then," said Lisbeth. "What's first?" Her teacher-mildly-bossy instincts came to the fore. I set her to work with some filing, while I tidied up my patient notes to hand over to my successor. Eventually, we entered the kitchen to leave notes for the diet cooks. The cockroaches were having a field day.

"This is gross!" Lisbeth was aghast. "Isn't there any spray or something?" Together, we found some insecticide and went to war! I wondered afterwards how many dead bodies were strewn on the floor the next morning. I didn't care! I wasn't going to be there!

Even now, hospital hygiene leaves much to be desired. A report summarising three years' worth of hygiene surveys by *Which? Magazine* showed that dirty equipment, cockroach infestations and un-refrigerated food were rife in the 50 hospitals that were reviewed. Thanks to the Freedom of Information Act, further damning pictures were revealed year after year.

Visiting the geriatric wards at the North West was not pleasant. I am embarrassed to say, I hated it. The wards were in little huts, physically away from the main hospital, which appeared to be ashamed of them and wanted no ownership or relationship with them. They all smelt of urine and a deep feeling of doom and depression pervaded. The patients were in neat rows in little cots, most of them with the cot sides up, so that they couldn't "escape". They looked like little grey-haired dolls.

There was even a special menu for them and for the mentally ill, which was different from that for the main hospital wards. It was almost always minced meat and mashed potato, with very little variation – maybe steamed fish on Fridays. Dessert was nearly always a milk pudding of sorts or maybe tinned fruit. Fresh fruit and nicely cooked vegetables were a rarity. In the enlightened present we would be horrified at such a thought but then it was commonplace.

Patients would wail and cry out in their dementia. "I want to go home…" A patient on the other side of the ward said to me quietly one day, "We are all going home soon", and she raised her eyes heavenwards. Later in my career, I would be passionate about caring for the elderly and infirm but for now, the quicker I was in and out of there, the better.

The hospital secretary, as he/she was called in those days, was responsible for the administration and general running of the hospital. Mr Woodall called in each day to say "Good Morning" to Charlie and myself and to ask if there was anything that we needed. I knew that, should I have asked for anything, he would do his best to accommodate me.

Matron would walk the wards and wish each patient "Good Morning" by name when she came on duty and "Good Night" when she went off. The nurse taking her on her rounds had to remember all the patients' names, their diagnoses, any treatments or medications they had had that day and how they were improving – or not. It was a nightmare to gabble that lot off at the speed of a matron's march, especially if it was one's first day on that ward!

Once the NHS was reorganised (or disorganised? see "Territorial Boundaries"), such manners and common courtesies seemed to disappear. Senior nurses gave the impression of plumping themselves up officiously and called themselves nursing officers; a new training programme for student nurses (Project 2000) based much of the training outside the wards, with the result that they then started to refuse to feed helpless patients, as they felt it was beneath them. What was happening? The whole ethos of vocational training and tender loving care was changing and I wasn't sure if it was for the better.

Nowadays, there is more emphasis and reliance on equipment and technology than there used to be. It seems that the personal touch has gone. Bed-ridden patients are lucky if they get a daily blanket bath. No more is the thermometer under the tongue or in the armpit; the hand gently resting on the wrist to take a pulse; the stethoscope and sphygmomanometer to take blood pressure; the discreet observation of the rise and fall of the chest to count the respirations. Patients are hooked up to machines that monitor all of these. Bedsore prevention has also changed. In the '60s, bed-bound patients were treated several times a day on pressure-sore areas by gentle but deep massage to encourage the circulation. Any nurse, whose patient developed a bedsore, was deemed to have reneged on her care and she was summarily fired. In fear for our lives, I once assisted a nurse whose patient was showing the early signs of a sacral bedsore. Current treatment then was to paint the area with insulin and dry it with oxygen, from the conveniently placed outlet by the bed. It somehow worked and we both kept our jobs!

Modern research suggests that water-beds, air-beds and

other pressure-relieving equipment are superior to rubbing bottoms, heels and elbows, but check with any hospital long-stay ward or nursing care home. You will find that pressure sores are considered to be an occupational hazard and viewed with an apparent lack of concern. I have seen a patient hoisted up high and the district nurse and myself peering up into the deep, cavernous recesses of her rear, where a pressure sore had broken down to a hole, big enough to put your fist in. Bone was clearly visible. Not only must it have been incredibly painful but such sores can lead quickly to infection and septicaemia, placed as they are, right by the body's effluent pathways.

Is your blood boiling? Mine is!

"Another NHS lottery," says The Patients' Association in their recent dossier on pressure sores.[4] It calls for mandatory monitoring and reporting of pressure ulcers (bedsores). It estimates that around 412,000 patients will develop a new sore each year in the UK. The costs of treatment are estimated at £1.4–2.1 billion per year. This figure represents four per cent of the total NHS expenditure. No monetary cost can be put on the discomfort, distress and pain suffered by such unfortunate patients.

Like many of my era, I yearned for those days when matrons ran well- disciplined and efficient hospitals. It is true, some of them were "dragons" and made life scary for young nurses, but underneath they had their values firmly rooted in what was best for the patient.

Later, "Modern Matrons" were established but again, they tended to be divorced from patient care, shutting themselves away in their offices to do battle with targets, policies, management and politically correct issues.

---

[4] The Patients' Association. 2010. *Meaningful and comparable information. Tissue Viability, Nursing Services and Pressure Ulcers.* September 21st

THE FAB GIRLS

"Man cannot live by bread alone"

"The Book of Deuteronomy", Old Testament

Hammersmith
July 1971

Darling Mum

It was lovely to chat last night. Sorry that there was a lot going on – the girls from College were here – we had a merry time!

I would love to get a job back there but there aren't any vacancies. I did hear that one of the girls at Ipswich is moving on – I should love to go back there – good social life with the doctors too! I'll have to see how things turn out. This month's jobs' list didn't offer much.

Susie and Sally came to supper last week: Susie thinks I would like the FAB very much. I have mentioned this to Valerie – she is not really inclined to move on yet so is quite willing if I want to go first! Though I feel badly, because we have staff problems at the moment – one cook has gone; another is on holiday and one of our porters is going soon.

Will 'phone at the weekend
Love, Mary xx

Hammersmith
August 8th 1971

Dearest Mum

Thank you so much for the letter.
I went to the Flour Advisory Bureau on my afternoon off.
I must say, I was quite enthusiastic about the idea of joining them.

54

The head of the Nutrition and Home Economics Department is very nice – about 30, I would think – and I also met the lectures organiser. I think that knowing some of the college girls who are already there, made me feel very welcome.

It's quite hard work but interesting and much more varied than the hospital. It really seems to include more of the public health aspect which I am keen to follow, including things like ante-natal clinics, schools, the elderly, health visitors' work and so on.

The main theme is "Healthy Eating" but presented in a variety of ways to suit each audience. Bread is added as a side-line – after all, the Millers are the people who pay us!

Apparently, the Bureau started just after the War and the first lecturers were, in fact, all dietitians but now they include people from home economics, institutional management and teaching backgrounds as well.

I think if I took the job, I would miss the medicine but I can always catch up with the journals and although there is a policy that one should stay for two years, they would probably accept a resignation after about 15 months.

They were very understanding about the set up at the hospital – Valerie can't make up her mind whether she is leaving or not!

She and Philip came to supper last night. I took them home at 2.00am and then had to come back and clear up!! Bed at 3.00am!

Marie (a school friend) 'phoned and we are going to the Proms tomorrow – taking a picnic! And wine!!
Loads of love, Mary xxx

Hammersmith
August 25th 1971

Dearest Mum

Thank you so much for your nice letters.

I had a horrid evening yesterday: there was a MOUSE! He has been in the kitchen cupboard under the sink and in the drawer! Ugh! I have cleared everything out, washed it all and put wire wool round the holes. All was well this morning, so I hope that it stays that way!

I rang the FAB this morning: they still have a vacancy so I think I may give it a go – everyone seems to thinks it's a good idea. The money is much the same, or even a little more. Only thing is, I shall need CLOTHES – AND a HAT!!! Apparently, this is de rigueur for the WI and Townswomen's Guilds meetings!!

See you at the weekend.

Lots of love, Mary xxx

Hammersmith
September 5th 1971

Dearest Mum,

It was lovely to see you at the weekend and I am looking forward to hearing your plans for the flat!

The FAB rang up yesterday to offer me the job! £1250 p.a. – £50.00 more than I am getting now! Although I would have been entitled to a rise in December if I stayed.

Marie invited me to supper yesterday too: she is so much more agreeable when there aren't any men in her life!! We had a lovely evening. She had been along to the Intervarsity Club to see what it had to offer: she gave it a good review .

I need a day off now to find some nice clothes for the new job! Or at least to get some ideas!

See you soon

Lots of love, Mary xx

The chairman introduced me. I stood up and faced the audience: 500 Women's Institute ladies, all wearing posh frocks or suits with hats. I was in a posh afternoon dress and hat too.

With other WI worthies, I was on a stage with my exhibits on trestle tables in front of me. I had shopped locally in the morning for all the different kinds of bread I needed for the display and managed to win an argument at the baker's as to whether her "brown" bread was a true wholemeal or not. It wasn't. Some of the breads were quite exotic and included a cholla and pumpernickel rye bread, as well as a bloomer and a cottage loaf. The other items on display included plastic models of different foods – vegetables, an egg, a lamb chop, a piece of fish and a lump of cheese, to illustrate how the basic "Balanced Diet" is achieved. There was also some cocoa and a little pot containing black treacle. Artistically, six slices of bread were arranged fan-shaped on the tray. In addition, I had made up tasty spreads at the London office and frozen them – these were now gently defrosting. Salad garnishes, little bags of flour (wholemeal and white), a jug of warm water, fizzing gently with dried yeast and an earthenware flowerpot completed my "props".

The back row of the audience was far in the distance. I could barely make them out. I took a deep breath and projected my voice.

"Good Afternoon Ladies. Thank you for inviting me to speak to you today. Our title today is 'Scandinavian Breads'."

My head is smaller than average. I turned quickly round to show one of my exhibits and my hat slipped over one eye. It was a nuisance and a hazard. To a polite ripple of giggles, I dispensed with it, putting it carefully to one side. I explained the history of bread, Scandinavian style, including the necessary information on nutritional value, how good bread is for you (it's what you put ON the bread that can add extra damaging calories) what "a balanced diet" is and how bread fits in with this in all its various guises.

I then demonstrated how to make open sandwiches and suggested unusual toppings and combinations – some of which had been prepared in my hotel room a few hours previously – it's amazing how one can improvise.

"And now, I'm going to show you how easy bread-making is." This was my *grande-finale* to the talk.

"You need four ounces of white flour and four ounces of wholemeal flour. (That's about 100g of each). Pop these into your mixing bowl..." I held my hands high for maximum theatrical effect and emptied the flour from on high. I never knew that flour could bounce out of a bowl so effectively! At least they had the grace to laugh, especially when it made me sneeze.

"And this is one that I made earlier" – nothing but the best "Blue Peter" tradition. Appreciative "Ahh's" from these doughty ladies as I displayed a flowerpot shaped loaf and, indeed, it had been baked in a similar earthenware flowerpot to simulate the brick ovens of old.

After this, I was gasping for a "nice" cup of tea. Everyone jostled to ask questions and to get their own refreshments. The bread from the display was raffled off and the remainder of the spreads and salad garnishes resolutely binned. The chairman then took me firmly by the arm.

"Miss Farmer, would you do us the honour of judging our competition?"

Competition? No one had warned me of this dubious honour! I hardly knew a bun from a bap and I had to be judge and jury of the Victoria sponges, scones and Madeira cakes on display. Anyone who has seen the film *Calendar Girls* will remember the wonderful scene where Helen Mirren's character wins the Victoria sponge competition by nipping off clandestinely to Marks and Spencer! That same film immediately transported me to the days of lecturing in similar venues, with the evocative sound of metal chairs being drawn back on a wooden floor in a draughty village hall.

All eyes were boring into me. Trying to be scientific about it and remembering our "experimental baking" at college, I dutifully cut each sponge in half; scrutinised "the crumb"; poked and prodded it and then ate a small piece, munching sagely, weighing up the pros and cons of each and entering into the solemnity of the occasion.

It went very quiet and I immediately sensed which of them expected to win but, of course, I did not know which exhibit was hers. What a relief when I pulled the "right" one into first place! Feelings on such things can run high.

I was one of the Flour Advisory Bureau girls dabbling with "Flour Power". As "FAB Girls", our job was to educate the masses on the wonders of nutrition and eating bread as part of a balanced diet. How many of you remember the slogan: *"Six slices a day is the balanced way"*? This was the one that was current and, of course, there was the usual quip – how big is the slice?

Reminiscing with a friend and fellow FAB girl recently, she told me that on one occasion the WI were locked out of their church hall. There was only one way in – through a window. As the thinnest and most athletic of those present, it was her job to climb in and unbolt the door. So, in best afternoon frock, high heels and hat, in she went! The lectures were free, so we were quite popular with groups of WI, Townswomen's Guild, Young Wives' groups, schools and colleges, who were always on the lookout for a free speaker to fill their diaries.

The address of the Flour Advisory Bureau was most prestigious: 21, Arlington Street, London W1. Many years later, a young friend took me to dinner at the famous "Le Caprice" restaurant.

"Gosh! I used to work opposite here!" I told him. We went to look at the plaque on the door. It still looks imposing and is still owned by the British and Irish Millers Association.

Hammersmith
October 8th 1971

Dearest Mum
This is just a quick line to say that all is going fairly well with the new job, though I felt like a fish out of water at first!

Everyone is very nice and I feel that, once I get the hang of things, it will be good fun.

I have sent you my "arrangements", so you can see where I will be next month or so ...

I've bought a COAT!! It cost ££££'s (£35.00) but it's very nice – Aquascutum – I dithered and dithered and in the end, got Lisbeth to approve! I got a tax return so blew it all in one go!!

Lots of love, M xx

St James' Street, Hammersmith
October 9th 1971

Dearest Mum

Today was the Nutrition Conference – held at the Hilton Hotel! What swank! It's given annually by the FAB, so that meant we were "hostessing" which was fun – but highly exhausting.

Lots of people were there whom I knew – Moira and Julia – the former very happy in her married state!

I went straight from there to Sheila's – my baby-sitting went OK – no squeaks! He's very good and a happy little chap now!

The christening is fixed for early November. I have been asked to be a godmother! Isn't that nice! I feel very proud and honoured!

The afternoon we spent in the garden: Shelia and me weeding and Tim mowing the lawn: very companionable!

Then a friend of Sheila's came to tea to show off her new fiancé – we all approved!

Sheila has lent me a pattern for a "sausage dog", so I can get cracking on making them as draught excluders – using up my remnants of material and stuffing them with old tights!

Lots of love, Mary xx

St James' Street
Hammersmith
November 6th 1971

Darling Mum

It was lovely to hear from you: thank you so much for your letters.

I had quite an afternoon today: went to have my hair cut at Vidal Sassoon's – a student was doing it and each time he snipped a bit, he had to go and check with the boss! It took over FOUR HOURS!! I was really ratty by the time he'd finished, not least because my neck ached from having to be in one position all the time…BUT it is very nice – a sort of bob style.

Well, I am playing "solo" now at the FAB – they have let me out on my own! I think it will be fun – at least I can't complain of two days being alike! It does make social life a bit more awkward though, with all the evening work.

Lisbeth thinks we will probably move to the maisonette she is buying in early December – I will be in touch when we know more so we can arrange collection of my bits and pieces.

I am off to a conference tomorrow and then a BDA (British Dietetic Association) meeting in the evening.
Love always, Mary xx

St James' Street
Hammersmith
November 12th 1971

Dearest Mum

Thank you so much for your letters: am so glad that you have someone to help with your move.

I saw Lisbeth's flat yesterday: it really is quite small but has quite a lot of character. There is a teeny back garden too – plenty of room for some nice pots.

12.30am: If I don't get something resembling a letter off to you now, I never will!

There is a lot going on at work, which makes social life awkward. If Lisbeth and I want to have someone round together, we have to check the diaries months ahead! She thinks we may be moving either the w/e of December 11th or the previous one. We need to arrange for all our bits of furniture to be collected between Manchester and Chichester!

Sorry this is so short: I have just come back from giving a talk at Ewell – they were such a nice group of ladies – but I feel that I didn't give a very good "performance".
Lots of love, Mary xxx

We were a team of six and between us worked a three-week rota of one "at home", which meant lectures in the London and Home Counties area; one was spent in the kitchen baking and one "away", which meant going anywhere in the British Isles, outside the "home" area. We stayed in hotels for which we had to make our own arrangements. I would always eschew the big towns, preferring to find a small, friendly, country guesthouse. Sometimes we flew to Glasgow, Edinburgh or Belfast, used buses and trains to the far north, east or west of the country, or drove, if we were lucky enough to have our own cars. I still have wonderful memories of flying over the Forth Bridge on a bright, sunny, icily cold day. It looked so romantic.

Llandudno
November 24th 1971

Dearest Mum
I am sitting in the hills, quite high up with a fantastic view of the sea – without a coat!!! Sun everywhere – beautiful sky – gulls wheeling round and calling loudly. The town seems really deserted but I expect that they get very crowded in the summer season – it's quite a popular resort I believe.
It's marvellous to have this wonderful air: the only thing that mars it is that I have no one to share it with – not even the dog!
Bangor was rather miserable – wet and cold. The hotel was fairly nice but there was no heater in my room. I had bed socks and a vest on under my pyjamas!! And nicked the eiderdown from the other bed in the room!
Gogarth Abbey is great! It's a large hotel and looks over the bay

with the hills, where I'm sitting, behind it. It's nice and quiet!

The two groups that I spoke to here were in very small villages, which means that they all prefer to speak Welsh! One of the reasons that I felt the talks didn't go quite as well as I'd hoped was that they had to listen to an hour's worth of English! I felt quite alien!

I had great fun getting the bread yesterday in Bangor: I ended up in "ye olde bakehouse" – a wonderful aroma as the hot loaves came out of the ovens!

Tonight, I am talking on "Sensible Slimming": It was so warm in my room, I asked the receptionist if my "perishables" could be kept in the 'fridge till I needed them: the staff were most amenable to such a strange request!

The shadows are lengthening: a pity that the days are so short, especially when the weather has been so unexpectedly wonderful – you would think it was early September! I'd love to come to this area again and do some exploring!

I managed to get in touch with Norah, Mrs Neale's friend: a bit older than me, she had done Institutional Management at Westminster Tech. and now works as a bursar at Bangor University. She came to collect me and we had such a nice afternoon, chatting over tea, finishing up with a martini! So I've had no time to be bored!
Lots of love, Mary xx

I had travelled by train to Bangor and fortunately, there were porters on stations in those days to help us with our heavy bags but there was a lot of waiting about on draughty platforms for many of our longer journeys.

That was when I spent my tax rebate on a "maxi-length", Aquascutum maroon and beige tweed coat and knee-high, maroon suede boots to match. I felt the "bees knees" and was warm as well.

When away from the office, we needed to spend each morning buying the breads locally that we needed for our display. It was amazing how many variations on a wholemeal bread there were – and still are. After our "shopping" in the morning, and preparing our exhibits, the rest of the day was our own until we had to leave for our talk, or be fetched from our hotel by a worthy member of the WI. I would often find a country walk in the afternoon and on one occasion assisted a farmer in righting a very pregnant ewe, which had fallen into a tractor rut and got stuck!

When staying away, I hated eating by myself in the hotel and would usually take a book or newspaper to breakfast. Dinner was largely omitted, as the talks were often in the evenings, so a decent lunch was the norm. It could be quite a lonely existence for that week. Often, there was no television in the hotel rooms either.

Chesterfield
December 2nd 1971

Darling Mum

It was lovely to chat on Sunday: you sounded really cheery!

Re: Christmas plans – John and I felt that if you would both like to come to Hammersmith, that might be best – I have said that I will take the following week off, so I wouldn't mind taking you back to Chichester. If you'd like to let us know train times, John or I will meet you at Victoria.

Lisbeth and I went to John Lewis to look at cookers for the flat: there was a Creda – quite a decent size and four rings – £51.00!

I went to a nutrition seminar last week: there were quite a few people from college and also, guess who! Prof. Thomas! I nearly fell over backwards – it's not often he graces these functions with his presence!

What horrid weather with all this fog! I'm not regretting that Aquascutum coat one jot!!

See you soon!

Lots of love, M xx

Our week in the kitchen was when we made the samples of our trade. We took the flowerpot loaf and different tea-breads and cakes with us as exhibits. A favourite was an "all-in-one" chocolate cake that contained black treacle – an excellent source of iron and calcium. There was a fig loaf too – extra fibre here. Much of the presentation depended on the title of the talk but we nearly always showed how to make bread and bake it in the clay flowerpot.

The original FAB lady was Patty Fisher, sadly now no longer with us. She was highly respected for her knowledge and her passion for taking simple but practical nutrition and health messages to the public at large. At her demonstrations and talks, she always wore a black hat, placed at an elegant angle, as well as fine leather gloves. Before the bread-making demo, she would peel off one glove and elegantly mix the bread one-handed!

Public speaking then was definitely not my thing and there were times when I couldn't imagine why I was doing this job: my first talk was a disaster. I simply dried up. Gradually, confidence grew and I enjoyed it. I was invited to address the WI Federation at their local annual conference, as already described. People were genuinely interested in food and nutrition and how they could better their health through diet. Titles of our talks ranged from "Feeding a Family"; "The History of Bread"; "Scandinavian Breads"; "Breads and Spreads" and of course, "Slimming".

Extract from *The Shrewsbury Chronicle*
March 31st 1972
Produce Guild Ladies told How to Use Their Loaf
At each of the Spring Area Meetings for Shropshire W.I., Miss M. Farmer of the Flour Advisory Bureau demonstrated "Scandinavian Ways of using Bread", which, of course, included exciting Danish open sandwiches.

Miss Farmer explained the nutritional value of a variety of breads – rye, wheat and "hard" breads, which are served with coffee – popular in Scandinavian countries where, she said, housewives would never dream of placing slices of buttered white bread on their tables.

Miss Farmer followed this by giving lots of useful tips on fillings and toppings.

Extract from *The Warrington Guardian*
December 3rd 1971
Flour Power

"Modern Life – Modern Meals" was the theme of a talk given by Miss Farmer, a dietician with the Flour Advisory Bureau, to the members of St. James' Church-Women's Fellowship in the Old Road, Latchford schoolroom on Thursday last week.

The next meeting of the Fellowship will include a demonstration by a representative of the Irish Linen Guild.

Extract from *The Bucks Free Press*
Jan 21st 1972

The majority of members braved the unpleasant weather to attend the January Meeting of Downley W I.

They were amply rewarded by the attractive appearance and lively personality of the speaker, Miss Mary Farmer, of the Flour Advisory Bureau, whose practical advice on choosing foods for health held her audience spellbound.

Of course, there were often embarrassing moments. One that immediately comes to mind occurred when addressing a small group of patients who were undergoing rehabilitation, after mental illness. As I finished and asked if anyone had any questions, a good-looking youth asked, "What are the best foods for sex, Miss?" I turned bright red and muttered something about oysters and other supposed aphrodisiacs! Once, I made a big mistake by talking about "unusual" vegetables, such as peppers and aubergines, to children in Falkirk, Scotland – I could see some of them turning visibly green. They had never heard of these "foreign" foods then! On another occasion, I was asked to give a talk to a large group of teenage schoolchildren on "Healthy Eating". The staff disappeared, presumably to have a much needed coffee and a smoke. It was immediately obvious that there was a little group in the combined classes, whose sole object was to make my life difficult. I had had no teacher-training skills. Discipline or respect for a visiting lecturer was non-existent. It was probably also a big mistake and rather rash of me to mention the word "constipation", when talking about fibre in the diet! I was easy game for them! I managed to separate the trouble-makers but lost the plot totally and, was eventually rescued by the staff. My estimation of teachers escalated.

And how difficult it was when addressing women's groups, not to keep making eye contact with the largest person in the audience, when talking about slimming! However hard I tried, my roving eye kept returning.

Fulham, London
1971

Dear Mum

I had great excitement last week: the Weight Watchers' Association and The British Nutrition Foundation got together for a conference and had invited a Prof. Sebrell to speak – he's the Medical Adviser to Weight Watchers.

I got back in time from my FAB talk to go to the evening presentation and didn't know a soul but in the end, met up with another two dietitians who knew Demetri.

We saw people drifting off afterwards, so we followed and found ourselves at a reception with drinks being handed round – NOT Slimline Tonic or Tomato Juice, but whisky and gin!!

I got chatted up by a professor from Birmingham University who "thought he'd seen me before sometime" – he did apologise for the old gag! Anyway, he was most interesting and said that if I was in the Aston area of Birmingham to look him up and give him a starch-free lunch!! I wonder if he meant it!

Last night, I finally braved myself and went to the IVC (Inter-Varsity Club) new members' social – with Marie for moral support.

It was a bit strained at first but I soon realised others were much shyer than I was! I met a guy who worked in immunology with special reference to rheumatoid arthritis. He was amazingly enthusiastic and I learned a lot. (I had heard of things like IgA and IgG – so he recognised that I had a glimmer of intelligence!!) I told him to keep up the research because of you!

And met some other people too – good practice for small talk! So now that I have broken the ice, perhaps I'll get to some more functions there.

Julia rang today to invite me to lunch as a kind of send-off for Valerie – she is getting married to Philip at the end of the month.

Lisbeth came back today but has to go into hospital to have a polyp removed from her nose! Sounds nasty!

Lots of love, Mary xxx

The electricity cuts of January and February 1972, due to the seven-week long miners' strike headed up by Joe Gormley in a clash with Ted Heath as Prime Minister, did nothing to diminish our activities. In the spirit of "the show must go on", we roamed the country with our displays and our entertaining and learned talks by torch and candlelight!

Fulham
February 26th 1972

Dearest Mum

Thank you for your letters – the post has been very odd lately and a whole load came all at once – the postmarks were December!

We've been extremely lucky in not being too affected by the cuts: at Romford, all the candles were at the ready but we didn't need them in the end!

The East Enders are quite a breed apart! What a journey! All the way across London into Dockland – lots of really heavy traffic – and pollution to match!

I've asked Susanne if I could take those two weeks off in June. She says it's OK but wonders if I'd like to have a 'bit of a busman's holiday'. There are three talks she wants me to do: Newton Abbott, Plymouth and Exeter. It might be worth considering – at least our petrol would be paid for! And you could have 2-3 nights in an hotel!!

We could think about it.

Susanne has just given me my April arrangements: I'm going to Scotland! Flying to Glasgow and then across to East Lothian and then to Fife. Crumbs!

Lisbeth is much better now: I think her iron tabs helped.

Lots of love, Mary xx

PS: I got a hat at Fenwick's! Beige felt Breton with white trimming

I'm not going to Bradford after all – swapped with someone else – so I don't go away until March 1st – to swinging Cleethorpes!!

Fulham

March 5th 1972

Dearest Mum

Thanks for your letters: I DID get the one that you sent to Bradford: the girl who went instead of me kindly forwarded it.

Isn't it marvellous to have finished with all the power cuts and a return to some normality?

Susie came up to town and we had lunch. She is very full of her wedding news – getting married on May 13th, so I've been told to keep the day free.

Last Wednesday, I went to Grimsby to give the talk in Cleethorpes. I arrived in the middle of a power cut – they have had four hourly ones there! – so I went for a "healthy walk" round the golf course that the

hotel overlooked. Apart from two lone golfers, all I saw was a hare –
I'm not sure which of us was more startled, as he suddenly jumped up
from the grass – I almost trod on him!

From there, to Gainsborough, where I had a most interesting evening.
I had written to Trevor (a former boyfriend) at his parents' address but
had not heard anything! Funnily enough, his mother had opened it in
error! 'Phone calls and messages went back and forth with the result
that his Dad appeared at the W.I. meeting, just as I was packing up! He
is the spitting image of Trevor! He and T's Mum came down to the hotel
and we had a very nice natter, including Trevor in a four-way telephone
call! He is married now – but not to Jackie! – and they have a little girl,
15 month's old. Proud grandparents showed me photos: she looks very
sweet. I am invited to stay with them the weekend after next, which I'm
looking forward to. They live near Wallingford, Berks.

Lisbeth and I met up with some old College students on Friday;
Sheila, baby and dog came on Saturday – I enjoyed it but I think Lisbeth
found it a bit much!! After the others had gone, she and I skipped off to
the pictures – "Diamonds are Forever" with Sean Connery!! He really
is rather dashing and every young girl's dream of The Ideal Man!!

Look forward to seeing you next weekend.

Lots of love, M xx

PS I have finished making my maxi dress: it's turned out well and
I'm pleased!

C/0 Beauchamp Hotel
Shrewsbury
March 23rd 1972

Dearest Mum

It was so good to hear from you and glad that the flat-hunting is
going well.

The weather here has been brilliant! Which is just as well, as I am
here all week! I have been exploring the countryside and so glad that I
did bring my car, which means I can go out every day! I've found some
lovely quiet spots to have my picnic lunch and rambling. I don't find it

so lonely when I'm outside.

On my way back from Ludlow, I stopped to look at Stokesay Castle – not open to the public until the summer but what I could see looked lovely and a very pretty setting. Then I rambled on the hills – it's so good to have the lighter evenings – and the lambs were so pretty, gambolling and skipping about. There are LOTS of farms here of course – I came across a dead sheep – the poor thing was quite cold and stiff – it looked as if it had fallen down a ditch and broken something – while I was examining it, all the other sheep in the field gathered round – odd, wasn't it? Anyway, I told a chap who was driving a tractor, so felt that I'd done my duty!

I saw a few hares as well – it was so still and quiet – just the birds twittering away – very pleasant!

It was about 8.00pm when I got back to the hotel, which is really nice: I have rather a small room but it has a beautiful view over the hills and I have my own loo and shower!

On Tuesday, I found such a pretty walk – by a brook with a ford – and the first lot of primroses.

Today, it's a bit cloudy and I've just come back from town from doing my bread-shopping. I've put in an order for the week at the two bakers here – that helps a lot.

The groups I've given talks to have all been very pleasant and interested and the numbers have been huge! 102 on Monday; 213 on Tuesday and 188 yesterday! Makes up for the low numbers I had with those rotten Mothers' Clubs!!

Mrs Everall is the produce guild secretary for Shropshire and is a charming woman. In her late 60s, I suppose with two grown-up daughters, one of whom did Institutional Management and is now the assistant domestic bursar at Christ's Hospital School in Horsham.

The other is married with two daughters. Mrs E tends to "mother me" a bit and has taken to washing and ironing my table cloths and tea-towels, which is very kind. She has taken me to most of the talks as well: she has to attend anyway and it seemed silly to take two cars.

Seeing Trevor with his wife and daughter was great fun and I really enjoyed it, though one or two "domestic tiffs" were embarrassing and uncomfortable. Catherine, the little girl – "Cathween" is her interpretation – is a darling and very affectionate. They rent the School House which is actually quite a large cottage and garden. Trevor has to teach on Saturday mornings and so Carol and I worked in the garden – until the lawn mower gave up the ghost!

I felt awful as I broke a plate while washing up! I hope to find a replacement at John Lewis.

I think I have a talk in Lewes next week, so will come on to you afterwards if that's OK – will let you know later.

Lots of love, Mary xx

Fulham
April 23rd 1972

Darling Mum

How nice to get your letters – thank you so much.

The Scottish trip went off quite well and the trains weren't too bad. And the flight was such fun! Except I really only enjoyed the going up and coming down! I wouldn't get very far if that's all I did!

The weather was very nice too, which makes such a difference. I had to go by bus from Haddington to Edinburgh and then to Cupar, which was a bit of a headache, carrying all those beastly bags. All that travelling took quite a long time.

On the way back, I went by train, so I saw the Forth Bridge both ways: it really is beautiful countryside but Kirkaldy wasn't very exciting, even though the fair was there, lending a holiday atmosphere. The Scots people I met were awfully nice – one of the ladies sent along her son to meet me – quite a nice young man!

Yesterday, we had a "jolly outing" from work to Chorley Wood in Essex, where the flour and baking research is done. It was a most interesting day and we went round all the departments, afterwards being entertained by the director and his merry men – all quite famous in their fields – I made a bit of a boob by not recognising the name of one of them!

Lisbeth's sister and her husband are coming round to the flat soon to help us put up a bathroom cabinet amongst other things: it will be a hive of activity – and a late night I expect!

This week has been quite tiring: relentless talks – most of them in the evening. On Wednesday, I had the new home economist and a student to accompany me. My! These Jewish ladies were chatterboxes! And what a sumptuous tea they had! There was caraway bread topped with roll-mop herring; tea-breads and rich cakes! Some of the ladies were quite plump! I now know why!

The Diabetic Group was a splendid crowd to talk to: very mixed – boys and girls; women and men all ages. I learned a bit about the diabetic "camps" that they hold each summer: I think that might be a better idea than being a Locum. I'm not sure if you get paid – certainly they pay your keep – it sounds fun and would be a good experience.

Susie is organising a dinner dance after her reception and she has asked Suzanne and me if we would go: it means staying overnight – probably Newton Abbott but I'll ask Suzanne how she feels about that …

I have fixed a B and B for the first night of our holiday in Wells: £1.13 each for the night.

Lots of love, Mary xx

FRESH AIR AND AN OPEN TOP

"Driving along in my automobile…"

Chuck Berry

Except that I didn't have a "baby beside me at the wheel" and I *did* have "a particular place to go"!

Following my stint at the FAB and shunning other possible hospital work, having never much enjoyed being enclosed in one building all day, I quickly applied for a job as the county dietitian for Woodlandshire. I have to admit that a certain amount of nepotism prevailed: my good friend who was in post was moving to the North and she put in a good word for me.

This was 1972 and community dietetics, as a separate entity and quite different from hospital dietetics, was just getting off the ground. The principle was simple: as there were so few dietitians in the country – at that time they numbered just over 1000 for the whole of Britain – it was deemed more effective to disseminate the principles of good nutrition through other professions and disciplines and thus, widen the net. Currently, the number of dietitians has increased by around five times, compared with what it was then.

Many people think of dietitians as holding endless clinics in GP surgeries and in hospitals, or sitting by patients' bedsides on wards explaining the vagaries of many and various diets, but community dietitians at that time could be described in modern "Management Speak" as "thinking outside the box". Initially, such posts were employed by the Health or Social Services

Departments of a county council, rather than by the NHS. When the idea was first put into practice, there was a true paucity of numbers. In 1972, there were merely ten across the UK. As it was essential to work alongside other professionals, strong links, and indeed friendships, were made with many. Health visitors, district nurses, school nurses, school meals advisory staff, school cooks, pharmacists, teachers, health education staff, lecturers at the local technical college and voluntary organisations, such as home helps and the Meals on Wheels services became our "students" and then, our "voices". Visual aids were often real food, which meant clearing out my food cupboard at home and arranging a colourful basket of fruits and vegetables. Rather than give advice to individuals, the emphasis was on preventive medicine and education. Much of the time was spent organising in-service training, "Teach-Ins" and conferences, taking part in community nurse training and providing back-up educational material for these other professionals to use. Patients attended the hospitals for individual dietetic advice. GP-based clinics for dietetic consultations did not exist then. These came later.

As previously alluded to in "How it all Started", research was suggesting that weight loss was more successful if patients belonged to a group. There was a sense of sharing, understanding, support and encouragement between the members. This principle underpinned a number of slimming clinics in the county, which were run by interested and enthusiastic health visitors, who had had initial training from the dietitian. School nurses followed suit for overweight children in their schools. Midwives, who organised antenatal classes, invited the dietitian in for a session or two and together with health visitors and health education officers (HEOs), teaching sessions on health and nutrition for pregnancy and the newborn thrived.

Home visits were, of necessity, kept to a minimum, but occasionally referrals were made by a health visitor or a GP.

Usually, these patients were babies, young children or breastfeeding mothers.

The school meals advisory officer for Woodlandshire was a gem. She and Jamie Oliver would have got on like a house on fire! She constantly ran in-service training programmes for her school cooks, with the result that children were welcomed in the morning by the aroma of home-baked bread, buns and cakes. "Nutrition in disguise" was her mantra. By this she meant that vegetables were secreted into Bolognese sauces, stews, meat loaves and casseroles; sugar content was reduced in dessert recipes and baked goods, including freshly made bread rolls, pies and tarts, were often made partly with wholemeal flour.

It is strange that "what goes around, comes around". In the early '70s, all school children were regularly weighed. Those, whose problems were highlighted, were referred for further advice. Very often, this meant advising the whole family on healthier eating patterns. Further, there was a School Meals Policy, which stated the exact quantities of calories and protein that should be provided in a portion of the school meal. In the '80s, free milk for primary schools and school meals was abolished. Some of you may remember the slogan: "Mrs Thatcher: Milk Snatcher". Mirroring the NHS non-medical services, school meals were put out to tender and bought in.

What a sad day it was when school meals were no longer! Especially as they also served as a practical example of good nutrition, often backed up by suitable posters, which at that time were hand made in-house, by the likes of yours truly and her colleagues, or we "borrowed" the services and skills of the technician who was employed by the Health Education Officers (HEOs). Luckily, I still had my box of watercolour paints from school days. Invention was certainly the mother of necessity! Latterly, a policy for school meals has been re-introduced but the Labour government of the day thought that it was their own new, clever idea.

The School Food Trust, "Eat Better do Better", is an independent body and, galvanised by Jamie Oliver's campaign, was established in 2005 by the Department of Education and Skills "to transform school food" and "to promote education and health of young people".[1] School food standards, which were revised in 2005, were to be phased across all schools over three years and implemented at the latest by 2008. Rather than be prescriptive as the original guidelines were, the current advice is more general, with the emphasis on provision of more oily fish, fruit and vegetables and dairy products. Confectionery, deep-fat fried foods, salt and snacks (except for nuts, fruit, vegetables and seeds) are restricted or disallowed altogether. (I have just re-read that and suggest that schools need to be careful about allowing nuts, in case a child is severely allergic). Stricter nutritional guidelines for school dinners in primary schools were set down in 2008, with those for secondary schools being implemented in the following year. In an attempt to further encourage the uptake of school meals, recent findings from The School Food Trust suggest that, in order to make packed lunches equally healthy and well balanced, parents need to set aside between 50 to 190 hours across the school year. If my maths is on the right lines, this is around 15 minutes to an hour each day. Perhaps some parents actually enjoy spending this time for their children? Continuation of the Trust's funding and in its present format is currently being debated. It awaits the outcome of the present (Coalition) government but it is understood that its commitment to "this incredibly important agenda" remains.[2]

Many of the school kitchens in the '70s and '80s doubled up to provide meals for the Meals on Wheels service. This meant

[1] Department of Education and Skills. 2009. *The School Food Trust*. Available at: http://www.schoolfoodtrust.org.uk/homepage
[2] BBC News Online. 2010. *School Food Trust faces quango axe*. September 24th. Available at: http://www.bbc.co.uk/news/education-11405066

that the kitchens were fully utilised throughout the school holidays as well as the school terms.

Because the county health departments were more generous in their budgets than the NHS, for the first time there was a move towards more professional looking diet-sheets and written information. Community dietitians started to produce their own glossy-looking leaflets and later some went into business, selling them to fellow professionals. These were a far cry from the untidy looking typed diet-sheets that had been copied using a Gestetner machine! The next step was to translate them into different languages. With the influx of immigrants of differing nationalities (mostly from Italy, several Asian countries and now, Eastern Europe), there was a strong case for facilitating the understanding of nutrition and dietetic information. Many food companies and organisations later joined this bandwagon and, to this day, produce attractive and usually nutritionally sound material, using the expertise of their in-house nutritionist or dietitian.

During the '70s, the number of county councils in Britain that were able to employ a dietitian within their health or social services departments rose to around 20. I shared an office with health education officers, who visited the schools offering education on sex and other topics, such as personal hygiene and road safety. Sex was the real winner with pupils and indeed, my own knowledge on the subject increased by leaps and bounds!

The perks of being employed by a county health department, such as Woodlandshire, were two-fold: firstly, I became a key-worker for its New Towns Commission, which meant that I was eligible for one of their apartments and secondly, the county council offered very enticing rates for loans, which meant that I could consider buying a new car.

The designated flats were in a row of six and were above

double garages – one for each flat. There was a large bed-sit, a kitchen, which measured eight feet x seven feet – just enough for my second-hand cooker and 'fridge – and a teeny bathroom. The "bath" was hysterical: I had never seen the like before. One end was overly deep and the other shunted up, making a "step" on which one could sit. On the first night, I slid down into the deep part with knees up to my chest, wallowing in the warm water which reached up to my neck and promptly had visions of getting stuck and having to call the fire brigade! Except that there wasn't a 'phone in the bathroom and mobiles had yet to be invented for the "common man".

The current boyfriend (who eventually became my husband) had just bought himself a white Triumph TR6. Not to be outdone, I swapped my ancient Morris mini-traveller (with the starter button and full-beam buttons on the floor) for a brand new, bright red Triumph Spitfire, Mark 4 – thanks to the loan by my employer. Woodlandshire is a big and attractive county and in the 1970s I was THE County Dietitian. Driving along leafy lanes in the summer with the top down and the wind in my hair was my idea of heaven, especially as I was getting paid for it. Dietetic students who came to visit had a glimpse of what appeared to be an attractive and rather glamorous job: applications for community dietitian posts soared!

Driving around a county doing one's work is not without its hazards. Animals, other drivers, other vehicles and traffic police all play their part. On one occasion, I had a clinic at a GP surgery in the county town of Borderland. It started at 9.00am but I liked to be early to sort out the paperwork I needed to take with me, familiarise myself with the computer (again!) and go through the notes of the patients who were booked in, some of whom would be new to me.

Going along a country road one particular sunny, wintry morning, I noticed that a cat on the opposite side of the road was running intently in the same direction as me. I slowed but the cat didn't. Suddenly, it was galloping across the road in front of me and then took a sharp left turn, straight towards my car. I braked sharply and heard a sickening bump. I stopped the car, got out and it had disappeared. Finding it crouching behind the village hall and not entirely sure how badly injured it was (one of its eyes looked decidedly swollen and a bit bloody), or whether it was going to go into attack mode, I scruffed it and examined its collar. Yes! It did have a tag with an address and 'phone number. I called the number. Of course, they were out, probably at work, like I was supposed to be. There was an answer 'phone. How do you leave a calm, professional message to beloved cat owners, indicating that it tried to commit feline hara-kiri in front of you? There seems to be no protocol for this. Somehow, I found suitable vocabulary. "Now what do I do?" I thought. I had no choice. I put the cat in the back of the car, where I had all my files and papers for the day, food samples and my Wellingtons for walking my dog later. Safely, the dog was the other side of the dog-guard. She was looking more than just interested! I knew of a veterinary surgery in the area, rang the number and thankfully, someone was there. On my way, I thought, "Oh No! Cats hate travelling! It's going to pee and puke all over everything – or even poo! Oh God!"

Arriving at the vet's, I went round to the back of the car. The cat had vanished. Looking harder, I discovered that it was face down in a Wellington boot. "Oh Lordy! It's a gonner!" I gently tipped it out. It wasn't. The vet was reassuring.

"It's probably just very shocked. Don't worry, we'll keep him in and put him on a heating pad." I thought how nice that sounded. I could have done with that! Now I was *really* late. It was just as well that there were no speed cameras on that route! I rang the vet at lunchtime. There were no queries from its owners. That afternoon, I was out of the office but when I returned, there was a message from the receptionist.

"Oh, Mary – there's a message here that I don't understand… something about a cat?"

"And?" I said hoping it was good news.

"It's fine," she said. "That's all it says here…does that make sense?" *Deo Gratias*!

Flat 7,
Bolam Court
Woodland
February 11th 1974

Dearest Mum

I have just had a weird and unnerving experience – the joys of working in the countryside, I suppose! A cow was loose in the road! It had no intention whatsoever of being caught! All of a sudden, it galumphed towards me – and missed! Phew!

I was just on my way back, having given a talk to some OAP's – they had given me a cheer!!

There is another interesting job in the dietetic jobs list this month: I'm going to write off for details – just for a laugh! It's at a health farm! As Keith says (a colleague at work) you go in at 9.30am, measure out the grapes, lettuce leaf and lemons – and that's it! Job done for the day!!

Of course, most of the clients would be overweight – but at least they would be rich ones!!

I'll 'phone at the weekend.

Lots of love, Mary xxx

Returning from North West Hospital one summer evening in my beloved and trusty "Egg", I checked my rear view mirror and noticed a very large policeman on a huge motorbike behind me. The Catholic guilt immediately flew into action. I checked that I wasn't speeding and everything else seemed to be in working order. My heart rate rose. I was very near to the flat that I shared with Lisbeth and took a small side turn. He followed. I took another little turn. He followed and then there was the roar of his bike in my right ear as he came alongside and waved me down.

"Oh Lord," I prayed silently. I wound the window down.

"Hello," I said trying to flutter my eyelashes. Though I was no mistress of coquetry, I could try. This was an emergency!

"Hello," he replied genially enough. "Did you know that your shock-absorbers are worn?"

"Er...?" more fluttering.

"Yes," he said, heaving himself off his bike, coming round and stretching his hands out, pressed his large bulk on "The Egg's" bonnet.

"Hey! Careful!" I was alarmed. "The Egg" was an old lady and need to be treated with respect.

"It's all right – they'll probably last! Where are you going?"

"Er...home..."

"Where's that?"

"Just round the corner..."

"Fancy a coffee?"

"Um...?" This was a surprise!

Loud and cheery laughter: "Ha! Ha! Ha! I may drop in sometime! Mind how you go!" And he gunned his engine. So this pantomime was just a chat-up line after all!

One is constantly surprised at people's kindness. I hadn't long been in Woodlandshire and was using one of the county fleet cars: a real "sit-up-and-beg" shiny black Morris 1000. I felt like the district nurse. In fact, the district nurses *did* use these cars! Returning from a clinic, I realised that petrol was running very low. I couldn't see a garage anywhere but did see a dairy and puttered in there to ask if they could direct me to the nearest petrol station. Eventually, I found a couple of chaps in the bottling area.

"Oooh...that's a few miles love...How much petrol do you have?"

"Mmm...it's running on the smell, I think..."

"Okay, Darling, come with me…" and the foreman took me round to where his own car was parked, picking up an empty glass milk bottle and a piece of rubber tubing on his way. Opening the petrol cap, he inserted the tubing, sucked on it and immediately siphoned off enough to fill the milk bottle with precious fuel. I started to thank him profusely.

"Not done yet," he grinned. Back to the bottling area, he placed our bottle on the belt and out it came with a silver cap. A very different kind of daily pinta!

Running late while taking a student to a British Dietetic Association meeting one winter's evening, I was hastening on, thinking that if we could average "a mile a minute", we should just make it. I could see that the petrol gauge was flickering dangerously towards empty. Just then, we topped the brow of a very steep hill. Switching the engine off, I freewheeled and came to rest gently and gracefully beside a petrol pump at the garage at the bottom. The student was quite impressed. I was just relieved!

One wet, drizzly morning, I was using a fleet car again and working in Woodlandshire. This time, it was a little red mini. Coming round a sharp right hand bend on the wet road, I hadn't expected to see a van backing out of a hidden driveway. I braked sharply and missed the van but the suddenness of it made the passenger front seat flip forward and smash the windscreen. I was very shaken. It is usually after such incidents that one thinks about the possibilities of what could have happened but I had to continue on to the morning's clinic. The department's secretary looked up as I arrived.

"Goodness Mary! You look white! Are you OK?"

"No…not really…" I explained.

"Oh dear…poor you." She was sympathetic which was A Big Mistake. It reduced me to tears.

"Look – don't worry. I'll get on to the fleet pool and arrange another car for you. You carry on with the clinic and I'll speak to you later." What a gem!

Minor road accidents are moderately common amongst community health workers. For this reason, the Calmershire Primary Care Trust actually organised a whole day on driving safely, through the firm that rented out the fleet cars. It was held on a disused airfield and all the instructors were former police officers. Scary? Mmm… But it was enormous fun. We learned how to work the Anti-Skid Braking Systems, how to park properly by weaving in and out of innocuous straw bales, and we were then taken out on the road for some fine-tuning of our driving skills.

I was thrilled to come home that night and say to my husband that the instructor had told me, "Don't change a thing! Just drive like that all the time."

Snow and ice cause all kinds of havoc for cars and it is amazing that, over the number of miles that one travels to and from and during work, that there aren't more incidences. Over the years, I had the occasional slide or spin on black ice but luckily no one else was around. I just embarrassed myself. However, one afternoon during January 2004, the country was hit by a freak snowstorm. On this occasion, a delay in managing to eat my lunchtime sandwiches served me well. It was 3.00pm and already getting dark.

Calmershire was becoming covered in the white stuff and I had a 25-mile journey to get home.

"Look at that! I think you'd better go now, Mary," advised the staff nurse at Tranquillity Hospital, the rehabilitation hospital in Calmershire, where I was working that afternoon. We were both staring out of the ward window at the swirls of huge snowflakes.

"Oh…it's OK," I said airily, "I'll just finish up and then perhaps go a little earlier."

Eventually, I slithered out of the car park and set off. I wasn't really worried and joined my usual route out of the city to go back to the office to collect what I needed for the next day, but I could barely see through the windscreen. As I reached the country road to go home, there was a long line of traffic in front of me – at a complete standstill. A coach looked as if it had got stuck on the hill. "It'll clear in a minute," I thought. To cut a long story short, I arrived home at midnight, having set off at 3.00pm. This was a journey that normally took 40 minutes at the most! Feeling a bit lonely, I 'phoned my friends on my mobile and caught up with some girly chat. I hadn't had time for lunch, so I ate half of my sandwiches, saving the other for later. I began to feel like an intrepid explorer who has to monitor his rations.

"Where are you now?" My husband was concerned and 'phoned at frequent intervals but my answer was the same each time.

"I've just gone another mile in the last hour," I would say.

"Oh NO!"

I was lucky: some motorists had to spend the whole night on the motorway. Fortunately, I have a good bladder, so did not need to have a "comfort stop". This is something that most community staff develop by necessity – one is constantly on the move and with no time between clinics, training sessions, meetings or home visits, it is just as well!

Returning home late one evening, having collected some enteral feed (artificial feed for tube-feeding) for a home visit the following day, I stopped off at a café to meet a friend for a reviving cup of tea. It wasn't until I was halfway down the road to go home afterwards and felt a huge cold draught of air, that I realised my rear screen had been smashed and two boxes of enteral feed taken. What on earth would someone want with those? If they tried to drink the liquid feed, they would have had a nasty shock: it tastes disgusting! The police were dutifully and equally puzzled and I equally dutifully filled out the Incident Form in triplicate. Needless to say, they were never found.

While driving, my brain would idle on all the various jobs that I had to do that day or the next, such as: 'phone so-and-so; write to Dr Thingy about Mrs B; take some food supplements to Mr D; enter the last clinic details on my palm top; check on Mrs X's enteral feed; write up the minutes of the staff meeting; prepare for the next training session at a care home; write to the matron and "cc" to the visiting GP about my last visit to her care home; claim my travel expenses and so on. Terrified that I would forget, I would scribble each one as it came into my mind on a post-it and slap it on the dashboard. When I parked up, even though many of these were totally indecipherable, these little scraps of paper were welcome *aide memoires* – I even used to keep a notepad by my bedside for the same purpose! Many a night of insomnia was soothed by the knowledge that I had it "written down somewhere".

THE DIETITIAN'S CLINIC

Patience is a virtue …
Children's Verse

My patience is now at an end
Adolf Hitler," Speech", September 26th 1938

"Good morning, Mrs Jone…s…" the smile petered out from my eyes but my lips were left in a frozen rictus. My friendly greeting was supposed to be welcoming and imbue reassurance, calm and good humour for that Monday morning. It not only went unnoticed but fell totally flat.

"Just give me a diet – I haven't time to stay and talk!" my overweight patient interrupted crossly. Hmm…wrong response. Two could play at that game.

Me, crisply: "Oh…OK…er, what kind of diet would you like? Low protein? Giovanetti? Low fat? Diabetic? Low potassium? Low sodium? High protein? Exclusion? Low residue? High fibre? Low lactose? And…there's more …"

No – I didn't really respond like that but it was tempting sometimes.

For many the word "diet" is synonymous with "slimming". In most people's minds, dietitians give "advice on slimming" and to be fair, a lot of the dietitian's time is spent doing just that – for better, for worse! Many patients are sent by their GPs or hospital consultants "to see the dietitian" and most of them *do* need advice on weight reduction, regardless of the underlying medical problem, which could vary from diabetes, osteoarthritis, heart disease, infertility, mental health or snoring, so they expect to be simply given a diet-sheet and told to get on with it. Anything else seems to them to be a waste of time and they just want to get in and out by the quickest possible route. Dare I say, that the dietitian's job is to find out more about people's lifestyle and their eating habits; about family history; medical history; medications; risks of various diseases; about meal patterns and shift work; likes and dislikes and so on and, with this information, tailor-make a regime that suits the individual. Many patients ask for a menu plan: it is entirely possible to do this for each and every patient, but it is excruciatingly time-consuming. There would doubtless be foods on it that the patient will not eat. So, from the dietitian's point of view, this chore can be a waste of valuable time and is generally discouraged.

Hospital dietetic clinics are sometimes held in the outpatient department, where a clinic room is allocated and usually everything one needs is available, like a table or desk, enough chairs and so on. Or it may be that the clinic is held within the dietetic department itself, if there is enough room. Hospital consultants, or their registrars refer patients for these. Pre-The Computer Age, we lugged all our paper patient notes from the hospital medical records department to wherever we were holding the clinic. Sometimes, these were pre-ordered and taken by a porter for us. We just hoped that all of them were there. Often there were one or two missing, which really threw a spanner in the works and held up the clinic while we made frantic 'phone calls and went on a search, often trudging over to medical records itself, which was more than likely based in the bowels of the hospital, or in a building several minutes away. There was a certain *frisson* of excitement, when, armed with the patient's hospital number on a scrap of paper, and ranging up and down the aisles in the department, one eventually discovered the missing notes – but it was very time-consuming. And very annoying to find that they had already been booked out to a consultant for that day.

Community clinics are generally held in a health centre, a GP surgery or a small, community (rehabilitation) hospital. Referrals for these are made by the GP, or occasionally by another health professional, such as a speech and language therapist (SALT), physiotherapist, district nurse or health visitor. Before these were set up, patients would have to trail several miles to their nearest hospital. Holding them in the GP surgery or health centre was much more convenient for them. Sometimes, there would not be enough room for everyone and I would find myself in an examination room with one chair for the patient and one for me but with no desk or table. If the patient brought a friend or partner, I would have to sit on the examination couch and spread the paperwork beside me. It often took on a life of its own, as it flew off onto the floor, leaving me scrabbling in an undignified state. Patients' notes for these clinics would be kept at the surgery and the receptionist would pull them for us. Occasionally one set would be omitted and we would have to fawn and grovel, so that we could have what we needed. Alternatively, we would keep our own set of notes together with any relative correspondence but it made more sense to have all the information together.

Referral letters from doctors were often succinct.

Dear Dietitian Lady
Mrs Smith has a BMI of 40.
Please advise.
Thanks.
(Squiggle as signature)

Or with a hint of dark, crude humour, that would not be allowed today.

Dear Dietitian
   Mrs Jones is an extremely large lady and has now developed

diabetes. Fortunately, her husband runs a car wash. I gather that is how she manages her personal hygiene.

Please advise her on how to get rid of more than a few of her excess poundage.

    Kind regards

Others might give a bit more information.

Dear Miss Farmer

Re: John SMITH
d.o.b. 01.01 1951
1, The Avenue, Anywhere

Please would you send this charming gentleman an appointment?

He has recently been diagnosed with diabetes and I have prescribed metformin. He is slightly overweight. He is a lecturer in Classics at All Saints' College and is keen to know more about his condition.

    Kind regards,

A legible signature

The letter might appear to be straightforward but then the patient offers further information.

"Yes, that's right, I do have diabetes but does it say that I am wheat intolerant as well?"

"Er...No, it doesn't. Just as well you told me."

"And does it say that I take *Amitriptyline*?"

"Um...No...is there anything else about that I should know?"

Ears prick up: *Amitriptyline* is prescribed for a variety of conditions but some of the side effects include constipation, dry mouth, increased appetite and weight gain. In fact, there are many medications that alter taste, food cravings, thirst, appetite and weight as well as interfering with mineral and vitamin status, so that the more complete picture one has, the better.

Mrs Kendall had irritable bowel syndrome. One of the tried and tested solutions at the time, depending on symptoms and history, was a low residue diet but with a bulk-forming supplement, such as *Celevac* (methyl cellulose).

On her follow-up appointment, she told me that she had had a horrid experience with the *Celevac*. What I hadn't known, because the information was not available to me, she hadn't told me and I hadn't thought to ask, was that she had a hiatus hernia, which is what happens when part of the stomach slides through the diaphragm into the chest. It can cause quite severe heartburn and epigastric pain. The tablet of *Celevac* had started to swell in her lower oesophagus (food pipe), just where the hernia was and caused her a lot of pain. This illustrates another good reason for getting as much as information as possible from the patient.

After this initial fact-finding, one goes on to Stage Two, which is taking a diet history. This can be more complex than you might think and is rather like asking for a coffee in a diner in the United States, or even in Starbucks.

"Hi! I'm Mary, your friendly waitress. What can I get for you today?"

"I'd like a coffee please."

"O-KAY...Would that be Regular? De-caff? Espresso? Cappuccino? (wet or dry)? Americano?"

"Er...Regular please."

"Arabica? Continental? Kenyan? Columbian? Blue Mountain? Java?"

"Oooh...Arabica please."

"Milk?"

"Yes please."

"Would that be full-cream? Half-and-half? Skimmed? Semi-Skimmed? Vitamin D-enriched?"

"Semi-skimmed please."

"Hot or cold?"

And so, the dietitian has to ask similarly to get all the necessary information, on which to base dietary assessment and then...Advice! And this is where the Powers-of-Persuasion, Counselling Skills and Silently-Willing-the-Patient-to-Agree merge in the consultation process.

Some patients are easily categorised:

Garrulous Patients often find it difficult to stop talking about themselves/ their children/ parents/ cousins/ the neighbours/ their garden/ the allotment/ their DIY/ the dog/ the canary etc. etc. They simply do not draw breath and without being rude, it is often difficult to stop the flow of irrelevant information. I have sometimes wondered if this may be a delaying tactic to avoid the real issues. The "open question technique" can be an open oral door! I have tried the usual non-verbal clues: looking away; looking at the clock; moving papers together; standing up and so on and unbelievably, none of these has resulted in the desired effect. One has to be firm: "I think that we may be getting a little sidetracked here: can I stop you for a moment and re-cap?"

The Silent Patient may be angry/cross/upset/anxious – body language tells all. This type of patient is tricky to help. I have humbled myself and almost knelt at their feet to get them to open up, smiling a lot to indicate that I am really a nice person and ready to listen to them. Open questions show that you have all the time in the world and that you are utterly and thoroughly interested in what they have to say. Awkward gaps don't have to be filled with chatter: silence can work too – but not all the time. Very often, one can be lucky in stumbling on what is holding them back, with the relief palpable on both sides!

The approach: "If you don't want to tell me about that now, we can come back to it later," works well but one needs to remember to do that: some patients like to play games.

The I-Know-It All/I've-Tried-It-All Patients are probably more difficult than either of the previous types, as they are questioning why they need to be at your clinic and/or why their doctor referred them. They know all the answers to their condition and it is obvious that the dietitian is wasting their time and they don't want to be there in the first place. Having won over such a patient, and arrived at a mutually agreeable point, I have sometimes smilingly challenged them with: "Well…you're here now! What persuaded you to come?"

"Oh well," rather sheepishly, "My doctor sent me, so I thought I'd better." Ah! The Power of the Medic! And generously, they admit that the session was useful.

The Angry Patient can be a hybrid of the Silent Patient and the Know-It-All. Often such patients are understandably fed up. They may have seen several doctors and therapists with no clear-cut diagnosis. They may be very stressed and worried about having to take time off work to attend the clinic but at the same time, concerned about their condition. Recognising and acknowledging this early on in the consultation is important, so that by the time one is finished, they are mere puppy dogs.

The Internet Patient arrives at the clinic with a neatly tabulated five-day diet record from their computer, a load of information (some good, some not so good) and a bunch of questions. When I worked at Calmershire, patients were routinely asked to bring a diet-record with them when they were sent their referral letter and this could save quite a bit of time. We LOVED these! Even so, with ready-meals and recipes, further questions need to be asked to get the full picture. Further, they have looked everything up concerning their symptoms and diagnosis on the Internet, their diet and all other recipes and treatments besides. They are probably a walking encyclopaedia of their condition. I've learned a lot!

Patients often present barriers to the suggested changes for diet and lifestyle, some of which are highly inventive. Part of the dietitian's job is to encourage a way round them and much of the consultation time is spent problem-solving the practicalities, and that's apart from the patient glancing at the diet-sheet and pronouncing, "I don't eat those! And I never touch that." The dietitian adopts a wheedling, persuasive manner but with undertones of insistence and resolution.

"How would it be if you just had one *Shredded Wheat* instead of two?"

"If you don't like breakfast, how would it work if you had a snack when you got to work instead, rather than wait until lunch-time when you must be really hungry?"

"Could you take fruit, such as apples or bananas with you, which are easy to eat, rather than the 'Greasy Spoon' café, when you take your break at the lorry park?"

And then there is the question of encouraging more exercise.

"How about walking or cycling to work? Using the stairs more? Getting off the bus a stop or two before you need to and walking the rest? Parking a bit further away?"

"What about hobbies? Do you like dancing, gardening or swimming?"

Then there would be some discussion, ideally patient-led but often with a bucketful of persuasion and coaxing on the dietitian's part as to when this might be fitted in. Eventually, there is some kind of compromise and promise on both sides, hopefully leaving the patient feeling that he/she has had their money's worth. And this routine is often then repeated with the next patient – and the next. And the next!

Because this is extremely time-consuming and, dare I say, quite wearing, the advantages of forming patient groups for this purpose can be appreciated. (See "Fresh Air and an Open Top"). More patients can be seen so it is a better use of everyone's time and there is mutual support between the members of the group.

It is a strange phenomenon that many patients, especially those who are overweight and who do not appreciate the extra demands that they are making upon their body, seem unable to make the changes for themselves and are often seriously uninspired. They need a prop – guess who that might be!

"I'll do it if you tell me to," they say.

Or "I'll do it for you…"

Or: "I need to report to somebody."

And it is extraordinary that many people still do not appreciate that eating fat of any kind *makes them fat!*

"Oh…but I always have sunflower margarine on my toast. I never touch butter now."

"Oh no – I don't have any fat – I use olive oil in my cooking."

In traditional Indian cooking, ghee (clarified butter) is used in large quantities to bring out the flavour of the spices but provides a "hidden" source of extra calories.

There has been so much emphasis over the past 40-odd years about the effects on cholesterol levels of "bad" saturated fats (like butter and lard) and "good" unsaturated oils (like sunflower, olive or corn oil) that their calorific values seem to have been forgotten.

Patients, who *are* well motivated and *really* want to reduce their symptoms, improve quality of life and get well again, are highly enthusiastic.

Mrs Edwards was in her late 60s and had high cholesterol. She followed her diet to the letter. In addition, her GP and I referred her to the local gym for the GP Exercise Referral Scheme. After a few weeks, she came for a follow-up appointment. She looked fit and well; her weight was down and her cholesterol levels were within normal.

"Well done!" I enthused. "You are my prize patient! A real star!"

"Thank you for your help." she said quietly. "I have to be strong to look after my husband."

It was only then that I found out that her husband had cancer and she was his main carer.

After the fact-finding mission, the instructions are handed out – usually on a printed diet-sheet, which sometimes has to be scribbled on to make the necessary alterations suitable for the individual. And then, there is the letter to write to the professional who made the referral – usually this is the GP but not always, in which case they are copied in, as is anyone else who might be involved in that patient's care. Sometimes this can amount to six or more, if many agencies are associated – I counted eight for a young patient who suffered from Huntington's disease. And, latterly, it was deemed A Good Idea to copy the patient in as well. Not only does this give written confirmation of what was said but it makes them feel Involved and Part-of-the-Team. (It also makes us very careful about how we phrase our letters!)

And so, if you have been getting annoyed and fidgety while waiting for the dietitian, you might now have some understanding of what is going on behind the door. It can take a while, which is why new patients are usually offered a 30-minute appointment. Even so, it is possible for up to 12 patients – a mixture of "new" and "follow-up's" – to be squashed into a "session" which is supposed to be three hours. It is thirsty work and one longs for a break when one can have a cuppa or even a glass of water! But it's not half as bad as a doctor who may have up to 80 patients on a clinic list!

Clinics are not without their moments of laughter, tears and frustrations. Going through a reducing diet-sheet with a young black woman many years ago, we soon realised that we were talking at cross purposes when she informed me that she had two stomachs: one for digesting carbohydrates and the other for protein. Where this idea originated, I have no idea but it caused us both some merriment.

Asking people about their life and food habits can throw up distressing memories and raw nerves. Bereavement, marital problems, children, stressful jobs and shift-work top the list. It is a privilege that these things are shared and although one is unable and indeed, unqualified to give advice on *les affaires des coeurs*, it gives a unique insight into people's lives and the rationale to modify or tinker with standard dietary advice.

On holiday one year, I employed a locum. She was a girl with whom I'd been at college and I knew her quite well. She had gone on to do (and still does) some highly erudite studies, had a Masters and a PhD but felt she wanted some "hands-on" experience, as she had never worked in an NHS setting. I was showing her round and she pointed out the box of tissues on the desk.

"What are they there for?"

"You'll soon find out," I grinned. She did!

"You were right about the *Kleenex*," she admitted, when I returned. "I learned a lot! Don't some people get their lives tied in knots?"

And then there is the total lack of common sense. Tanya was a young lady in her mid-30s. She was employed by a headhunting firm and had gained a lot of weight recently. She worked hard and played hard, going out with her friends at weekends to enjoy a meal and a drink. She had persuaded her GP to prescribe a weight-reducing medication to help her lose weight fast. Like many patients who wake up one morning and suddenly find that they are fat, forget that this took a while to pile on and they want it sorted...NOW! The drug that she had been prescribed is called *Xenical* (Orlistat). This works by not allowing the body to absorb fat. It doesn't take much imagination to guess where any dietary fat goes: yes! That's right! Down the pan! So, reducing fat intake is paramount. The main side effects are enough to put one off: oily leakage from rectum; flatulence;

faecal urgency; liquid or oily stools; abdominal distension and pain; tooth and gingival disorders. Instructions might as well also say: "Ensure that you always have a spare pair of clean knickers available."

Tanya had several appointments so that we could check on her progress. Her weight wasn't falling off as we both hoped.

"So what do you think is going on?" I asked.

"I don't know," she pondered.

"Well..." I metaphorically sucked the end of my pencil. "Let's start again and go through what you are eating and drinking. What are you having for breakfast?"

Everything seemed in order and then Tanya said, "I do like a drink at the weekends with my friends."

"OK – don't we all?" I smiled. "How much are we taking about?"

Thinking she would tot up a glass or two of wine, I wasn't prepared for her reply.

"Well...over the whole weekend, probably a couple of bottles of vodka and the same of wine and a few shots at the night club..."

I tried my best to make my face non-judgemental. Still in shock, I totted up the calories: they amounted to more than 5,000 for the two days.

"Er...did you not realise that alcohol has roughly one and a half times more calories than an equivalent amount of protein or carbohydrate?" Now it was Tanya's turn to look sheepish.

And then there are the dropped bricks. By me.

"So...I just need a little more information, if that's OK," I said to the affable young man, with attractive, shiny, blond, floppy hair and engaging grin. He had been referred for advice on weight reduction.

"Yeah...fine."

"Do you still live at home?"

"Yeah...I'd like to get a place of me own though..."

"Are you working?"

"Yeah – I'm at the meat-packing factory down the road from here."

"OK...and what about any drugs you might be taking?"

Without batting an eyelid, "Well...I've stopped the smack now but still have a bit of a smoke... y'know – weed..."

I looked up from my note-taking and felt my face go red.

"Oh...I'm really sorry...I actually meant whether you are taking any medications at all..."

Unfazed, he chuckled at my discomfiture.

"No, no...that's OK...I haven't been given anything by the doctor."

Food, health and their interaction are eternally fascinating subjects; so much so, that many of us succumb to a multitude of magic claims that are made, often not backed up by good scientific studies. Many are totally unfounded and potentially dangerous. These quasi-scientific claims for diets, supplements, herbs and other panaceas prey on people's vulnerability; their hopes and fears; their yearnings to be well and prayers to be slim, eternally youthful, healthy, intelligent and beautiful.

Mrs Hammond was an elderly lady in her 70s and was plagued with arthritis, which was very painful. Not surprisingly, she was eager to try almost anything that offered some respite. By the time that she was referred to our clinic, she had more than her arthritis to contend with. She had ingenuously been following a very strict diet, which claimed to cure her condition. She had eaten no meat; no dairy products of any kind, no eggs; no citrus fruits or tomatoes and very little sugar or high carbohydrate foods for nearly a year. She was very thin; her bones were crumbling, she was anaemic and as her vitamin C status was extremely low, her immune system would also have suffered. She was amazed to learn what damage she had, quite unwittingly, been doing to herself.

Children in the clinic could be a distraction. If the child was the patient, it was usually easier to see them in their own homes. They got bored in the clinic room, in spite of the box of toys that they would happily clutter over the floor. However, sometimes they just had to tag along if the parent was the patient. This meant that the parent, usually the mother, had half her attention on what we were trying to discuss and half on her child.

I could see that Mrs Ferris wasn't with me. Her attention was focused on her little two-year-old boy, who was getting more and more fidgety. Her eyes constantly flicked from me to him.

"I think he wants to use the potty…"

I got up to open the door to direct her to the lavatory but in an instant, a blue plastic potty with bunny pictures running round the rim was whisked out of her bag. Mrs Ferris undid his romper suit. The child sat on it there and then in the clinic room. We held our collective breaths. Dietetic consultation was temporarily suspended. After much grunting and going red in the face, the little chap produced a poo. Jubilation on the part of his mother.

"Clever boy! Well done! Did you do a big poo? In your big blue potty? With the bunny rabbits running round?" She looked up at me delighted.

"Isn't he a clever boy, Miss Farmer?" I stretched my mouth into what I hoped was an admiring smile but fear it turned into a tight, mean little grimace. I was just wishing he hadn't been quite so clever in my clinic!

Mrs Ferris wiped him and then went in search of the loo to dispose of the offering. I went in search of air-freshener spray – raised eyebrows from Bridget, the receptionist, along the lines of "What are you up to away from the clinic?" I rolled my eyes and made a face.

"Don't ask," I mouthed. "Tell you later!"

Bridget often brought me a cup of tea in the middle of the clinic. Or, on A Good Day, one of the receptionists at the GP clinic would do the same. What a welcome sight that was! It's amazing how thirsty one gets talking and explaining, especially when it tends to be rather repetitive. But it was torture too!

"You'd better have that, while it's hot!" some patients would say. Others would hint that they'd like one too. ("Milk – no sugar please!") Occasionally, I would take a gulp but it seemed to me rather rude to do this in the middle of their consultation, however parched I felt. More often than not, it stayed cooling rapidly on the desk and would end up thickening, shrinking and forming an unappetising scum, as only cold tea can. Bridget also occasionally used this opportunity to see how I was getting on: she was the one who was privy to the grumbles in the waiting room.

"Mr Gardner says he can't wait much longer," she murmured, as she placed the steaming cup in front of me.

"OK, Bridget. Thank you," I would mutter back, thinking "Oh God! How can I get this lady to stop chattering and come to a close?" Sometimes, one would have to be downright blunt.

"I'm really sorry Mrs Coles but there are other patients waiting. We need to wrap this up and agree some goals." Even then, some did not take the hint.

Bridget was an enigmatic lady. Some days, she appeared to be quite inscrutable. On others, she showed tremendous insight and empathy.

"Can you come and see this gentleman, Mary?" Bridget poked her head round the door of the office from the reception area one afternoon. I was annoyed. I had planned to catch up on paperwork and was luxuriating in the anticipation of having the whole afternoon clear to do it and maybe even leave on time. I sighed inwardly.

"OK, Bridget. Just give me a minute."

It was a miserable, wet, cold February day. A small, rather

bent, neatly and well-dressed elderly gentleman stood politely in reception. He twisted his hat in his hands. He looked chilled and forlorn.

"Hello," I greeted him. "I'm Mary, one of the dietitians. How can I help?"

"I have an appointment for the dietetic clinic this afternoon but your receptionist tells me that there isn't one today."

"No – that's right, I'm afraid there isn't. Wednesday is about the only afternoon that we don't have one." I paused, puzzled. "Do you have your appointment letter with you?"

He dug into his coat pocket.

"Yes – here it is. See? It says 'Wednesday, 26th'". It did indeed, but it also said "March", not "February" and the appointment was for 12.30pm, not 2.30pm.

"You're a month early," I tried to joke. "Most of our patients aren't that keen."

His weather-beaten face crumpled. "Oh no, how silly of me. I was so looking forward to discussing things." He started to turn away, crestfallen and woebegone. The paperwork could wait.

"Can you tell me what it's about? Why don't you pop into the office for a minute?" Behind him, with eyebrows raised and a questioning expression, Bridget made the sign of a "T" with her fingers and mimed drinking. I nodded and smiled, "Thanks".

Poor Mr Watson. He had been widowed for four years and was finding living on his own very hard. He missed his wife terribly and recently, had lost weight as he hadn't been looking after himself. His doctor thought chatting to a dietitian would be a good idea. He told me that he was longing to have a little dog as a companion but his sons vetoed it, as they thought he was too old to care for it properly. Tears fell as he spoke. After he had composed himself and dried his eyes with a pristine, ironed hankie, he told me that he had been a jockey and was used to starving himself.

"Just raw eggs and vinegar was all we had on the morning of a race," he told me. I wrinkled my nose and made a face.

"You get used to it," he said with a smile, as he sipped his tea (Bridget had even found some biscuits). He started to cheer up and we discussed his racing career – and Dick Francis' novels, which had provided me with my sole source of information on the subject. I promised I would let the dietitian whom he would be seeing eventually, know that we had already had a chat.

Most older people enjoyed the old chestnut: "Would you like your weight in French or in old money?"

"Oh…old money please! I can't understand these kilo-wotsits!"

Most of the clinics had stand-on scales with a dial, showing the weight. As a large person stood on these, it was sometimes difficult for me to actually read the weight, because of the large and pendulous stomach that was in the way. This meant that I had to bend down to do this but this was sometimes distinctly unpleasant and hazardous, as there was often the whiff off "cheesy" bare feet in summer, or of urine off an elderly gentleman's trousers. There could be good reason for this: prostate problems; diabetes; or simply not knowing when he had finished passing urine. I was never sure how to broach these sensitive issues and wimpishly avoided any mention of them for fear of further embarrassing my patients, but would then discreetly use the air-freshener after they had gone and before the next patient entered.

Genuine shock often registered on patient's faces, when they stood on the scales and were told their weight. Younger women especially had no idea that they had been quietly piling it on over the years, until they were either referred by their GP because they had seen him/her for another unrelated problem, or there was a sudden realisation and wake-up call.

"Are you *sure*?" they would ask.

"Are your scales right? I'm not this weight on mine at home."

"I *can't* be!"

"Oh! That's just *awful!*"

What I could never understand, and still don't, is how such people get to such a state: are they not aware that their clothes are getting tighter? And why don't they take steps to rectify the small increments in weight before it gets out of hand? I would sometimes be really worried about their reactions to the revelations about their weight and what their ideal weight should be, hoping that they wouldn't turn into an anorexic overnight, or jump off the nearest cliff – which fortunately, in the land-locked county in which I worked, was a long way away!

Great reliance is made on charts detailing heights and weights or, in the case of children, growth percentile charts. Over the past years, much emphasis has been placed on Body Mass Index (BMI), which is one's weight in kilograms, divided by the square of one's height in metres (kg/m^2).

Based on information compiled by actuaries, BMI replaced the former Metropolitan Association's chart of healthy weights and heights. It is deemed to be more accurate and certainly simpler to use. Most people now know and are familiar with the coloured bands on the BMI chart:

A BMI under 18.5 (often coloured pale green) suggests that one is unhealthily underweight; between 18.5 and 25 (emerald green) is considered "normal" and between 25 and 29 (yellow) is classed as "overweight". After that, enter the orange zone (BMI values between 30 and 39) and you are classed as obese. Anyone who has a BMI more *that* is in serious trouble and classed as *very* or morbidly obese (brick red!). This means one's weight is a direct threat to one's health if not now, certainly in the future.

However, these charts have their limitations and interpretations should be made sensibly. For example, they don't take into account genetic tendencies or the constituents of that weight. For someone who is highly muscular and fit, the BMI might veer into the overweight band but they are not FAT. And it is body FAT that is the health problem. There is a variety of specialised equipment that can measure percentage of body fat – often found in gyms and swimming pools – each having varying degrees of accuracy. Sadly, as they are rather expensive, there are few dietetic clinics that have them, unless they are research-based metabolic units.

At the time of writing this chapter, the names of those in the Lions Rugby Team had been published in the paper. A quick Google on some of the names, and Wikipedia gives intimate details of their heights and weights. BMI values vary from 27–30 but one could hardly say that these chaps are unhealthily overweight or obese. They are full of muscle, fighting fit and have the number of "caps" apiece to prove it!

Further, *where* that body fat is distributed has, for many years thought to be significant: "pear-shapes" (weight around the hips) were not at such risk of diabetes and heart disease as were "apple-shapes" (weight around the abdomen). Now, new research suggests that excess body fat *per se* is still important in determining the risk of heart disease, but regardless of whether it is around the tummy or the hips.[1]

Mr Harding was a fit 35-year old, who had been referred to us because his weight veered into the "yellow" zone on the BMI chart. His build was stocky, he was not very tall but he was extremely muscular. He was cross that he had been referred

[1] The Emerging Risk Factors Collaboration, 2011. Separate and combined associations of body-mass index and abdominal adiposity with cardiovascular disease: collaborative analysis of 58 prospective studies. *The Lancet Online*. March 11th. Available at: http://www.thelancet.com/journals/lancet/article/PIIS0140-6736(11)60105-0/abstract

because he did not think that he needed advice from us. I questioned him as usual about his food intake and exercise. He rowed for a local club, went to the gym and hardly ever seemed to sit still! I had to agree with him that he probably did not need to come to see us although his food intake did need a minimum of tweaking. He calmed down and went away happier but that left *me* cross, that his GP had misinterpreted the BMI findings on the chart.

Older people do not conform to these tables either. As we get older, body composition changes: we lose muscle and cartilage and bones get thin. Some medical conditions cause fluid retention. Such changes are reflected in body weight.

Accurately measuring the height of someone who is very bent due to old age or illness is virtually impossible. To overcome this glitch, the academics propose that the demi-span is measured. Many people are familiar with the Leonardo Da Vinci sketch of *Vitruvian Man* which depicts a man standing in a circle, his arms and legs stretched out straight. Measuring fingertip to fingertip from one side to the other is the same as his height. Measuring from one fingertip to the centre of the breast bone should therefore be half his height. Many older people would be unable to stretch one arm out sufficiently straight in order to make an accurate assessment like this. Undaunted, these same academics also offer a further alternative, using the knee-height from the floor and some complicated equation. But this involves the patients sitting upright with their feet firmly on the floor and the knees at 90 degrees, in order to make the measurement. Hmm – tricky if you have osteoarthritis and bowed legs!

As a Scottish friend of my father-in-law said to him about his arthritic, bandy legs, "Eh, Fred! It's a guid thing ye dinna keep pigs!"

"Whaat? Why's that then?"

"Aye...t' buggers t'would run between yer legs!"

Many dietitians who work in elderly care keep a check on weight changes but dismiss converting them to BMI's. As you can see from the above, they are fraught with inaccuracies and mean precious little. Even so, some inspectors of care homes emphasise their importance.

Mr Rai ran a small care home on the outskirts of Calmershire. I had visited previously and enjoyed a spectacular lunch with his ten happy and contented residents. It was beautifully cooked. Wine or sherry was offered before the meal and we all sat round a table together. About a week later, he rang me in a great state to say that the inspectors had been and expressed their concern about one of the residents, who had lost a massive amount of weight quite suddenly. What the inspector hadn't asked was "Why?" The answer was simple: this lady had heart failure and had been retaining fluid. Her GP had prescribed diuretics (water pills) and so what she had lost was fluid, not fat or muscle. As "a pint of pure water weighs a pound and a quarter," this would not be insignificant. Poor Mr Rai was truly worried that his home might be closed down.

"Listen," I ventured. "How about I write to the Inspectorate and tell them what this is about?" His gratitude down the 'phone line was audible. "Yes please," he breathed.

On another occasion, I was asked to see a young girl who had severe cerebral palsy. Jenny was about 13 years old and her parents were worried that she was too thin. Many people with this condition tend to be underweight, due in part to the physical difficulties of getting enough food into them but also because of their constant and uncontrolled movements.

Jenny's parents wanted the full works: her height; her weight; a dietary assessment and some advice. Her height posed a problem. She could not stand and her spine was very distorted.

"Shall we lie her on the floor?" they asked. I was dubious.

"This isn't very dignified." I addressed Jenny. "What do you think?"

"That's OK," she indicated.

And so, as Jenny was gently laid on the floor, I crawled beside her on hands and knees, wielding the tape measure. All three of us got involved, grovelling beside Jenny. There was much giggling but I was constantly reminded of a story I was told by a fellow dietitian.

An enthusiastic, young doctor was researching heights and weights of old people in care.

"We've got to get their heights," he urged the care staff.

"But most of them can't stand unaided," countered the nurse in charge.

"Well – tell you what – let's lay them out on their beds and measure their lengths," he suggested. It doesn't take much imagination, even with a dash of dementia and a smidgen of confusion, to guess what these poor souls were thinking...

"We are being measured for our coffins!"

Needless to say, Jenny's length measurement was subject to a multitude of errors but it gave the her parents some basis to work on, however scientifically shaky.

Children are a completely different kettle of fish. Adult BMI charts are *not* applicable as children grow at different rates and anomalies like premature births and genetics also need to be taken into account. More appropriately, the Institute of Child Health has carefully compiled their heights and weights, which are related to their age, into growth charts. These were considered pretty accurate for years, as they were based on growth rates of thousands of healthy children, who grew up to be fine upstanding pillars of the community. Latterly, however, it came to light that most of these children had been bottle-fed and put on weight at a greater rate than their breast-fed counterparts, increasing the likelihood that they could develop into overweight adults and therefore, were not exemplary "ideal weights".[2] In an era when "breast is best", and when many breast-fed children appeared not to gain as much weight as these charts suggested they should, breast-feeding mothers had felt pressurised to start feeding formula milks. Embarrassingly, the whole system suddenly lacked credibility and the charts had to be re-written, using healthy, breast-fed babies' lengths and weights as the basis, together with new information from the World Health Organisation (WHO). As these new charts are being introduced, so the number of babies and young children who are classified as "overweight" will just about double.[3] [4]

There is further cause for red faces: recently the National Information Centre has "'fessed up" to a software glitch in the Parental Feedback Tool of the National Child Measurement Programme.[5] Understandably, parents who received letters from the programme informing them bluntly that their children were overweight and could be at risk of heart disease, diabetes and cancer, were shocked and angry. Several of these cases were highlighted in the press. A five-year old girl, who had had a height and weight check at school, was wrongly deemed "overweight", while a little boy, was equally wrongly deemed "obese" by the annual Child Measurement Programme.

These children's statistics were within the recommended healthy range of the paediatric growth charts but, for some inexplicable reason were plotted against a BMI Chart and were

[2] BBC News Online. 2006. *Baby growth charts to be revised*. April 24th. Available at: http://news.bbc.co.uk/1/hi/health/4938234.stm

[3] Smith, R. 2009. New growth charts will classify more babies as overweight. *The Daily Telegraph*, May 7th

[4] Bedford, H. and Ellman, D. 2009. New infant growth charts, *Community Practitioner*, June, Vol. 82,No.6, 36-37. Available online at:

http://www.ucl.ac.uk/paediatric-epidemiology/pdfs/CP_growthcharts_June09.pdf

[5] NHS Information Centre. 2010. *National Child Measurement Programme Error*. October 28th Available at: http://www.ic.nhs.uk/news-and-events/news/national-child-measurement-programme-error

found to be in the overweight band. Even more worrying is a case in which one young girl is now refusing to eat because she had been labelled "fat".

Any interpretation of children's measurements should also take family origins into account. I saw a number of young children who had been labelled "thin" by a health visitor. Checking the charts suggested that this was indeed the case and then I looked at the parents. They were Japanese and tiny! Many people from Asian or Eastern cultures tend to be small-boned and of delicate stature; why should their offspring conform to a Western-style build?…

I am reminded of a story, told to me by a former medical officer of health (MOH) who worked on occasion as a locum in the 1960s. The doctor from whom he was taking over was doing earnest and laudable research into the heights and weights of schoolchildren in Ireland. Dr O'Brien took over. He looked at the height stick, measured himself and found that he had grown two inches. Interesting! Looking closer, he could see that the base was indeed two inches above floor level. Oops! So much for so-called scientific research!

I am often asked if being a dietitian influences my own dietary habits. I have found this hard to answer. I suppose, if I am honest it has, but then I was lucky in that my mother was an excellent cook and there were always seasonal fresh fruit and vegetables on the table. Dietitians, like the rest of the population, come in all shapes and sizes, though it helps if one is a reasonable shape oneself, being neither too fat nor too thin and I think it is fair to say that most of them are. It could be highly embarrassing if I saw a patient who had been previously seen by one of my larger colleagues.

"How DARE she tell me to lose weight, when she's overflowing on that chair!" Conversely, if the previous consultation had been taken by a very thin colleague.

"It's all right for her! She's probably anorexic!" Sometimes you just can't win.

And then there is the question: why do people choose this profession? Do they have a healthy or an unhealthy attitude to food? It could be argued that there are some who already may have anorexic tendencies and like to learn more about the values of foods. Hopefully, this is not too common. Most dietitians enjoy the science and the medical aspect and are fascinated by the effect of food on human physiology, psychology and biochemistry. On the whole, whether consciously or intrinsically, dietitians probably do think more about what they put into their mouths, compared with the general population. After all, they have "the knowledge" and the wit to practise it!

Skipping meals while working in the community is inevitable. Too often a clinic, a home visit, training session, visit to a care home or a meeting would run late and one had to be somewhere else. I would take sandwiches for lunch and sometimes eat them as I drove to the next appointment. Breadcrumbs, sliced tomato and cottage cheese would unavoidably fall into my lap and did little to enhance my concentration on driving. I would give up and often take my sandwiches home, put them in the 'fridge and start again the next day. If they didn't make it to my mouth that day, the dog had them! The day that I was caught in a snowstorm and hadn't managed to have my sandwiches at lunchtime served me well! Hunger pangs would go away while I kept busy but dehydration was more of a problem: it is well-known that concentration levels dip when hydration levels are low and thirst is not always a good indicator that one needs fluid. Then, as Nature intended, what goes in must come out and finding a handy loo then becomes paramount! Not always easy when travelling round a large county!

Clumsiness happens to us all but on occasion my hands would

take on a life of their own. One of the clinics I took fortnightly was in a GP practice in the county town. It was a large practice with several doctors, nurses and receptionists. In addition, there were visiting staff like myself, which included a podiatrist, a speech and language therapist (SALT) and a counsellor. It was a friendly practice. Its partners took care to ensure that their staff were valued, including arranging a Christmas party each year for them all at a local hotel. It was good fun and an opportunity to get to know everyone, when they let their collective hair down. The senior partner was a very kind and sensitive man. For some unfathomable reason, try as I might, I always seemed to do something stupid and inept every time that I saw him.

I was coming down the steep stairs from the staff room, which was at the top of the rambling, converted house, where, if there was a break in the patients' list, one could sneak up and have a welcome cuppa. Dr Roberts was coming up, holding a basket full of letters, blood results, patient notes, prescriptions, X-rays and various forms. He waited courteously for me at the tiny half-landing and nodded a greeting. Some force of darkness made my hand twitch in response and my arm grew in length by at least two feet. The basket flew up in the air. Papers went everywhere. I scrabbled on the floor, trying to be helpful.

"*Don't*" he hissed. "Just *leave* them!"

Mortified, I slunk on my way, feeling my face go red as red could be. A year or so later and not long before he retired, Dr Roberts suffered a mild stroke. How he would have hated that! He was such an active man. I wrote a note to express my sympathy and to wish him a speedy recovery. Much to my surprise, I had a hand-written note a few weeks later, thanking me so sincerely for the note and for *"the sensitive and kind way in which I had treated his patients"*. What a gentleman! But the question in my mind was – how on earth did he know how I treated his patients? I am sure that he didn't have his ear to the door! Similarly, when I left that area to work in Calmershire, again I had a handwritten note from Dr Roberts thanking me for my services. Gallantry and courtesy are surviving!

At his retirement party, all the staff put on a surprise review. Rehearsals had been clandestinely carried out at lunchtimes, when the eternal paperwork is normally done. There were poems, song and dance routines and little vignettes, poking gentle fun at the NHS, the government and medical care. There was some definite talent, no longer hidden under the proverbial bushel and it was an enjoyable way of cementing working relationships. It was a model GP practice!

BLOW THE WIND SOUTHERLY

Yet Freedom! yet thy banner, torn but flying
Streams like the thunder-storm against the wind.

Lord Byron, "Childe Harolde"

The three Ps stand for Pee, Poo and Puke – the greatest of these being poo. Perhaps those of a sensitive and delicate nature might like to skip this chapter: not everyone is intrigued or fascinated by the inner workings of the digestive system!

It is a simple fact that gastroenterologists, nurses and dietitians are utterly fascinated by poo, with pee being a strong contender in second place. There is even a special chart from which you can compare your patient's malodorous offerings. It is called the "Bristol Stool Chart". Yes! You can even Google it! It gives you not only descriptions – colour, consistency, frequency; whether production is explosive, uncontrolled or needs effort ("Push hard, dear" takes on a whole new meaning) – but also little drawings which help to give clear definitions of the classification of faeces into seven categories.

This may sound like rather "too much information" and excess attention to detail bordering on the obsessive but, in fact, if someone has "diarrhoea" what does this really mean? Does it mean an occasional loose stool or squatting and squitting all day long (and night too, if you're really unlucky)? Close questioning on everything that you need to know, such as colour (yellow to black); the presence of mucus, "jelly" or blood; whether the stool is stringy, watery or semi-solid, whether it is explosive and so on can eliminate (pardon the pun) whether

114

there is an infection (such as *Clostridium difficile*), an allergy, a food intolerance, some kind of inflammatory bowel disease (IBD), reaction to medicines such as antibiotics, damage from radiation to the gut area, excess alcohol, overuse of laxatives, cancer or food poisoning.

Unsurprisingly, not all patients share this fascination. It is embarrassing to talk about, so the dietitian needs to steer a course during questioning, between what the patient understands, clear definitions and, of course, a small dose of lavatory humour. I was amazed recently to see a poster in our local GP surgery of a series of pictures of...well...bare bottoms! Of all shapes, sexes, colours, ages, musculature and sizes. The title was *"The Doctor has seen them all before!"* and was supposed to encourage patients to talk about their unusual bowel habits in a bid for bowel cancer prevention. It would be intriguing to know how effective this was!

Mrs McDonald was a sweet woman, who worked as a laboratory assistant. She was very, very thin. She came to our outpatient clinic with her husband who was ANGRY. Oh Boy! Was he a cross man! He did not need to speak; the body language said it all. Mrs McDonald's GP had sent a letter to our department suggesting that the lady had food allergies. The poor woman existed solely on cooked rice and peppers, which strangely, seemed to be the only foods that did not reappear in the lavatory pan a few hours later. She had lost nearly a stone (6.4kg) in weight in a month and her husband was incensed because he did not think that her problems were being taken seriously. We talked for a long time, in between calming Mr McDonald. I could understand his anger; he was really worried and concerned and had good reason but I had to be firm and ask him to allow me to hear the story from his wife alone. After covering pretty much every aspect of what went in one end and came rapidly and violently out of the other, I was pretty sure that Mrs McDonald did not have any allergies or intolerances. Her husband agreed and was relieved that at last someone was doing something. He started to calm down. I asked Mrs McDonald if she had ever been asked to provide a stool sample.

"Well…No…" She was surprised. "Do you think that would be helpful?"

I hand-wrote a letter there and then for her GP and told her to pop into the surgery for a sample pot. I apologised for having to ask her to do this – not nice – but in the circumstances, necessary.

A few days later, the 'phone rang.

"Miss Farmer? It's Mrs McDonald here. Thank you SO much," she enthused. "You'll never guess – I had an environmental health officer on my doorstep yesterday, asking if I worked with food! I was riddled with *Clostridium Difficile*! I'm on really strong antibiotics and already am feeling heaps better! Thank you for all your help."

Mr Lane also presented in the clinic with a letter from his GP, this time suggesting that he had Irritable Bowel Syndrome. He was a librarian and, as he scaled up and down ladders checking books, running to the lavatory in between, was unsurprisingly very physically fit. He found it difficult to talk about his problem and had lived with it for some time before seeking help, putting his symptoms down to the fact that he had had radiation on his abdomen for a previous cancer. Occasionally, he had to go to London. He knew every public lavatory on the Victoria and Piccadilly Underground Lines!

He was naturally anxious and embarrassed but we were soon able to inject some gentle humour into our conversation. He later admitted that he nearly didn't keep the appointment, as he felt that it would probably be a waste of time. We agreed he might find a low residue diet helpful but with the addition of a bulking agent. Amongst other things, it transpired that he did eat a lot of bread. We agreed that it might be worthwhile trying to cut down on this, together with the other advice. Several weeks later, he appeared in the clinic and sat down with a happy and contented smile all over his face.

"I never thought that I would say this," he began, "but I've just had the most normal poo for the first time in years! I'm now so glad that I came to see you! It was brilliant! Would you believe, I actually enjoyed it! Thank you so much!"

Afterwards, he took the trouble to write such a nice letter, thanking me for my humour in tackling his humiliating and ignominious problem.

Irritable Bowel Syndrome (IBS) can present a number of wide-ranging symptoms and I sometimes wonder if it is a convenient label to slap onto patients, where a true diagnosis is elusive. Suffice it to say, it can cause a lot of discomfort and pain through bloating, heartburn, wind and backache. Naturally, there is also anxiety when there is diarrhoea, fatigue, general distress and the feeling that one's bowels control one's life. In some patients it may be latent coeliac disease masquerading as IBS, or it can even be confused with gynaecological problems. It is a common "functional" bowel disorder. Symptoms come and go but it is NOT a precursor to bowel cancer.

Causes are unclear and vary: in some, symptoms may have been triggered by an infection, a parasitic infestation and/or after a course of antibiotics; there may be food intolerances and/or over activity of the nervous system supplying the gut. Some patients, like Mr Lane, already "have a feeling" that a particular food, or class of foods may be the culprit. As a result, treatments vary from encouraging the use of "good bacteria" to re-colonise the gut (though latterly, there is some scientific discussion as to the validity of this); changing the fibre content of the diet; attempting to isolate any food intolerances and avoiding stimulants (which would increase gut movements), such as *Coca Cola* and coffee. At one time, it was suggested that patients should avoid sugars and yeasts, with the idea that the gut was over-fermenting these and contributing to a *Candida* (fungal) infection, which might be causing the symptoms.

Several years ago, it was noted by a psychiatrist that patients with depression who were being treated with an anti-depressant, such as *Amitriptyline*, were suddenly aware that their IBS symptoms disappeared. Having said that, one of the main side effects of this drug is constipation but the role of stress in the aetiology of IBS should not be overlooked.

The role of fibre in treating IBS has also changed over the years: now it seems that it is the type of fibre, which is crucial. Increasing the intake of soluble fibre is thought to be helpful for some patients. This is found in oats, pulses, some fruits (such as apples), nuts and seeds such as psyllium. Bran is an insoluble fibre and is best avoided. Some patients benefit from avoiding nuts, seeds, pips and skins, which seem to cause a "mechanical" mini trauma on the gut. As symptoms improve, foods can be gradually re-introduced. From this very brief paragraph, you can begin to get the idea that finding a solution for such patients is not easy. They need a long time in the clinic room!

As a dog-owner, who has to frequently go on "poo patrol" and "pick up", talking about the products of one's nether regions becomes less embarrassing or inhibited. Further, as our current dog has a form of IBD, like Crohn's disease, and through no fault of his own has, on more than one occasion, decorated the kitchen overnight with his own personal and unintentional "dirty protest", I now have no problem in discussing such issues! It seems to be a peculiarly British attitude that we shy away from such details. It is not usually a conversation topic of the month, or at posh dinner parties, and yet, if one suffers from such problems, the activity of one's bowels is never far from one's thoughts. We use euphemisms, such as "number two's", "using paper"; "jobs"; "passing solids"; "a call to nature" or in nursing shorthand, "B.O.", which does not stand for "body odour" in this context – but "bowels opened". Many of us do not understand the workings of our bodies and for some, the particular workings of the gut are disagreeable and distasteful in the extreme. Did you know, for example, that the average colon is nearly five feet (one-and-a-half metres) long? Or that 70 per cent of food residue is excreted within 72 hours of it being eaten? The remaining 30 per cent may remain in the colon for a week or more.

IBS should not be confused with IBD, of which the two best-known varieties are Crohn's disease and ulcerative colitis. These are serious. Any blood in the stool and/or accompanying weight loss necessitates a timely visit to the doctor.

The flip side to such problems is constipation, which has been estimated to contribute to around one per cent of consultations in the GP clinic. NHS spending on laxatives is considerable: in the elderly population, and particularly those in hospital, laxative use appears to be without any proper rationale or assessment. Many of us self-medicate. Older people may have been brought up to believe that regular bowel motions and the need to purge "toxic waste" are essentially healthy. (The Victorians took antimony salts regularly which caused vomiting and diarrhoea, so that they could be totally cleansed internally). And yet how do we define "constipation"? Like its counterpart, diarrhoea, there appears to be no accepted definition. It is open to individual interpretation, thus causing difficulties with assessment and appropriate treatment. For some, it may mean that they "miss going for one day". Some feel that normality is going after each meal. For others, normal bowel function could mean that they "go" only once a week. Passing "rabbit pellets" (one patient described her lavatorial activities as dealing with the "rock of ages"), or straining are pretty good indications of being bunged up.

The consequences of constipation can include general

abdominal discomfort, including bloating, cramps, heartburn, passing wind, nausea, lethargy, headaches and bad breath. It can impact on a person's physical, psychological and social well being. What *is* important is that any sudden change in bowel activity, or the presence of blood, is noted and reported to a doctor.

Overcoming chronic constipation often means looking at psycho-sociological aspects as well as lifestyle and diet. Children may not like to use the lavatories at school, for example, because "they are smelly" and so "hold on" when they feel the urge to defaecate. In time, if the messages from the gut are constantly ignored, the reflex action answering "the call to stool" becomes inhibited. Lack of muscle tone and inability to "push"; bowel motility and transit times; various medications, such as cough medicines, which contain codeine, or morphine-based pain relief and acute and chronic illnesses, are also implicated.

Denis Burkitt, known affectionately in nutrition circles during the 1960s and '70s as "The Bran Man", showed convincingly that lack of fibre was the root of all colonic evils. Professor Burkitt had been an army surgeon. East Africa during WW2 was one of his postings, where he stayed for five years. Both he and Professor Hugh Trowell had worked in Uganda, where they observed that dietary fibre was essential in prevention of disease. Professor Burkitt's definitive book on the subject was a best seller and revolutionised dietary education.[1] He loved to compare "poos" contributed by native Ugandans eating a traditional diet, with those produced under stress and strain by British white people, who consumed highly refined foods. His photographs contrasted the Ugandan "cowpats" with the "white-man's pathetic hard offerings". One of his favourite observations was the installation of telephones in all the hotel bathrooms so that constipated businessmen could make their calls and appointments while sitting on the loo!

---

[1] Burkitt, D.P. 1979. *Don't Forget Fibre in Your Diet.* Martin Dunitz.

Rather than increase their intake of fibre by eating more fruit, vegetables and wholegrain bread and cereals, some people prefer to buy a supplement that is based on bran, psyllium seeds or ispaghula in order to address their problems. This is all very well but it is essential that attention is also paid to fluid intake. These supplements swell in the fluids of the gut and, if there is not enough fluid intake from the top end, can actually clog up the system even more. Further, coarse wheat bran can act as an irritant in some people and interfere with the absorption of minerals, such as calcium, zinc and iron. It looks like chicken feed, smells like chicken feed – and guess what? It *is* chicken feed!

Increasing fluid intake is always a sensible first line of treatment; the longer that food residue is stored, the more fluid is reabsorbed from the gut, leading to firmer stools. A rough and ready rule of thumb is to increase fluid intake, especially from water and fruit juices, to 60-65ml/kg body weight/day. Tea and coffee can be included in the overall daily fluid but the tannins in these tend to be astringent, preventing full uptake of fluid in the gut tissues.

Laxative use should be properly monitored. Over-use can make the condition worse by affecting gut motility and muscle tone. None knows this better than bulimics and anorexics who, in their attempts to prevent calories seeping into their system from a binge, hurry the gut up to expel as much nutritive value as possible.

In Borderland, there was a unit for elderly patients that had a separate catering facility. It was noted that laxative use was rife. Together with the visiting doctor and the nurse in charge, the catering manager and I sat down one afternoon with the menus, the patients' care plans and drug charts. We made changes to the menu to include more wholegrain cereals, fruit and vegetables, suitably prepared for wobbly dentures, and ensured that fluid intakes were improved. Within a short time, laxative use decreased dramatically.

'ELF AND SAFETY

In the multitude of counsellors, there is safety

The Book of Common Prayer

Strands of the ubiquitous Health and Safety Executive web weave themselves into every part of working life.

The Health and Safety at Work Act stems from 1974 and is there *"to prevent death, injury and ill health to those at work and those affected by work activities."* [1]

For staff in the NHS, regulations regarding Moving and Handling, Fire Safety and Control of Substances Hazardous to Health (COSHH) are those aspects of 'elf and safety which are most applicable. It is mandatory for staff to attend training sessions under these headings annually. In addition, there may be certain items of equipment for which risk assessments are done separately.

'Elf and Safety has been ridiculed because of some asinine derisory rules that have been made under its umbrella. In one area, for example, a beautiful row of chestnut trees were cut down because the conkers might have fallen on children's heads. A 93-page guide on how to ride a bicycle has been drawn up for the police. Titled *The Police Cycle Training Doctrine* (2009), it reminds officers, amongst other little nuggets of information, how to turn a corner and not to detain a subject, while in the saddle!

[1] Health and Safety Executive. Updated, 2006. *Health and Safety at Work Act, 1974.* Available at:
http://www.hse.gov.uk/legislation/hswa.htm

Children are warned by the Food Standards Agency not to pick fruit from hedgerows, thus putting the kybosh on yet another innocent outdoor pleasure: gleaning one's own produce for free. Ironically, this coincides with the current government's aim to reduce the burden of "health and safety madness" and to blitz the inevitable "compensation culture".

A *Sloppy Slippers* project for the Over-50s, which gives advice on wearing slippers safely, has been published at a cost of £3,500. Per-leeese! In its defence, it is claimed that this initiative will save money in the long run, as it will help to prevent falls. Not surprisingly, this has been criticised as being "patronising and a waste of tax-payers' money". Even cemeteries are targeted: people could stumble over artificial flowers that are laid on graves. And don't forget your doormat! Someone could trip or slip and have a nasty accident. Curtains and flowers come into the fire hazard category! The list goes on. However, it is easy to err if one does not think of every possible predicament in which Mr and Mrs Average and Mr and Mrs No-Common-Sense might find themselves. And, as my dear departed mother used to say, "Common sense isn't very 'common' these days!"

In the new offices in Calmershire was a spanking, brand new waiting room for the outpatient clinics. Most of the nicely upholstered chairs had arms, which made it easier for older people to get in and out of them. Unfortunately, some of the extra large patients who were waiting to see the dietitian got stuck in them and there was a call for those without arms, so that there was enough room for any "overflow".

Weighing heavy patients was not without its difficulties and not all scales go beyond 24 stone (152.4kg). Those who are in wheelchairs present further complications. Before Health and Safety started to take more notice, we were issued with specialised equipment for weighing patients in wheelchairs in clinics and in the patients' homes. These consisted of a pair of ramps resembling skis, which could be connected by wires to a digitally-read scale. They were made of steel and were incredibly heavy. I never weighed them but I would estimate each to be about a stone. However, we would put them in the car and lug them to the patient's house. The tricky part was aligning the wheels of the chair correctly in line with the ramps, and occasionally we would have to lift that part of the chair with the patient in it!

Millie was a very large lady in her late 50s. She was often in her night-dress and her downstairs sitting-room had been converted into a bedroom. It was difficult not to stare at her huge size and her breasts which, totally unsupported, drooped and sagged towards her stomach, which in turn, folded down to her thighs. Part of the assessment meant that I had to take measurements around her upper arm and also her waist. I could barely get my arms around her middle to do so. Her husband came to the rescue by holding one end of the tape measure. She was indeed "60 inches wide" just like the song, *Here Comes the Bride.*

She lived in a delightful Borderland village with her husband and her son, both of whom, thankfully, were strapping and strong, due to the physical demands of their work. Her husband was a market gardener (I would often be presented with a "bouquet", such as a swede or a bunch of greens, after my visits) while her son was a gravedigger at the local cemetery. Millie was employed at a jam factory but then health problems took over and she could no longer work. She was in a wheelchair because she was riddled with arthritis and had chronic mobility problems. Add to that, she had visual problems, which included a very pronounced squint (her glasses were as thick as the bottom of a milk bottle), together with diabetes and an underprivileged upbringing. It was extraordinary that Millie never complained, was eternally grateful for anything that anyone did for her and had a sense of humour that matched her size. I became very fond of her and her family.

On our first visit, we had to get Millie out of her wheelchair, so that we could weigh it on its own. I had taken a colleague with me, as this was the first time that I had used the ramps. With three of us assisting, we attempted to put Millie on her bed, as there wasn't another suitable chair. This was no mean feat, as we eventually discovered she weighed in excess of 25 stone (158.7kg). Trying to dodge the furniture and people in the over-crowded room, Millie missed getting far up enough onto the edge, and she collapsed serenely against the spongy springiness of her air-bed. Like Mr Blobby, she slid down and folded gently onto the floor, with the grace and effortlessness of a popped barrage balloon. All of us also ended up on the floor, except for Jan, my colleague, who stared open-mouthed at this whole procedure. Nervous giggles infected us all. In spite of the helpless laughter bubbling up inside me, in the back of my mind I was thinking, "Oh No! Here comes the litigation!"

"Are you all right, Millie?" we kept asking.

She didn't speak. "Oh No!"

"Millie?"

Her whole body started shaking: chins, shoulders, breasts, tummy. Everything wobbled…with laughter, tears streaming down her face!

"Oh my goodness…" she gasped. "What a performance! Help me up then!"

Eventually, after much huffing and puffing, heaving and shoving, pulling and pushing and without much dignity, we managed to get Millie safely on the bed and professional relations were resumed. But then we still had to manoeuvre her in her wheelchair onto the ramps. More huffing and puffing and backbreaking work but at last, the job was done.

It was no surprise that, soon after I moved jobs, these wheelchair scales were outlawed on grounds of health and safety. I couldn't say that I was sorry but it did mean that patients then had to be transported to the hospital, where there was more suitable equipment, which was highly inconvenient for them.

Later, when I had moved to work in Calmershire, our department acquired portable chair-scales, with rear-only wheels. These comprised a bucket seat of moulded plastic, that could be detached from the metal base on which was the digital display unit. We did our own risk assessment on these, dismantling them; finding how easy they were to lift into a car; wheeling them to the car park; sitting on them and rocking to see how steady they were and so on. Our manager passed them as fit to use and off we went thus equipped. These were invaluable for weighing patients in their own homes and residents in care homes, where, either the home did not possess suitable scales, or staff did not weigh them regularly, even though Care Standards clearly said that they should. Even so, subsequent health and safety rules did not allow us to use these either, on the grounds that the base was too heavy to lift into a car, especially if this was not a hatchback type. Thus, the responsibility for weighing residents regularly lay fairly and squarely on the care home staff. The scales were expensive to buy and many of the smaller care homes simply could not afford them.

I regularly flouted these new rules, taking the scales to those homes which were on my caseload, despite the fact that others in my department were dubious about this practice. My argument was that if I didn't, until the care homes organised themselves properly, their residents would never get weighed and this was one basic method of checking on their nutritional status. It was also an ideal opportunity to "eye-ball" them for myself and assess them overall, apart from which the residents enjoyed this regular ritual and it became a social occasion too.

Some of them were suspicious of this new-fangled equipment. Jessie had severe dementia and was somewhat aggressive at times. The carer gently explained what we were trying to do. Jessie turned her head away.

"No!" she said firmly, folding her arms, crossing her legs and clamping her lips. I decided to take a turn.

"Jessie," I started. "See this chair – could you sit in it for me, like this?" And I sat in front of her to show her what I wanted.

She turned her head graciously towards me, suddenly very ladylike.

"You wan' me to try i' ou' for yer, do yer? Yeees...orl righ' – if you want me to," she condescended. "Wass this all abou' anyway?" she demanded.

"Well...it's a special chair that weighs you, Jessie."

"Coo-er...well I never...clever innit?" But then on another occasion, she wouldn't be so cooperative.

Some poor souls were so difficult to move, they were unable to sit properly and their legs would be draped over the foot-rest. Others would be unable to keep still. The digital display would waver and wobble and an intelligent "guestimate" would have to be made.

Very often, several of them, especially in the Elderly Mentally Ill Units (EMI), would leave a wet patch on the plastic seat. I soon got used to the idea that I needed to carry some antiseptic wipes and an old dog towel with me! But this was far more serious as it meant that staff were not checking their residents regularly, asking if they needed the lavatory, having their incontinence pads changed, or ensuring that they were suitably hydrated.

Rosa was one such resident. The carer who opened the door of the residential home to me that morning looked near to tears.

"Hello Carole – what's up?" I asked.

"Come in, Mary," she invited, "I'll tell you...we're all in an awful state."

I was making a routine monthly visit to her care home to

weigh and review the residents. I loved coming here. It was a happy home with only 12 residents, most of whom had dementia to varying degrees and who were looked after lovingly by the devoted staff. Add to which, their cook, Jeanie, made the best scones in the area! My dog would illicitly accompany me, much to the delight of the residents and especially Rosa, who loved to "look after her" while I went on my rounds. She would hold the lead proudly and chatter nonsensically away to her. Over tea and the famous scones, Carole explained that the new Care Standards meant that they would have to close and that all the residents would be split up and have to move to different homes. Too much money was involved to bring their house up to the new standards. They simply couldn't afford the structural changes necessary. Now it was my turn to be sad; not only would I miss my visits but, I was very concerned about the changes forced on a small group of confused, vulnerable and frail old people. I promised Carole that I would follow them up.

And so it was that, in due course, I was doing my rounds in another home and saw a lady in her room in a very distressed state. She was hunched up, crying, whimpering and sitting astride her chair, holding herself between her legs. It was Rosa! I barely recognised her. She had lost weight and looked dreadful. She didn't know me, or the dog. What was going on here? When I made enquiries, it transpired that Rosa had a urinary tract infection (UTI) and was also constipated. She was severely dehydrated. No wonder she was in such a state. Water is essential to life. One often forgets that enough fluid is essential not only for proper brain function (water content of the brain varies between 72 and 82 per cent with more water being present in the grey matter – the nerve cells) but also for proper functioning of the kidneys and bowels. Mouth infections, such as "thrush" (candidiasis), can flourish if the mouth gets too dry. It has been revealed that doctors have misdiagnosed several diseases in one in six older patients, including dementia. Confusion can arise due to a variety of factors, such as vitamin B deficiency, thyroid imbalance, side effects of medications, grief, depression, fatigue or dehydration. It is more than likely that at least some of these patients were dehydrated, amongst other things, and thus muddle-headed. If left unchecked, dehydration is fatal. The body becomes less able to maintain adequate blood pressure, deliver enough oxygen and nutrients to the cells and to rid itself of waste products.

When caring for older people, ensuring that sufficient fluids are taken is crucial to their good health. Any tummy upset with diarrhoea and vomiting causes loss of body fluids. Medicines such as diuretics ("water pills"), which are often prescribed to treat high blood pressure, add to the problem. They encourage excretion of not only water but of salts such as sodium and potassium. Other drugs that are used to treat urinary incontinence may compound these issues.

Thirst, unlike hunger, is not such a strong urge. Indeed, once one feels really thirsty, one is already at risk of becoming dehydrated. Professionals emphasise that, especially during hot weather, we need more fluids than our thirst indicates, especially if we fall into the older age bracket – 65 years and more.

Some while ago, the BBC Panorama programme showed undercover filming of the care of older people in a hospital.[2] Some of the patients had not been offered a drink all day.

In this day and age of complex medical ethical issues, where phrases such as "assisted death", "advance directives" , the wishes of the patient", "patient competence" and "the patient's best interests" are being bandied about, should we not look

[2] BBC News. 2005. *Panorama: Undercover Nurse*. Broadcast on BBC One, July 20th, Available Online at:
http://news.bbc.co.uk/1/hi/programmes/panorama/4655929.stm

first at *basic care* and ensure that the patient is fully hydrated, fed and comfortable, before we take decisions on his/her competence? (See also: "Prolonging Life or Tender Loving Care?").

One way of estimating one's degree of hydration is to check the colour of the urine. Ideally, this should be light straw coloured; anything darker than this and it indicates that fluid intake needs to be increased. A useful rule of thumb is 30-35ml of fluid/kg body weight/per day. For constipated individuals, this should double. (See "Blow the Wind Southerly"). However, what goes in must come out and if getting to the lavatory is a problem, or if there is a real fear of "having an accident", then many older people "self-regulate" themselves by refusing to drink more than they think they need. This is where good care is essential. Carers need to be able to pre-empt the need to go to the lavatory by offering assistance before the individual feels he/she has to ask for it. This way, dignity remains intact. There is nothing so demeaning as having to ask for help on this subject.

For those in one's care who already have continence protection, it is crucial that pads or other equipment are checked and changed regularly. Leaving someone wet and/or soiled for any length of time is extremely distressing for the individual and can contribute to skin infections and pressure sores, to say nothing of the smell.

I contacted the district nurse who visited Rosa's new home.

"I'm glad you 'phoned," she said. "I've been very worried about these residents. Shall we arrange to meet the manager together?"

Together, we gave the manager the Third Degree. Her response was the usual.

"I just can't get the staff – and not all of them understand instructions because their English isn't up to it." We were firm.

"We understand this but you have a duty of care, which is not being met."

It wasn't long after this that we learned that there was a new manager. We hoped for a better future for these residents.

TERRITORIAL BOUNDARIES AND THE NHS
(God Bless Her and All Who Sail in Her!)

If you can keep your head when all about you
Are losing theirs and blaming it on you,
If you can trust yourself when all men doubt you
But make allowance for their doubting too ...

Rudyard Kipling, "If"

"I think you'd better come in here, Mary," said Phil.

I had just returned from a week's holiday. What was this about? I was hoping it wouldn't take too much time. There was plenty in my diary to attend to that day. Phil was our line-manager. The fact that he was a physiotherapist and hadn't a clue about dietetics, dietitians or how we spent our days, didn't seem to worry him. What annoyed my two colleagues and myself was that he didn't seem to want to find out or care. He just counted the money that we spent from our miserable budget and consequently constantly nagged us about it. This attitude fuelled a "Them and Us" split, which developed between management and staff in not just our department but in others too. Staff often felt that management was totally divorced from what they really did, as exemplified by our own therapy managers, both at Borderland and Calmershire. They then had the audacity to make ridiculous decisions as to how our service should run, based on ignorance of what was needed.

Phil was looking serious but then he never did smile much, so I didn't think too much of it. He silently handed me a letter.

As I read it, that funny feeling of blood draining from my face came over me. I felt rather sick and my mouth went dry. There was a sort of ringing in my ears.

"Dr Bird is furious," he added.

Well, that didn't mean anything; Dr Bird was *always* cross and hated any kind of changes made to his patients' enteral feed prescriptions.

The letter was from the dietitian at the main hospital in Borderland.

She accused me in no uncertain terms of stepping on to her patch. Not only that, I had upset the GP, Dr Bird, by suggesting a change of artificial feed for one of his patients. The patient in question and his family were upset and I "had been clinically unprofessional" in advising loperamide (an anti-diarrhoeal agent) for him, when he had an infection of *Clostridium difficile* (*C.diff*).

Well! EXCUSE ME!

Michael, a young man in his early 20s, had multiple sclerosis (MS). He lived at home with his parents in a lovely country home, deep in the midst of rural Borderland. He had to be fed by a tube into his stomach (known in the trade as a "PEG" – per endoscopic gastrostomy) and needed total nursing care, which was lovingly provided by his parents and the district nurse (DN). Now that he was home from hospital, I had been asked to see him by his DN, to review his tube-feeding and to see if we could sort out his diarrhoea, which had been chronic. While in hospital, he had been advised to take massive amounts of vitamin C to stop his urine crystallising out and blocking his urinary catheter. Excess vitamin C can certainly cause diarrhoea, so I suggested that this might be reduced. And then I suggested that a change in the type of feed he was having might also help. At no point did I suggest an anti-diarrhoeal medicine and no one had mentioned that he might have a *C. diff* infection. I wrote all of this up for the GP and the DN. End of story!

I had been about to go on holiday and had made a date to visit again when I returned. I went away and worried about Michael for the whole week. On my return, I went straight to his home before going to the office, as he lived quite near. Michael's mother opened the door and looked embarrassed and uncomfortable.

"Er..." she began. "We've been told that you shouldn't visit anymore...did you not get a message?"

Now it was my turn to feel uncomfortable.

"Oh...er...I haven't been to the office yet," I explained. "Could I come in for a chat anyway?"

I made small talk while my brain was racing wondering what was going on, and learned that the hospital dietitians were now involved and that they wanted to take over Michael's care.

At the time of this incident, I was employed by the community Trust. Our duties were many and varied and included monitoring patients who were having tube-feeds in their own homes. Once a patient had been prescribed a tube-feed, the hospital dietitian advised the GP, who then wrote the prescription for the company that made it, faxed it through and the company then delivered it direct to the patient. Once a patient was home, the community staff took over the care, much as a hospital nurse relinquishes her care to the district nurse. As community dietitians, we could also change the type of formula for the tube-feed, if we felt that this would be beneficial and/or if a change in the patient's circumstances appeared to warrant it. It meant requesting the prescription direct from the GP and then going through this process all over again, incurring further expense. These feeds are *not* cheap and it was the GP who paid for it. Any feed that had already been delivered to a house, could not be re-used and had to be discarded, even if it had not been opened.

Until Primary Care Trusts were set up, getting agreement for payment for a new patient needing a tube-feed was a further nightmare. Various forms for the feed company had to be completed, as it was what was then called a "Non-Stock Requisition", and were copied to the person responsible for payment – our locality manager. First, we had to rush upstairs from our office to the computer that was shared by all the staff in the building and hope that there was no one else using it. This was so we could log the patient's details on to the system and then arrive at what was called an MPI number – or personal index. Without this, we could proceed no further. More information had to be entered, such as the diagnosis, the GP and *his* codes and then our own details. Because this was such a hassle and there was always a delay, we usually ended up keeping a stock of feeds and giving-sets (the necessary tubes and connections), so that we could whiz off to deliver them ourselves, allowing patients to have enough for the weekend. All this sounds simple but it could take up to an hour or so, while frantic 'phone calls are made, the computer is being used or crashes and the Primary Care Trust refuses to pay.

Returning to The Letter. After feeling sick, I then felt very angry. I felt that this could have been addressed politely and professionally between the hospital dietitian and myself being, as it was, a total breakdown of communication between the two Trusts. I was horrified at the injustice and felt just as I did at four years old, at my first convent school, when another girl leaned across the boy next to her and pinched my pencil. When the teacher turned around, it was me that she saw trying to retrieve it. And it was *me* who was put in the corner! I still smoulder at the memory. And I still hate the name, "Beryl"!

I asked Phil if I could have a copy of the letter, so that I could respond. Initially, he said he would, but it never materialised. I rang Dominic, the DN who had made the referral to me. He hadn't been advised that this patient should be seen solely by the hospital staff. Nor did Dominic know that the patient had *C. Diff.* In any event I wrote a response, as I knew that that horrid letter would be in my personal file, held by Phil. It was along the lines of why couldn't a fellow dietitian just lift the telephone with an explanation; why did they not advise the DN and above all, why had they not informed us that the patient had a *C. Diff* infection? I further explained that I would not, under any circumstances whatsoever, advise an anti-diarrhoeal medicine, without recourse to the GP first. My colleagues were sympathetic and aghast. Very kindly, they assured me that they would have done the same in my place. There was no response from anyone to my letter. Surprised? Me neither.

This was 1990, when the Conservatives introduced their NHS and Community Care Act. GPs were offered the opportunity to be responsible for their own costs. For the first time, the so-called "internal market" in the NHS was mooted, made up of "purchasers" and "providers". The former were health authorities and some, not all, family doctors, who became "Fund Holders". The latter were hospitals, learning disability services, mental health services and ambulances. As it turned out, GPs who opted out of fund holding made the right decision. Eventually, the "purchasers" and "providers" became Trusts, each with their own management. Competition between providers was encouraged and the NHS was set on a steep learning curve of business management. How ludicrous a notion this was felt to be! Anyone who has been involved in caring for others knows just how unpredictable people and their ailments are. Senior staff in many departments spent ages and valuable clinical time writing business plans. Clinicians – especially doctors – simply wanted to do the job for which they were trained, without too much interference. They did not want to become accountants or businessmen and women overnight.

It seems as if the NHS has undergone more organisational changes in its history, than you and I have had hot dinners. It has been in an almost continuous state of what has been dubbed "redisorganisation". It would appear that every time things become difficult in the NHS, The-Powers-That-Be change the names of the organisations and introduce more managerial posts in the hope that things will get better.

It doesn't. In fact, not only can constant change have negative effects on staff, it also costs a lot of money as new stationery, new logos, new uniforms, name badges and new corporate labels all have to be made, to say nothing of new policies (which are usually the same as the old ones, but sexed up a little so as to make them even more incomprehensible). Staff are moved to different offices and teams are split up. Job descriptions may alter. More managers are appointed and no one likes change. And, when it was reported that adding a number to the NHS 60th anniversary logo cost £6,000 per digit, which took two designers – sorry, I mean, *"A Creative Director and Senior Designer"* – ten days to complete, one is forgiven for being cynical![1]

Part of the 1974 Reorganisation wasn't all bad: in fact, in theory it boded well, as the theoretical goal was to provide a "seamless service" (management speak!) between the hospital and the community. I could see it also working well in practice, from our profession's point of view. It *should* mean that the same dietitian who had seen the patient in hospital would continue to treat him/her once he came home and was referred back to his GP. So far, so good.

From the dietetic perspective, this meant that county (community) dietetic posts were scrapped. (See "Fresh Air and an Open Top"). The County Health Department became

[1] Gosden, E. 2009. Government paid £6,000 a digit for NHS 60th anniversary logo. *The Times*, December 26th. Available at:
http://www.timesonline.co.uk/tol/news/politics/article6968036.ece

absorbed into the NHS, which then became an Area Health Authority. Most counties (areas) were divided up into Districts, each with its – yes, you've guessed it, another management level – a District Health Authority. Overarching the lot was the Regional Health Authority. It was a three-tier management system and already, staff were complaining that there were "too many Chiefs and not enough Indians". It was supposed to be managerially driven by consensus, allowing all employees to have a voice in decision-making. It soon earned criticism and within a couple of years a Royal Commission on the NHS was appointed to examine the problem areas.

As community dietitians, formerly employed by local health or social services departments of county councils, we now had to apply for "District Dietitian" posts, of which there were four in our county of Woodlandshire. (Not all counties were divided similarly: small ones actually became single District Health Authorities). Our new posts meant that we had hospital duties as well as our existing community duties, although the catchment area (and the population served) was smaller.

In practice, the catch came because hospitals go by the clock. They are highly regimented in terms of ward rounds, clinics and catering all at certain times and days of the week and seem to forget that there is "another world" outside. This did not fit comfortably with community work, where the emphasis was strongly on preventive medicine, nutrition education and "spreading the word" through other professions as well as the necessary administration and preparation. Much of this work has already been clarified in the chapter, "Fresh Air and an Open Top". Community dietitians are used to making their own diaries, not being dictated to by others, or have them make their daily arrangements. For a single-handed dietitian like myself, there were often clashes on the time-table. I was amused by a course that was then organised specifically by the NHS for dietitians in these new posts: it was about management and managing staff. The fact that I didn't have any staff to manage appeared to be omitted!

One morning, when working at Woodlandshire, I climbed all the stairs to the dietitian's office on the sixth floor of the hospital as usual, where I had a morning clinic. The first two patients were already waiting on the chairs outside. I wished them a bright "Good Morning", asked that they wait a few moments while I sorted myself out and unlocked the door. It was totally empty! No desk, no chair, no files or filing cabinets… nowt! On the floor was a forlorn telephone.

"Um…" I was completely thrown! "It seems we don't have an office this morning, I'm afraid." I tried to be cool and act as if this was an everyday occurrence. "Do you mind waiting, while I make some 'phone calls?"

I sat on the floor and started dialling. This was not funny. Time was ticking by and more patients joined the queue. Eventually, after several calls, someone said, "Oh…I think it's been re-located to outpatients."

We all trailed down (in the lift this time) to the outpatients department on the ground floor. A red herring. No dietitian's office. More 'phone calls. Eventually, our wild goose-chase led us to a sideward off one of the medical wards. Up in the lift again and there was everything from my office, dumped unceremoniously on the floor. A clinic that I, and I am sure, my patients, will never forget! But the funny thing was, it was I who felt guilty. I felt so stupid and embarrassed that I had had to air the inefficiencies and ineffectual communication within the hospital – such professional glitches should be away from the public gaze. Further, collecting patients like the Pied Piper of Hamelin, as we trailed through the hospital, meant that they were seriously inconvenienced. I was outraged that the hospital manager had not had the courtesy or foresight to warn me that this might happen and advise me of the details. Courtesy and good manners seemed to have been thrown out of the window together with other old-fashioned niceties.

The gap between management and staff widened: when I left Woodlandshire, three people were employed to do my job. I was cross and told the hospital board so. What had I to lose? I was off to another job! To add insult to injury, one of these dietitians could not drive but was allowed to take taxis to all her community appointments!

Soon after this reorganisation, it became clear that things weren't working out as they should be. A highly expensive and well-known American-based management team of consultants was brought in to put it all right. Those of us "on the workshop floor" felt that we could have told the chief executives and management what was wrong for peanuts! As it was, the NHS was billed large sums of money for a statement of "the bleeding obvious". Are the management going to re-structure, so that there are less of them? I don't think so!

Stranger things started to happen: 1974 and onwards saw nurses sloughing off their starched aprons and caps overnight, clutching "colour-coordinated" clipboards instead; ward sisters whipping off their butchers'- blue uniforms, plumping themselves up and taking to power-dressing and expensive hair-do's very seriously indeed.

In 2009, The Patients' Association published a dossier suggesting that a million people had suffered poor treatment by nurses, or worse, been cruelly treated, in the last six years.[2] A catalogue of neglect and abuse included being left on the floor after a fall, being left in soiled clothes and sheets and not being fed and hydrated adequately. One hears anecdotal evidence of sheer thoughtlessness: food being left out of reach or the call bell

[2] The Patients' Association, 2009. *Patients...not numbers, People...not statistics.* August 27th

placed on the affected side of a stroke patient. In 2010, a Government Review suggested that nurses should be more caring,[3] and the Royal College of Nursing has given guidance on nurse staffing levels to address this.[4]

A letter from a hospital doctor to *The Daily Telegraph* describes the reason for an experienced theatre sister handing in her resignation: her new job description prioritised patient care as number seven. [5] And most damning of all, as this goes to print, is the report from the health ombudsman over the "callous treatment" of elderly patients in the NHS.[6] Where has basic care, compassion and awareness of patients' needs gone? A recent initiative, the "Productive Ward" is aimed at helping nurses improve efficiency on the wards by "releasing time to care". [7] Erm…isn't that what nurses are supposed to do?

With the 1974 Reorganisation, there was a change of attitude too: no longer were they matrons or assistant matrons but "Nursing Officers" and they wore badges to tell you so. Later, they suddenly became very arrogant and refused to feed helpless patients because it was not part of their duties or job description; that it was demeaning, or that they were too busy to monitor

[3] Department of Health, 2010. *Prime Minister's Commission on the Future of Nursing and Midwifery in England – 2010.* March 31st. Available at:
http://webarchive.nationalarchives.gov.uk/20100331110400/http:/cnm.independent.gov.uk/

[4] The Policy Unit, Royal College of Nursing, 2010. *Guidance on Safe Nurse Staffing Levels in the UK.* December. Available at:
http://www.rcn.org.uk/_data/assets/pdf_file/0005/353237/003860.pdf

[5] Gladstone, J. 2009. When patient care slipped down the managers' list of priorities for nurses. "Letters to the Editor", *The Daily Telegraph*, August 29th

[6] Parliamentary and Health Service Ombudsman, 2011. *Care and Compassion?* Press Release. February 15th. Available at: http://www.ombudsman.org.uk/about-us/media-centre/press-release/2011/nhs-is-failing-to-meet-even-the-most-basic-standards-of-care-for-older-people,-warns-Health-Service-Ombudsman

[7] National Nursing Research Unit, 2010. *Improving healthcare quality at scale and pace Lessons from The Productive Ward: "Releasing time to care" programme.* NHS Institute for Innovation and improvement. Available at:
http://www.institute.nhs.uk/quality_and_value/productivity_series/productive_ward.html

food. Excuse me? Where nutrition and hydration are the keystones to recovery, this seems a strange attitude to take! It has been suggested that nurses need better training to prevent elderly and frail patients being malnourished. Maybe they didn't appreciate the massive impact that this could have on such vulnerable people, who thrive on small, tasty, nutritious, frequent meals and snacks. Without this kind of attention, they can go downhill very quickly.

Research also suggests that nurses spend less than half their shift actually nursing patients due to poor layout of hospital wards, which means spending time finding equipment and drugs and, of course, the ever-dreaded paperwork. Even the Health Secretary, Andrew Lansley admitted that nurses spend too much time filling out forms to satisfy the NHS bureaucracy, thus compromising their quality time with patients.[8]

Many of these unwelcome observations have been attributed, not only to the changes in the structure and management of the NHS but also to the changes in nurse training over the past 40 years.

Project 2000 – A New Preparation for Practice (1986), was a revolution in British Nursing.[9] For over a century, from the 1870s to the 1970s, nurse training involved an apprenticeship system, around syllabi set by the General Nursing Council, exams, practical training and development of moral fibre to make a good nurse. Not only did nurses' duties involve overseeing cleanliness in the ward but they were also responsible

[8] Devlin, K. 2010. Nurses spending only a third of their time with patients. *The Daily Telegraph.* June 9th

[9] United Kingdom Central Council for Nursing, Midwifery and Health Visiting, 1986. *Project 2000: A New Preparation for Practice.* May 20th. ISBN: 0-95114 40-006. Archived Publication available from Nursing and Midwifery Council website (Formerly UKCC). Available at: www.nmc-uk.org

for the overall care of a designated number of patients. This included their personal hygiene, clean bedding, giving appropriate food and fluids, special diets, dressings, bedsore prevention, medications, mouth care and their psychological welfare, all of which were supervised by the senior nurse or ward sister. The student nurse retained a handbook, in which each skill was ticked as competency was achieved and signed off by the ward sister. When off duty, it was each nurse's responsibility to ensure that she "handed over" her patients to a colleague for the duration.

Four principles formed the foundation for the development of a good nurse: to develop moral character; to equip her with the requisite knowledge and skills for patient care; to learn by example of the ward sister; observing and practising techniques with guidance and finally, building relationships with colleagues and patients. The needs of the patient were supreme: any deviation or neglect of these resulted in strong disciplinary action or even dismissal. Critics of this "old-school" style of training suggested that student nurses were exploited as cheap labour and that their well-meaning but possibly inexperienced actions could be dangerous for patients.

Introduced in 1989, Project 2000 embraced the idea of pushing nursing into a more professional footlight, to put it on a par with other degree or diploma courses and improve the career structure. This meant more academic training, which did not take place in the hospital-based nursing schools as previously, but in colleges and universities and was paid for by the hospitals. (The changes in nurse training are clearly set out in Ann Bradshaw's book).[10] Even so, some experts suggest that our nurses are poorly qualified and that only a few have a degree. Since Project 2000 was introduced, there has been

[10] Ann Bradshaw. 2001 *The Project 2000 Nurse: The Remaking of British General Nursing, 1978-200.* Paul Wiley

continuing unease amongst the profession and the government as to its success, or lack of it. Its critics not only suggest that students, who do not go near a ward or a patient for the first year of their studies were divorced from their ultimate aim and were unable to practise what they had learned, but that the workforce on the ward was severely depleted. The government compensated for this by increasing the number of healthcare assistants (HCAs), who were non- or semi-trained.

Now, new rules from the Nursing and Midwifery Council (NMC) suggest that from 2013, all nurses should have a degree. There are concerns that those who might make excellent nurses may be discouraged from applying for training. But others, such as Ann Keen, a junior minister and former nurse, suggest that such a level of training provides nurses with the decision-making skills in an increasingly complex NHS.[11] Conversely, would those who attain a degree then be "too posh to wash their patients" or "too clever to care?" The basic fact remains that nursing is essentially a caring and vocational career and that this, together with flawless levels of competence, should be paramount. How that competence is achieved is perhaps what should be questioned.

1982 saw another re-structuring of the NHS, which abolished the middle, area-management tier. Around this time, a strange *patois* also developed. People started talking in riddles and codes. We were encouraged to "think out of the box"; to "have dialogue"; to "get a handle on things"; "have joined-up thinking". "Rafts of policies" were "run past" us; "flagged up" or "rolled out". Then there were "windows of opportunity"; "strategic overviews"; "cascades of information"; "task forces", "listening exercises" and "key initiatives". Together with

[11] Devlin, K. 2009. Degree-only rule 'will deter nurses'. *The Daily Telegraph*. November 13th

"Mission Statements", "Visions" and Regional Champions", these became popular everyday speak. "Organisational Developments" were referred to by management as "O.Ds". To us on the ground, that abbreviation meant only one thing – "over dose"! Or even "overdraft"! I could go on – but I think you are beginning to get the idea.

If you can keep up with them and "talk the talk", you are tipped to become a manager. It was always a mystery to those of us "lesser mortals" as to how this language developed, or how it became acceptable. Worryingly, it even diffused into our own meetings. We want nurses, not "ward managers" and patients don't want to be "clients". Bring back plain English PLEASE!

By the late 1990s, staff felt that they were considered to be totally incompetent at their jobs. CPD or Continuous Professional Development portfolios appeared and failure to keep these up to date could mean a disciplinary hearing. There were "peer reviews" and "mentoring" of both senior and junior staff – some called this sneaking and grassing. Sharing reflective practice with colleagues was encouraged. By now there was an all-pervading sense of "Big Brother Watching". Lawyers were having a boom time, as patients (and staff) discovered litigation. Patients' care slipped down the list of priorities and staff were warned that they had to watch their backs. They felt vulnerable, knowing that they had to record every single detail of their contacts with patients – legibly and irreversibly.

"If it ain't written down clearly, it never happened," cautioned legal advisors. The NHS Litigation Authority has seen "a significant increase" in the number of claims received.[12] Total payouts rose by more than a fifth in 2009, compared with the previous year, topping £800 million. Total claims (which

---

[12] Devlin, K. 2009. NHS legal payouts top £800m, *The Daily Telegraph,* August 10th (Original report available at: NHS Litigation website: http://www.nhlsa.com/ Claims/)

included clinical and non-clinical) increased in number by 1,000 over the 2009/2010 period.

This atmosphere did not lead to happy working teams. Professional confidence dived and there was an undercurrent of uncertainty. How one carried out one's work was constantly questioned. People started to feel a bit "precious". Staff unions were swamped with cases of bullying (more of that later).

In addition to one's job, which was hard enough at times, there were the unofficial "add-ons" :

- Clinical Governance
- Evidence-Based Medicine
- Increased documentation and paperwork
- Clinical Effectiveness
- Clinical Audit
- Clinical Supervision
- CPD (as above)
- NICE Guidelines
- Policies and Procedures for everything
- Risk Assessments from the moment you fall out of bed to come to work
- Changes in the NHS structures (notably, former Trusts to Primary Care Groups to Primary Care Trusts)
- District Nurse Review
- Health Care Assistants Review
- Therapists Review
- Staff Attitude Survey
- Improving Working Lives
- Investment in People
- Ethical and Legal Aspects
- Appraisals
- Staff Reviews
- Strategies
- Self Assessment Tools (a tick sheet to good competence) – later these became Continuing Professional Development (CPD)

- Beacon Status
- Centres of Excellence
- And, would you believe, there was even a policy document for policy making! All of these against an already overloaded background.

I am sure that these are very laudable in their own right – but no one gave us the extra time to address them – nor, in many instances, could we see the point of them. As those of us who were looking forward to our retirement years would say, shaking our grey curls: "How on earth did we manage without all this stuff and still give good care to our patients?"

Most readers will be familiar with Parkinson's Law, which states that "*work expands to fill the time available for completion*" (Cyril Northgate-Parkinson, 1909-1993). I think we can see how this fits in with this kind of management.

You may feel that I am ranting unnecessarily but I am not alone. Mr David Nunn, an Orthopaedic Surgeon at a South London Hospital shows he is a man after my own heart. [13]

In a letter to *The Daily Telegraph*, he wrote: "*Vast amounts of money have been spent on employing people who manage pathways, policies and protocols but who have no direct patient contact and who do not answer to clinicians. As a result, these people have no incentive other than to see that their particular box has been ticked.*"

He concluded: "*Until the present government-driven management culture – in which far too many people are employed to do far too little except to obstruct – is abandoned, the poor quality of care in the NHS will be perpetuated.*"

Then there were the committees and sub-committees; focus groups – usually human-resources led – which included discussions on long-hours culture, flexible working hours, a

---

[13] Nunn, D. 2009. Poor patient care. "Letters to the Editor". *The Daily Telegraph*. October 19th

healthy workplace, equality and diversity, child care and work-life balance; steering groups; working parties and...meetings and, would you believe, PRE-meetings. Oh Boy! Were there meetings! Frustrated patients and colleagues trying to speak to someone were often given the platitude: "I'm sorry, Miss So-and-So isn't available. She is in a meeting."

In spite of reassurance that all these changes were based on "consultation" with the staff, (consultation documents were constantly written, re-written and updated) it always seemed that the results were a *fait accompli*, in spite of putting in one's penny's worth! The government of the day ends up doing its own thing and the slaves, the managers, do their best to execute their commands.

Anyone who has worked in the NHS and then writes about it, enjoys a polemic about the management – or lack of it. It is almost "obligatory". Praising it too highly would be a bit like saying that you like school or school dinners. And of course, I am directing my derogatory comments solely to those who appear not to understand what good management is all about. All would most likely agree that the NHS is an amazing organisation to work for, especially if the staff work within the original spirit, as envisioned by Nye Bevan in 1948. It is second only to the Chinese Army in being the largest employer in the world.

There is true loyalty within the ranks and it is because of this, that feelings run high regarding NHS expenditure and management style. The total number of employees is now around 1.43 million (2009 figures) but, wait for it, the fastest increase is amongst managers, which is growing four times faster than nurses. Its financial control and day-to-day management have been the butt of severe and lengthy criticisms, which is hardly surprising when we learn that the NHS is facing its gravest financial crisis yet. In 2009, it faced a shortfall of £15 billion over five years. [14] Increasing expenditure on management, administrative and clerical staff has been ridiculously out of proportion to salary rises for clinical staff. It's not getting any better and management is still top-heavy.

Over the years, management consultants have been drafted in to "put it all right" and billed the NHS vast amounts of money for their efforts. Latterly (2009), there were hints of nepotism, as deals were made with firms, which hired senior Labour personnel. Many chief executives of NHS Foundation Trusts now earn more than the Prime Minister, David Cameron.[15] No wonder people aspire to these dizzy heights!

But as the number of managers has risen twice as quickly as doctors and nurses under the last government, is this sustainable or ethical? It's all too much. It is not surprising that many doctors *are addicted to every drug under the sun"* says Dr. Clare Gerada, medical director of the Practitioner Health Programme.[16]

In addition to The Big Spend, NHS Trusts everywhere have been splashing out on bizarre, incomprehensible extras and apparently needless purchases, such as buying umbrellas for staff, chandeliers for a health centre, or spending £8,000 on a booklet which suggests ways that staff and patients can tackle climate change, one idea being putting pot plants in patients' rooms. Or, information on how staff can reduce their carbon footprints by walking and cycling more. [17] Or, encouraging the

---

[14] Smith, R. 2009. NHS will face £15bn budget shortfall due to effects of recession managers warn. *The Daily Telegraph Online.* June 10th. Available at: http://www.telegraph.co.uk/health/healthnews/5485814/NHS-will-face-15bn-budget-shortfall-due-to-effects-of-recession-managers-warn.html
[15] Roberts, L. 2010. The 300 NHS chiefs who earn more than Cameron. *The Daily Telegraph.* July 5th
[16] Devlin,K. 2010. Doctors are addicted to 'every drug under the sun'. *The Daily Telegraph* January 29th .Available Online at: http:// www.telegraph.co.uk/ health/ healthnews/ 7102415/ Doctors-are-addicted-to-the-every-drug-under-the-sun.html
[17] Faculty of Public Health, 2008. *Sustaining a Healthy Future.* Faculty of Public Health, January. ISBN: 1-900273-28-4 Available at: http://www.fph.org.uk/uploads/r_sustaining_a_healthy_future.pdf

Over-60s to have more sex. *"It's never too late to experiment,"* this booklet suggests. The mind boggles! Surely, "Nanny" should keep out of the bedroom! That's not all.

NICE (the National Institute for Clinical Excellence) appreciates that managers overall are one of the biggest threats to staff mental health. Guidance is aimed at reducing the £24 billion cost to the economy of staff absence through stress and, although not aimed specifically at the NHS, is to be adopted by it.[18]

Figures from the NHS Health and Wellbeing Review suggest that 45,000 staff call in sick each day.[19] Staff receive full pay plus a selection of benefits when they are on sick leave. It all mounts up. The Boorman Report, based on a series of surveys by the Healthcare Commission, revealed that one in three NHS employees suffered stress and pressure in the workplace each year, that this accounted for 30 per cent of sickness absence and cost the tax payer £1.7 billion a year.[20] Ouch! If sickness levels were reduced to an acceptable level, £290 million might be saved. Back-pain and work-related stress are the two most common reasons for NHS staff going on sick leave, with stress now in the lead. Part of the problem, says Cary Cooper, Professor of Organisational Psychology, is because of all the organisational changes that keep taking place in the NHS. People feel threatened about job security and feel they are losing control. Bullying is a growing issue in the UK workplace. Managers themselves are stressed, pressured by lack of resources, and too

[18] NICE. 2009. *Promoting mental wellbeing through productive and healthy working conditions: guidance for employers.* November.
Available at: http:// guidance.nice.org.uk/PH22/Guidance/pdf/English
[19] Bloxham, A. 2009. Over 45,000 NHS staff call in sick each day. *The Daily Telegraph.* August 19th.
Available at: http://www.telegraph.co.uk/health/healthnews/6049107/Over-45000-NHS-staff-call-in-sick-each-day.html
[20] Boorman, S. 2009. *NHS Health and Wellbeing the Boorman review. Final Report.* Pub: Department of Health. Available at:
http://www.nhshealthandwellbeing.org/FinalReport.html

often do not spot the signs in their staff.

Add to that huge workloads ("the job is never done"), cuts in staff and you have a recipe for disaster. Sometimes, it is overwhelming. There is a greater risk of car accidents, depression and suicides. Readers may remember the case of a dietitian in Manchester, who stabbed herself and jumped out of a high window. A friend and former colleague of mine, who is a dietetic manager, is on sick leave with depression as I write; she has already tried to commit suicide three times. These incidences make me sad and angry; these are good people who are simply using their skills to help others but they become damaged in the process, due to the systems surrounding them and their inability to override them and cope. Such a waste of talents and potentially fulfilling lives.

Even the NHS Fraud Squad adds to the general NHS deficit: fraud is estimated to cost the NHS £115 million a year but the squad itself costs three times as much to run, as it recovers.

But the shortfalls and figures in red are not all the fault of the NHS. By missing appointments, patients themselves add to this bill to the tune of £600 million a year. Go to the Naughty Corner! There is nothing more dispiriting than running a clinic in which 50 per cent of patients DNA (Do Not Attend). If away from one's office, one cannot always catch up on other things in the resulting gaps.

Gerry Robinson, the man who attempted to disentangle the messy management at one NHS Foundation Trust in Rotherham, concluded what most of us on the shop floor have been saying for years: *"Cure the NHS with far fewer managers"*. [21] As he points out, at the end of the day, the systems in place are highly risky. The wrong people are in the top (management) jobs; common

[21] Robinson, G. 2009. 'Cure the NHS with far fewer managers'. "Feature article". *The Daily Telegraph*. March 28th

sense and good business practice do not exist; chief executives surround themselves with other managers who tend to be "Yes Men and Women", rather than extricating themselves from their (nicely furnished and carpeted) offices, meeting medical and nursing staff and finding out how patients are actually cared for. They have a duty to the public, who is paying their (not insubstantial) salaries. Dr Peter Carter of the Royal College of Nursing (RCN) claims that up to £5 billion could be saved by addressing the NHS *"scandalous financial waste"*.[22]

Not all NHS managers are ineffective but the snag is that many come from within. Like any other genetically inherited trait, bad management breeds bad management, which is unwittingly passed down the line. The medical needs of patients are being increasingly overshadowed by the need to meet targets. There is a change in emphasis from patient-care to balancing the books, as NHS Trusts are being run like businesses. To make matters worse, it is suggested that half of our hospitals are misleading the public on their standards of care. Facts and figures on the self-assessments have been manipulated and massaged, in order to achieve targets. There has been a power-shift away from clinicians but *these* are the experts in patient care – not managers! Doctors want an NHS with patients, not profits. Once again, management consultants have been drafted in to advise on meeting the government target of saving between £1.5billion and £20 billion between 2011 and 2014. Their invoice to the NHS for this was around £350 million.

At least two doctors of the Consultants' Committee of the British Medical Association (BMA) have the right idea and the courage to say it.[23] In a letter to *The Daily Telegraph*, they wrote:

[22] Carter, P. 2011. NHS needs to take responsible approach to financial crisis. *The Daily Telegraph*. February 7th. Available at:
http://www.telegraph.co.uk/health/healthnews/8303334/NHS-needs-to-take-responsible-approach-to-financial-crisis.html
[23] Fielden, J. and Porter, M. 2009. Cut consultants. "Letters to the Editor". *The Daily Telegraph*, June 13th

"Independent management consultants are costing the NHS in England an estimated £350m a year, yet their benefit to frontline care is often unclear."

Hooray for good sense! But will anyone "up there" take any notice?

One of my "extra-curricula" roles was to attend Trust meetings. Money, or lack of it, was always on the agenda. Staff were constantly asked for suggestions on how to make cut-backs. Many of us would have liked to suggest that the management cut back their staff and/or their salaries! Instead, wards in the community hospitals were closed and staff were asked to be vigilant. The silly thing was that in the following financial year, one was penalised for such thrift. Accountants would look at the preceding budget and assume that the department would not need so much the following year.

And just don't mention the new computer system for the NHS which cost around £12 billion. In his weekly column in *The Daily Telegraph*, Dr Max Pemberton describes it as an *"ill thought-out wasteful and unnecessary white elephant, that is not fit for purpose."* [24] Because of its failure to allow communication between other departments and Trusts, it can hinder clinical practice. Delays in its implementation suggest that this cost may be even higher. And because the NHS is a political pawn and, at the time of writing, an election was looming, it was being rushed through so that opposing parties could not cancel it. Already, more than a million patient records are on the database, assuming that they haven't been deleted by the impish activity of 8,000 viruses.

"Agenda for Change", the new pay-scale system was heavily

[24] Pemberton, M. 2009. The chaos of the NHS's electronic records. "Finger on the Pulse". *The Daily Telegraph* December 14th Available Online at:
http://www.telegraph.co.uk/health/healthadvice/maxpemberton/6787809/The-chaos-of-NHS-electronic-records.html

invested in, both financially and by working extra hours. Designated staff laboured long and hard. Several years later and there are still many disgruntled staff, feeling that their assessment has put them on a lower pay scale than they should be. It was no surprise to read in the press that,

"A scheme to modernise NHS pay has delivered no evidence of savings or increased productivity according to the Commons Public Accounts Committee...Agenda for Change had failed to cut the NHS £28 billion wages bill." [25]

Over the years, the NHS has lurched from one "disorganisation" to another – many would say allowing no time for any assessment of a positive outcome, before the next. Successive Secretaries of State have come and gone, leaving a trail of White Papers. Staff have become disillusioned and feel that the embryonic, particular and special dream has become fogged, distracted and over-run by bureaucratic details, resulting in a "trained incapacity". Government ministers appear to see only what they want to see, not what the staff want them to see.

It is recognised that, by comparison with health care in other developed countries, the NHS is grossly under-resourced. The former Labour government, under Gordon Brown, promised extra funding for a further five years (up to 2011), but mis-management of GP and hospital consultant contracts, together with the debacle over junior doctor's jobs, (MTAS) and fast-track training for doctors and nurses, meant that this backfired and further chaos resulted.

The last review of the NHS (Lord Darzi) is unique in that it was viewed from the clinical aspect.[26] In an article by Lord Crisp, who was one-time chief executive of the NHS and

[25] Devlin, K. 2009. NHS pay reforms 'delivered no evidence of savings'. *The Daily Telegraph*. June 18th. Available Online at:
http://www.telegraph.co.uk/health/healthnews/5559433/NHS-pay-reforms-delivered-no-evidence-of-savings.html
[26] Darzi, A.W, 2008. *High quality care for all: NHS Next Stage Final report*. Department of Health. June 30th

permanent secretary at the Department of Health, it is suggested that the NHS should be freed from political control and left to run itself. [27] I think many would agree and say, "Amen" to that!

As I write, the new Circle Hospital at Bath has opened. The whole ethos of hospital architecture has been challenged and re-defined. Described as being innovatively designed by Norman Foster and Partners, more like an hotel than a hospital, there is daylight everywhere, a beautiful view, a calm atmosphere and it is owned and run by the professionals who provide the services to the patients. Think: John Lewis Partnership and you get the idea. Staff are fully engaged. In such a stress-reduced environment, it is suggested that patients will respond positively, thus lessening the number of days in hospital. *Circle* is Europe's largest partnership of clinicians, a highly ambitious project which aims to re-engineer healthcare to achieve excellence. It's maybe time to think afresh and we watch their projects with keen interest.

The poor NHS is a ship foundering in ever rising and troubled waters, buffeted and battered by violent storms and knee-jerk reactions. The crew pull feebly on the sheets to calm the flapping sails. The Captain has lost control. More passengers climb aboard. The many and various suggestions and advice to try and right her blow in on the strong winds, but are often conflicting, and into deeper and rougher water she sinks. For how many more years will she be seaworthy? It is the dedicated crew who battle on, plug the holes and bale out the water to keep her afloat. The ship's owners fuss over the manifests comfortably on dry land.

Will the current coalition government's plans be enough to

---

[27] Smith, R. 2009. Free NHS from politics former chief says. *The Daily Telegraph,* November 20th

put the NHS back in the black? Pilot schemes are just beginning which will empower GPs, allowing them responsibility for their share of the finances from the Primary Care Trust and to spend as they think best for their patients. (This sounds like a return to fund holding to me). GP consortia are already asking for financial advice from those expensive consultants. Will the proposed job cuts be confined to administration and management? Clinical staff are very worried indeed; there is in-fighting and territorial aggression. Not only are there personal concerns about job losses or changes in status, but also about deterioration of services and patient confidence, to say nothing of the projected cost of it all. The spirit that Nye Bevan envisioned in 1948 is wavering in the atmosphere of "distance management", bureaucratic dictums and meaningless euphemisms. Times have changed in terms of systems, science and medical advance but the very heart of the NHS is still beating – just. A "pace-maker" seems timely.

NUMBER CRUNCHING AND TECHNOFOLLY

"Contrariwise" continued Tweedledee, If it was so, it might be; and if it were so, it would be; but as it isn't, it ain't. That's logic"

Lewis Carroll, "Through the Looking Glass"

Time had stood still for me, while working as a freelance dietitian, rubbing shoulders with magazine editors, P.R. companies and journals, tapping away on my little Olivetti portable typewriter! I was blissfully unaware of changes that were rumbling through the NHS. My return after ten years was a harsh wake-up call. I had kept up with changes in general dietary advice but now, not only were there things like ready-made artificial feeds to grapple with (see "Tubes and Twiddly Bits") and the complicated sums required to work out the rate that they should be administered, but staff were now talking about something called "Körner". It turned out that this was not some new Hungarian recipe, or an allusion to the blues musician but a new system of counting. It was used for analysing and translating into numbers the amount of work that we were doing. How on earth could someone imagine the possibility of auditing the sort of care and time that involves being kind and considerate, as well as all the little deeds for patients that are the very essence and backbone of why people went into the caring professions in the first place? It is one's heart that defines this choice: not career structure, money or family expectations. Just to make things naturally more complex, as seems to be the way in the NHS, not all health authorities followed the same accounting system.

At Borderland we had a 50-page handbook, which told us which codes to use for each and every activity to account for every minute of the day. Things like going to the lavatory, blowing one's nose, making tea or having lunch were mercifully omitted, though amazingly, a former colleague from another Trust has told me that staff have recently been asked to record non-patient activities in ten minute units. It is thought "the commissioners would be interested". An invitation for some amusing and childish creative writing if ever there was one!

There were codes for meetings (of course!); for training – and this differed if you either received or were giving the training; clinics – and the location of each clinic then had to be notated; hospital work – and again, the location of each hospital; travel time (amusingly coded T-time); "admin" – which meant time in the office for telephone calls, writing letters and reports, collecting samples of nutritional supplements, or preparing visual aids and hand-outs for talks and training and so on. Patient contacts were further broken down to elucidate whether these involved telephone calls and letters or direct contact (face-to-face), or whether one liased with another fellow professional. Oh yes…and then there were the patients' details! Each one had to be logged on to the system, so that they had their own MPI (Medical Personal Index). Within this identification number were details of each patient's GP (each with their own code, naturally!), the diagnosis and the type of diet prescribed. You can imagine that this took some time to compile and a while to learn the codes. Thankfully it seemed that no one added up the number of hours taken for each activity and compared it with the hours on duty – though that might have thrown up some interesting incompatibilities! But see further down.

At the end of each month, all our daily paper records had to be transferred to The Computer, which was located at the top of the building. There were three monitors for all the staff. It is not surprising that many of us would drive over at the weekend, hoping to find one that was free, in order to do this wearisome task. If activities hadn't been written down, they were often forgotten and/or simply made up.

I learned several years later from someone who worked at the Department of Health, that "They only look at the patient numbers – the rest is thrown in a heap in the corner of their office!" Whether that was actually true or not, I have no idea but it made us feel understandably cross. However, after that revelation we didn't worry so much about the inaccuracies, so perhaps it was A Good Thing.

Later, when I moved to Calmershire, there was a similar system but instead of a paper record, we were issued with palmtops – little hand-held computers. Again, this caused equal frustration, as the codes did not always offer exactly what one needed and again, a certain imaginative streak was deployed. Determined to make this work, I became pedantic to the extreme. I recorded every conversation that I had with each and every patient, nurse, therapist or GP; every letter or report written; every visit and so on. Not surprisingly, our manager reported at one staff meeting, "our elderly care contacts have increased by 80 per cent"! Funnily enough, we were never told what our actual targets were, only that we had under-achieved, achieved or exceeded them.

It's the same in other services. Talk to any doctor or police officer – and the story is identical. They roll their eyes and plead "Don't talk to ME about paperwork and targets!" The really bad thing about this was that initially, I found myself deciding in advance how I would code a particular "contact", diagnosis and noting the time that the consultation took, instead of listening to the patient properly.

As time moves on, so does "technological progress". I now gather that the staff at Calmershire have "smart cards" which allow them to access the palmtops and the computer systems at the GP surgeries, where the dietetic clinics are held. Now it seems that The-Powers-That-Be have caught up with the idea of ensuring that one's hours spent on patients *do* add up properly. The percentage of total clinic time with each patient also has to be recorded. As do the minutes worked compared with the minutes that one *should* work. Hmm...intriguing! (And time-consuming).

A former colleague told me that anyone can access and view staff's e-mails, voice-mails, recorded activities and one's diary via the main computer system. How muddling that must be when the essence of community dietetics is that by and large, one fills in one's own diary. Do managers really not trust their staff? Are they so totally unaware of the amount of unpaid overtime that they work? Not to mention the amount of time that these new "stats" take to put on the system. Big Brother has truly arrived! And that's a Bad Thing. As I write, an editorial in *The Daily Telegraph* suggests that the target culture "is positively dangerous".[1] The piece refers specifically to A and E patients but the principle has an effect across the board. Further, an independent Nuffield Review laments the inundation of schools with "bureaucracy-speak" – such as "customers"; "performance indicators"; "deliverers"; "commissions" and "audits".[2] The basics of care (and teaching) have got lost in all this meaningless twaddle.

Part of our work at both Borderland and Calmershire involved holding dietetic clinics in GP surgeries. OK so far. But then computers insinuated their way into these surgeries, on which patients' records were kept and which were supposed to not only provide us with the information that we needed, like past medical history and lab. reports, but on which we were also

---

[1] Editorial. 2009 Missing the Target. *The Daily Telegraph*. June 10th
[2] The Nuffield Foundation 2009. *Education for All. The Future of Education and Training for 14-19 Year Olds*. Routledge, June.
Available online at: http://www.younglancashire.org.uk/webfm_send/80

supposed to input our own findings and the advice given to the patient. For a Luddite like me, this was a real headache. The learning curve was very steep (especially as we did not have a computer in the department on which to practise). Compounding this problem was the fact that each of the GP surgeries in our area had chosen different software programmes, so you can imagine the muddle of the early days until we got the hang of them all, bearing in mind our surgery visits were usually only once a month. On more than one occasion, the patient would see me getting very red in the face, pressing buttons ineffectually, smothering swear words and generally giving the impression of being totally inept (which I was!). The whole essence of the consultation would be lost in this techno-muddle. Often, the patient was far more IT-savvy than myself and would help me out: the epitome of patient-professional teamwork!

"Can I help you?" they would say and I would thankfully turn the monitor round with a sigh of relief.

Appraisals and CPD, or "Continuing Professional Development", are now part and parcel of many companies and guess what? The NHS blindly follows suit. This is not all bad. The intentions are good in that such practices ensure that staff are competent and not likely to kill off a load of patients – at least not knowingly or intentionally. The appraisal process is supposed to be two-way: your manager goes through your workload and asks how you think you are coping with it, but you are also offered the opportunity to have your say in how you are managed and what further training you think you need. When I was at Borderland, computers insidiously wormed their way into the work place. We were familiar with the main computer on which we had to record our patient-contacts and daily work but a PC in our office was a very new animal indeed! One of our team, Louise, was familiar with this strange beast and she used it to record all the details regarding enteral feeds.

To the rest of us, this was a skill that was shrouded in mystery.

"It's all just logic," said Those-in-the-Know.

Hmm…I wasn't so sure. It seemed to me that these new machines were all part and parcel of some new Force of Darkness to bewitch and bewilder older NHS staff, like me!

You might ask dear reader – and this would be highly justified – why didn't I have proper training? Indeed! Why didn't I? In the early days of the computer invasion, it was managers who had the training and the PCs on their desks. It doesn't take an Einstein to guess that "targets" and number crunching became an object of derision by the rest of us. But these were the magic numbers, based on the good old British method of "muddling through", on which future health service decisions were made. Now, in the name of "progress", the NHS has spent billions of pounds on attempting to computerise the whole system and what has happened? It breaks down repeatedly and files are "mislaid". Whatever happened to old-fashioned and (generally) reliable paper records?

"So what training do you think you need?" asked Phil during one of these appraisal sessions.

"I would really like to know how to use a computer," I responded.

"Why on earth do you want to do that?" queried Phil, genuinely and positively puzzled.

"Because it is something that I think will be used more and, supposing Louise was off sick or something, we would need to know how to record the enteral feeds…" I trailed off, as his face blanked.

"But you don't need training…it's easy-peasy!" as he whirred up the PC on his desk. "So simple and logical," as he whizzed the cursor around the screen, like a fly with ADHD. "Nothing to it," as he double-clicked on various icons and flooded my view with multiple screens. "Piece of cake," he insisted, as he generated a PowerPoint presentation. "A real doddle," as he opened up a spreadsheet.

I stood my ground. "Look – it may be easy-peasy-lemon-squeezy for you but I haven't had any experience at all with this. It's lemon-difficult – and I would rather learn how to do it myself than watch you."

"Oh – all right," he appeared to capitulate. As I expected, nothing happened.

And so it was, on my first day at my new job, at Calmershire, one of the other dietitians was going off on a sabbatical. I was to take over some of her work.

"Here you are: it's all on here." She handed over a laptop. "The password is *soufflé*." And she was gone.

I looked at this unimpressive black box. After ten minutes of fiddling, I managed to open it. Now…how did I find the "ON" button?

After another ten minutes, I asked our secretary, Sally. Together we found it. I managed to enter the password and the screen flickered into life.

"Then what?" I asked myself. I gingerly and tentatively pressed a few buttons. Could I find the programme my colleague had advised? Could I hell? I wanted to burst into tears and run away. I managed to keep it together for a bit. Other jobs suddenly seemed more pressing.

"I think I won't do this now," I said to Sally, as coolly as I could. "I'll pop out for a bit and do those home visits."

"Don't blame you," she said with a sympathetic grin.

Eventually, I managed to persuade the Trust to send me on a course for basic computing and by this time I had my own laptop – a gift from my husband. And eventually, things began to fall into place. But I was not alone in this unnecessary confusion. It suddenly seemed that not only did we have to be trained to do our clinical jobs but that, overnight, we had to be computer literate as well. It was very stressful, especially when one computer had to be shared by seven of us and one's Inbox would be flooded by unsolicited and non-applicable e-mails via the Trust Intranet. For those, like me, who did not have teenage children at home who were all whiz kids on their laptops and PCs, it was like being told to drive, but without a car to practise on!

TEAMWORK

Dr Meredith Belbin defines a Team Role as "our tendency to behave, contribute and interrelate with others in a particular way"

Meredith Belbin, "Management Teams – Why they Succeed or Fail"

"What's the good of argifying?"

Rudyard Kipling, "Life's Handicap. On Greenhow Hill"

Working in the NHS, there are times when everyone is your friend and you really feel part of a team. However, there are also times, when you wonder why there appear to be gross gaps in your patient's overall care. Getting ideal and holistic care becomes a battlefield with The Managerial Forces of Darkness and can take an incredible amount of time to overcome.

I regularly made home visits to a patient who had multiple sclerosis (MS). Her husband was her main carer and was absolutely wonderful. He really got stuck in to the business of caring for someone with this horrible and debilitating condition. As a former engineer, his attention to detail could not be matched. The Internet was relatively new but he made good use of it to find out as much as he could about the condition. "Mary! Knowledge is power!" he told me. I learnt a lot from him.

Sometimes I would visit with the speech and language therapist and together we would assess Frances' progress. I also needed to weigh her regularly and it was Alan who came up

165

with the suggestion that I borrow the connection from the Wheelchair Department that would fit onto her hoist and give us a digital read-out of her weight. This little gismo made the whole procedure easy for me and relatively comfortable for Frances. There were many times that I made use of that bit of kit and I wished that I had had known about it with another patient – that story is under "'Elf and Safety"!

On one of my visits to Frances and Alan, I asked how her sacral pressure sore was progressing.

"Well," said Alan, "Part of the problem is that Frances is only allowed three incontinence pads a day. They are not that big, so she is wet for longer than she should be and that is not really helping."

It all hinged on, yes, you've guessed it – COST (only 12p more per pad for the larger ones). Add that to the fact that, if she were to have more frequent changes, it would mean more additional visits from health care assistants. They had to come in pairs because of moving and handling rules, regardless of the fact that this lady had a hoist and other useful equipment. Further, because the pressure sore was not healing, this lady had to have extra visits from the district nurses (costs therefore including their time and their petrol, as well as the dressings) and antibiotic therapy, which probably didn't help her appetite and gut function, all because the Area Health Authority (AHA) wouldn't cough up an extra 36p a day!

The people in the AHA were "the untouchables" in their ivory tower and, as an 'umble dietitian, one rarely met them, let alone talked to them. I only knew one person by name in that exclusive club because I had been to a meeting about something quite different, but he was Director of Primary Care. Fighting my patient's corner, I wrote to him setting out my argument in fairly blunt language, pointing out that their "housekeeping" could do with some attention. Hey presto! About a month later, I had a fax from Alan to say that Frances had the bigger pads and things were improving. Another small battle was won! But there were times when I pondered that, as a mere dietitian, I would never have thought that I would be challenging the management about incontinence pads!

When assessing someone for the first time, it is obvious that one asks questions that are pertinent to the problems of nutrition, mealtimes, meal type and so on but to get the "big picture", one also needs information about lifestyle habits, medications, bowel and kidney functions and anything else that seems relevant at the time.

I had been asked to see an elderly gentleman who had Chronic Obstructive Pulmonary Disease (COPD). This condition is highly energy-demanding and patients often lose a lot of weight. Every breath is a struggle and it can be extremely frightening. Mr Love had been a paratrooper. He was slight in build and sat bolt upright during my visit. He was as neat as a pin and obviously took a military pride in his smart appearance with knife-creased trousers and a neatly trimmed moustache. He was rather quiet and it was his wife who answered most of my queries, in spite of my attempts to draw him in.

"I can talk the hind legs of a donkey," she laughed. "He just sits there!"

We went through the process of gathering information. I made some suggested changes, which Mr Love agreed to and I knew that, from his background, he would accept them as an "order". As I was packing up my things, I asked neutrally, "Bowels and waterworks all OK?"

Mrs Love's expression changed. "Ah…"she hesitated and looked fondly at her husband, who looked embarrassed.

"Well…he did have a bit of an accident recently…"

Poor Mr Love. He had soiled himself and was so upset. It all fell into place: his military career, pride in his immaculate appearance and the attention to detail. How he would hate that kind of ignominy. It was obvious that he was limiting his intake of food with the reasoning that if less went in at the top end, maybe less would come out of the other. Gently, and what I hoped was tactfully, I suggested that they might like to meet the continence nurse and talk things through with her. They both relaxed and agreed that this could be helpful. Exit dietitian stage left. Enter continence nurse, stage right.

Saskia also had MS. She lived on her own and was fiercely independent. Her grown-up daughter popped in occasionally but relationships between them were strained. I was asked to see her because she wasn't eating very well and was losing strength. She was confined to a wheelchair for most of the day and like this, was quite mobile around her flat. The problem arose when she demonstrated to me how she made tea, boiled vegetables etc. It was a disaster waiting to happen! Because of the different levels of her wheelchair, kitchen worktop, hob and bed, she had to fill a kettle with water, place it on her lap to go to the power point and then, with the kettle now hot, reverse the process, cradling hot water in her lap. I had nightmares! This was not a dietetic problem. I called the occupational therapist and we discussed how the different levels could be adjusted, so that Saskia could safely use the hob and the kettle, as well as transfer herself to her bed.

My dictionary at home defines "care" as "provision of physical needs, help or comfort". All of us who are in the caring professions need to look at the total care requirements for each individual – it is often not enough to do just what is requested on the referral letter. A symbiotic relationship between those involved and the patient results in overall improvements. Ideally, we should be prepared to go the extra step, that might be beyond the call of duty. And so it was always with a spring in my step and a song in my heart that I would make my regular visits to the rehabilitation hospital that was part of "our patch" in Calmershire. Patients were referred there from the acute (and dare I say, rather well off) hospital Trust. Many of the elderly patients had had a stroke or a broken hip and were in a sorry state when they arrived at Tranquillity Hospital. Quite often, the medical notes accompanying them suggested that the patient had not long to live.

I would tease the nurses who worked there that they looked after their patients too well so that they forgot that they were supposed to die! One lady outlived all expectations: she had been there for 15 years. The care was excellent. I got on well with the nurses and was always made to feel welcome and part of the team. Many of our discussions would revolve around arranging a tube-feed and, rather than continue with the rigid and often complex regime that had been started in the acute hospital, we made changes together, so that it better suited the patient, as well as the staffing levels and shifts on the wards.

It would be nice to think that all members of other departments similarly get on well, are supportive of each other and that everything is tickety-boo. I am sorry to say this is not always the case.

Part of my training in the '60s included a stay at Stanmore Hospital, which specialises in orthopaedics. I had to live on-site and had a room in the nurses' home.

The chief dietitian there was an expert in the metabolic work associated with various bone diseases. Intake of minerals and vitamins, such as calcium and vitamin D (vital for healthy bones) was carried out with great precision, involving accurate weighing of food intake, its analysis and ditto any left-overs. This was then compared with output – yes, you've guessed it, urine and faecal collections. I don't think that the patients liked it much either! She was exacting and, with her innate Teutonic thoroughness, worked her students hard and was known to put the fear of God into them all. Most of them were reduced to tears at some point. Having been forewarned, I was determined that I wouldn't do the same. My sense of humour saved me and I didn't.

Dearest Mum
  Well, here I am at Stanmore.
  It's a funny place – very nicely set out but very far from anywhere – I suppose that's the characteristic of former TB Hospitals.
  The nearest "village" is Stanmore: it is very quiet! I took a walk down there last evening to get my bearings – it's all quite countrified – quite nice but I am beginning to wish I'd brought my bike! The hospital itself is all spread out – mostly low buildings – just one floor.
  The nurse's home is quite nice but the food is AWFUL!! It seems dreadful to have to pay with these vouchers for such ghastly stuff!
  There isn't a hospital shop and Stanmore is a good 20 – 30 minutes walk there and back so one couldn't really shop successfully.
  I think some of the girls look after themselves though – there are cooking facilities of a sort, but I think it's a case of warming up packets!.
  Will write more soon,
Lots of love, Mary xx

When I moved to Borderland and was part of a new community Trust, I was "first on the scene" for the dietetics department and my brief was to set it all up. I had a nice little office with my own 'phone line that was in a health centre, so I was happily surrounded by community nurses of all kinds – salts of the earth! I started making 'phone calls, introduced the service and myself and it wasn't long before word got about and I was soon very busy. Louise then joined me, whom I knew vaguely from a training course. She was part-time but highly efficient and energetic. We got on well. Then it was a case of "two's company, three's a crowd".

  Cynthia arrived. We were simply told that she was to join us. Neither Louise nor I had met her, nor were we involved in her interview. She was also highly energetic and accomplished but our personalities just clashed. All three of us were of a similar grade and experience but Cynthia was simply not a team player and blocked all attempts at a good working relationship. This meant that no one accepted the authority for heading the department and it lead, ashamedly and unprofessionally, to intra-department squabbling. Unfortunately, Cynthia also had a very rude and abrupt manner. It wasn't only us that bristled. Health visitors and other staff complained. Management did little to help. "Sort it out yourselves," said Phil. "You are all grown women." Which was true, except we expected that Phil, as our line-manager, would suggest that one of us take the lead role. Instead, he washed his hands of us. He was mightily puzzled as to what kind of species dietitians were! Now that we were three in number, we had to move to a new, larger office, which was a room in what had been a local cottage hospital. Here, all our calls had to go through the operator. We had no direct line to the outside world, which further exemplified total misunderstanding on Phil's part, as to the way that we worked. As we were setting up the department, ordering new diet leaflets and getting in touch with other professionals, the 'phone was our only means of getting in touch. (This was well before e-mail systems were in use). Operators on the switchboard soon got fed up with us, asking for outside lines all the time. It was they who made the suggestion that we have a direct line, which was an enormous help.

We have already discussed the territorial boundaries between the hospital and community Trusts. You would think that diet-sheets and other instruction leaflets would be designed and collaborated upon by dietitians working in both the local hospital and the community it served. Common sense dictates that this would be less muddling for patients; that it would show we were working together (seamless service?) and that it would save money and time. Dietitians are very possessive of their material and it would be some time before the common sense approach was widespread. And the differences *did* cause confusion. If a patient was given a diet-sheet by a hospital dietitian and then saw a community dietitian in a GP clinic, who gave slightly varying advice, the patient whipped out their original instructions, with the beginnings of confrontation.

"Oh…but is says here that I should avoid grapes."

"Oh really, let's see…so it does…well, we would say that, provided you don't over do them, then it's OK. I'll have a word with them and see what they say…" Which is what we did, but this then became a prelude to a metaphysical argument about the whys and wherefores of this and other details. At one time in Borderland, both the hospital and community dietitians *did* get together in an attempt to design universal diet-sheets. Many hours were spent in discussion over such minutiae!

It was at this time that the NHS decided, in its wisdom, to run this unwieldy bundle of tangled wool as a business. Regional Health Authorities had been reduced from 14 to eight and hospital and community Trusts were separate entities, each with their own management structure. Sadly, the initial spirit of "community dietetics" from the 1970s was gone: this new wave of community dietitians approached their remit quite differently. GP-based clinics burgeoned and became widespread and overall, there was less collaboration with outside services. Part of that also meant that departments had to hunt around for work, marketing their "wares", the theory being that if more work was brought in, one would be given the extra staff and funds to deal with it. Hmm…I took the defensive stance that we shouldn't make promises we were uncertain of fulfilling. Further, dietitians are one of the smaller professions – as my husband loves saying, "They are thin on the ground", and I wondered how many applications we would get for jobs. Cynthia would have none of that! She was keen to tout for work but her marketing enthusiasm didn't match her zeal for actually doing extra time. This was often the basis for the start of a fight.

Internal wrangles were one thing. Chatting to a former colleague recently, who is now a chief dietitian at a university hospital, I learned that she was putting together a weight-management bid to submit to the commissioners. I was aghast to hear that this was in direct competition with the dietitians of the community Trust. Initially, the dietitians had agreed amongst themselves that they would work together but the commissioners had other ideas and effectively set the two departments against each other.

Later, when I moved to Calmershire, there was Moya. As an older dietitian in the department, she didn't trust any of us to carry out our work properly. She wasn't the manager but as she had been there the longest, seemed to think that she was. She had a lot of experience and though we respected that, she wanted every procedure to be done as she would have done it, regardless of the circumstances and the fact that time moves on. She was quick tempered and often didn't listen to an explanation. On one occasion, she embarked on one of her patronising monologues over the telephone, shredding my already wavering self-confidence into tiny pieces. I held the 'phone away from my ear and timed her. I was amazed that someone could think of all those words without pausing for breath or thought. It was exactly five whole minutes non-stop! And the whole tirade was due to a total misunderstanding about a talk that I had been asked to do. She hadn't appreciated that there were two of the same title in the same week but at different venues. She simply hadn't listened. It was the trigger for venomous verbal floodgates to open. When she shouted that I wasn't fit to work at a senior level, it was my turn to get angry. "That's not fair!" I yelled. Neither of us should have been at work anyway. It was after 6.00pm and I was wishing I hadn't answered her call. She did have the grace to give me a grudging apology the next day. Many was the time I would come home and rail about her to my long-suffering husband. Working mostly with other men, he couldn't understand this all female in-fighting.

"If that was in our office, we would just say f*** off and all would be forgotten! Tell her to bog off," he would say.

"I can't!" I breathed, thrilled and excited by the prospect, horrified and appalled by the obvious fallout.

"Well, I will," he threatened.

"You'll do nothing of the sort!"

We wrangled and shouted and then there were tears. And so on. It affected my health. I couldn't sleep. I had indigestion. Each evening I felt I needed that glass of wine! And suddenly I experienced a strange shutting down of my vocal cords. I couldn't project my voice. I saw my GP.

"Work for the NHS, don't you?" he looked at me sideways.

"Mmm..." I replied, with a wry grin.

Shaking his head in sympathy, he prescribed me a small dose of *Valium*. It was wonderful! Moya could rant all she liked. I didn't give a shit. Water off a duck's back now. My self-confidence soared. I could make decisions. I slept (and dreamed wonderful dreams). A friend, who is an expert in management training, serendipitously and unexpectedly popped in one day. He asked me how things were.

"How much longer do you have to work?" Graham then enquired.

"Two years..."

"That's a long time to be unhappy. You have to do something about it."

Tears began to prick my eyes.

"Remember that the first thing you say will set the scene," he had counselled. "The other thing is to keep focused on how you want this meeting to end and what you want to achieve.

This Moya-person has to appreciate your feelings. No one can argue with those."

On his suggestion, I took the bull by the horns and tackled Moya. I 'phoned her and, as coolly as I could, suggested that "we stay behind and have a chat" after one of our staff meetings. I was quivering inside and could feel my pulse racing. Graham's advice echoed in my head and I began by setting the scene.

"Do you realise how you make me and others feel when you act like that?" I then asked neutrally.

She looked utterly puzzled. The wind went out of her sails. She tried to explain how she felt pressured by others but it wasn't convincing.

"How are WE going to tackle this?" I continued, quoting verbatim from Graham's "manual" remembering not to use either the first or second persons, "I" or "you".

Although we never became friends, there was an uneasy truce between us and I was eternally grateful to Graham, whose timely visit had been at just the right moment.

This is but a small example of bullying in the NHS. It may come as a surprise to those who are outside the organisation but it has become widespread. (See also "Territorial Boundaries"). In my opinion, it reflects the extra constraints on staff from government "initiatives", but it is unfair to take these out on one's fellow men and women. Bullying takes many shapes and forms. There are control freaks; selfish holders of information that should be shared; power seekers and bulldozers, who enjoy getting their own way, whatever the cost. Then, there are "Mother Hens" who have to cluck over everyone in the department and professional and personal jealousies that get in the way of the "common cause". "Dumbing down" and constant undermining have a strong impact on work output and efficiency, through lowering of self-esteem. When this falters, it gives further ammunition and opportunity for unfair criticism. Poor management is often to blame and/or lack of recognition of an individual's behaviour and fragmentation of the team.

Where so few are doing so many different jobs, as in many NHS departments, it is possible to forget the needs of the staff and the "blame culture" is endemic.

Later, in one of our staff meetings, I described the plight of Joyce. (See "Prolonging Life or Tender Loving Care?"). This was part of what is known as reflective practice and one shares with colleagues certain cases and incidents. When I mentioned that I gave Joyce a hug, simply because I didn't know what else to do or say, everyone fell quiet and I could feel them sympathising. Moya piped up.

"Well, you have to be careful about that," she carped. "Some patients don't like being touched and you could have been accused of abusing her."

"You weren't there, Moya," I said quietly but firmly. "And you haven't met Joyce. You don't know her. It seemed the right thing to do at the time."

Inside, I'm thinking, "Oh! for goodness' sake! Leave it out!"

We were encouraged to share our experiences of clinical supervision, which is in place to help staff cope with their work. These sessions are entirely confidential. I had mentioned that I had found it helpful, that it was an opportunity to get things off my chest, be made aware of other perspectives and that I felt I could talk to my supervisor about anything and everything safely. Moya again – like a terrier which won't let go: "This isn't the principle of clinical supervision and may I remind you, that if the supervisor feels that a member of staff is practising unsafely, that they have a duty to report this?" My sessions were more informal than she would like – but increased formality might destroy the openness and ability to share.

The effect of this and other failings in the NHS can result in serious outcomes. Staff are leaving the NHS in droves. Others are suspended every day. A former colleague who works in the Learning Disability Service told me recently that a multi-disciplinary team within this service had written much-needed guidelines for a patient who had a very complicated and awkward history. The manager didn't like them and suspended the whole team – just like that!

Addressing and dealing with bullying is under-pinned by a raft of legislation; primarily, it becomes a health and safety issue, with managers having a duty of care to their staff. It is difficult to attract good staff to the NHS or other care agencies and there is much to be said for carrying out exercises such as The Belbin Questionnaire to ensure the ideal skill mix, but bullying and poor management is something else. It takes a very special skill to create a happy environment where staff feel valued and have job satisfaction.[1]

Downright impertinence and bad manners outside our department was an unpleasant surprise. A rude awakening.

Daphne was in a bad way. She had had the most horrific diarrhoea for several weeks. It smelt terrible and, I was informed, was often yellow and "frothy". She was in her early 80s, had quite severe dementia and was being cared for in a nursing home that was on my caseload. The staff were finding it very difficult, especially as Daphne tried ineffectually to clean herself up after each episode, which resulted in an even greater mess, not only on her clothes but around the bathroom as well.

It had already been suggested by a colleague that she might be intolerant to gluten. From the matron's description, it also sounded as though there might be secondary lactose intolerance. Luckily, the visiting G.P. was present on the day that I called and, together we discussed the merits of excluding both of these items from Daphne's food intake. The G.P. agreed it was worth a try for a few weeks. I wandered round to the kitchen to speak to the chef. He was sitting in the staff room, with his feet on the

<hr>

[1] *The Belbin Questionnaire.* (Date unknown). Available at: http://www.Belbin.com/

table reading a newspaper. He looked up crossly as I explained my errand.

"I'm on my break."

Rather taken aback, I asked when he might be free to talk.

"30 minutes."

As I had several other visits that afternoon, I couldn't hang around for 30 minutes, while he took the weight off his feet. I returned to the matron's office and reported the short interview. She rolled her eyes, muttered an apology and left the room. She returned a few minutes later.

"Gary will see you now."

As it turned out, Gary became an ally, not least because he had trained as a diet cook in a London hospital. He was sceptical at first but when I offered to buy the necessary special items that they would require and go through his menus, highlighting where changes needed to be made, he became more enthusiastic. We both worked hard and hoped that Daphne's mishaps would cease. Unfortunately, in spite of our best efforts, they didn't. She stole other residents' food and it was difficult for the staff to stop her. Thinking about it now, it seems likely that she may well have had an infection such as *C.Diff* and she probably could have benefited from further investigations.

LITTLE PERSONS

A child should always say what's true
And speak when he is spoken to,
And behave mannerly at table;
At least as far as he is able.

Robert Louis Stevenson
"A Child's Garden of Verses. V. Whole Duty of Children"

Paediatric dietetics is decidedly complex and not for the likes of my Small Brain. During my training in the late 1960s, it was rare to meet a child with an "inborn metabolic disorder". Most of these were treated by specialist dietitians at Great Ormond Street Hospital in London. They included cases of hypercalcaemia (too much calcium circulating in the blood, which is dangerous, as it can calcify and cause hard deposits in soft tissues like the kidneys or the brain) and "favism" (deficiency of the enzyme, G-6 phosphatase) which can cause a kind of anaemia. I do remember a case of hypercalcaemia while I was a student. Miss Newcombe was thrilled and we were all invited to view this little example of one of Mother Nature's hiccups and to note the characteristic physical and facial deformities. I can't imagine that the little girl in question, nor her parents, were as excited, or intrigued.

Over the past few years, the incidence of intolerances and allergies to foodstuffs has rocketed. Whether these are due to the ways in which we grow and process our food, or whether people have become more sensitive, is a topic for hot and

179

prolonged debate. Add to this melting pot, a degree of neurosis and imagination and we have a stew, which is a mix of the real and emotionally charged. Needless to say, many of these incidences cause extreme distress and necessitate significant changes to people's lifestyles.

Adverse reactions to food are common but not all are due to allergy or intolerance. By far the largest potential sources of harm in food are due to bacterial contamination. Research into allergy and intolerances is relatively new and the subject is surrounded by controversy.

"Food intolerances" is an umbrella term used to describe food allergies *and* food idiosyncrasies. A food idiosyncrasy can be a non-pathological inability to digest particular foods, or even a simple dislike.

"Inborn errors of metabolism" are examples of defined food idiosyncrasies and occur when certain enzymes are missing from the digestive tract and/or elements from the process of absorption. These are due to a genetic glitch, such as a primary lactase deficiency (in which lactose, or milk sugar cannot be properly digested) or phenylketonuria (PKU) (in which the essential amino acid, phenylalanine, cannot be metabolised). A secondary lactase deficiency can sometimes temporarily follow severe gastroenteritis or untreated coeliac disease. It is possible for a food allergy and a food idiosyncrasy to be present in the same patient, which can add to the confusion!

True "food allergies" are different again and are mediated through the immune system, which creates antibodies to destroy a substance that it recognises as "foreign". Such reactions cause classic immunoglobulin-based responses, such as urticaria from eating strawberries, or some food colourings, say, or sickness and diarrhoea from shellfish.

Sometimes, these reactions are extremely severe, the best-known example being anaphylaxis from eating peanuts.

Immunology has been described as a game of "hide-and-seek" of unparalleled complexity that is going on all the time in humans and animals alike.[1] Unfortunately, the terms "food allergies" and "food intolerances" are often used together but in fact are not quite the same.

Coeliac disease has been latterly described as being neither an allergy nor a food intolerance. The Coeliac Society refer to it as an autoimmune disease, triggered by gliadin, present in the wheat protein, gluten. Interestingly, coeliac disease was always thought of as being a "childhood disease" but it is increasingly now diagnosed in the adult population. Further, these conditions have sparked a whole new wave of "health and allergy specialists", many of whom offer tests for foods and non-food substances, the basis of which are not always scientifically sound. There are pulse tests, radionics, hair tests and many more besides, some of which are of doubtful value.

It is estimated that one in five Britons think that they suffer from a food allergy or intolerance but recent research from Portsmouth University suggests that of these, only two per cent actually do.[2] As a result, these people follow extremely rigid and restricted diets in the hopes that their symptoms will disappear, but in effect, they can also be starving their bodies of essential nutrients. This is where the services of a dietitian who specialises in such problems are essential. He/she can offer not only guidance on the range of foods that would be safe to eat but also in-depth advice about manufactured and processed foods. Manufacturers are now wised up to the fact that questions will be asked about the ingredients they use and so label their foods as best they can. Even so, items such as "hydrolysed fats" or "proteins", "starch" or "cereals" do not always tell you the

[1] Scowen, P. et al. 1985. *Food Allergy.* B. Edsall and Company, London.
[2] MacKenzie, H. 2010. Britons may be avoiding wheat unnecessarily. *University of Portsmouth News.* January 20th. Available online at:
http://www.port.ac.uk/aboutus/newsandevents/frontpagenews/title,107159,en.html

exact original source. As around two million food allergies are diagnosed in error, NICE has now issued guidelines for GPs, which were disseminated in February 2011.[3]

The problems of food intolerances do not seem to be the prerogative of humans either: more and more domestic pet owners are requesting help on this subject and a cursory glance at available pet foods shows that many of these are labelled "hypoallergenic" or "sensitive".

My own experience in this field is somewhat limited. More usually, the hospital dietitians see such cases but it is extremely satisfying when the detective work proves to be correct. Alice was a new mother and originally from the Caribbean. Her little girl was vomiting and her nappies were less than savoury. Cows' milk intolerance was suspected. Alice, to her great credit, was breast-feeding, so she agreed to follow a diet without cows' milk herself for the duration. It worked! She was thrilled and so was I. Latterly, however, research suggests that this is not always helpful and that more harm than good can be done, by restricting the mother's food during breastfeeding.

Very often young children grow out of such intolerances by the time that they reach school age and so it was with Alice's baby. It is worth noting that many people from the Caribbean and Asian countries are genetically intolerant to lactose. As babies, they produce the correct enzyme, lactase, in the small intestine but this wanes as they develop and grow and finally peters out. As adults, they *may* be able to take reasonable amounts of hard cheese and yoghurt. Milk without lactose is also available, which may be tolerated. Some, not all, may be intolerant to the cows' milk proteins, in which case it, and all its products, need to be avoided. Alternatives to cows' milk include

---

[3] NICE, 2011. *Food allergy in children and young people.* February. Available online at: http://guidance.nice.org.uk/CG/Wave21/2

milks from goats, buffalo and sheep and extracts from soya, rice and oats. There are cautions attached to all of these, not least the possibility of brucellosis and other bacteria in unpasteurised goats' milk. One-third of all babies who are intolerant to cows' milk may also react to soya milks. "Milks" from rice and oats are not nutritionally complete for a young child.

Professional advice is essential; self-diagnosis and treatment can lead to further problems, at worst, severe malnutrition. Dietitians are able to prescribe special baby milks for those who need them.

In the community at Borderland, we were more likely to be asked to see children who were either "fussy eaters", "failing to thrive" or who were overweight.

The "fussy eaters" were true eye-openers. I had never met such small persons who ruled the roost before! They were adept at calling the shots. The poor mothers were at their wits' end, dancing to the tune of their precocious offspring, trying to produce something that would be acceptable to their diminutive despot. It is not surprising that every meal ended in a row and/or tantrums – on both sides. Naturally, mothers were worried that their child would starve. Having very little experience of small children I was at a disadvantage but I did have experience of puppies! It seemed to me that the principles of establishing a pecking order in the family hierarchy were somewhat similar, which all goes to show that dietetics is often not about the food *per se,* but about other psychological aspects and family dynamics.

Chloe was three years old. I arranged to visit her and her mother at home. I always felt that this gave a truer picture of family interactions, compared with asking them to come to the clinic. It also meant that the child was in familiar surroundings and need not get bored.

It was Chloe who answered the door: my first clue. When

we sat down, it was obvious that she was in charge, telling me where to sit, helping herself to items from the 'fridge, interrupting our conversation and pulling the cat's tail. Poor Mum looked understandably harassed and confessed to losing her temper when Chloe refused to eat. She needed a lot of reassurance that Chloe would not suffer and some tips on ways to hide her reactions.

Recently, fussy eaters have again come to the fore. Mothers need to be comforted that most young children will not willingly starve themselves and that, with dogged and patient determination from both parents being consistent and establishing house-rules, they will eventually end up eating normally.

It is not only physical symptoms related to foods that have become increasingly noticeable amongst children.

Lewis was six. His parents were separated and he lived with his mother, who was sure that he reacted to food colourings and excess sugar.

"If he has these, he's off the wall!"

While he was with her, they managed very well, but problems arose when he spent a weekend with his father, who lived with his new girlfriend.

In spite of exhortations and pleas by his mother, they loved to spoil Lewis by treating him to all the foods that he liked but which caused his behaviour to deteriorate. Poor Mum had to deal with the consequences when he came home. The dietitian is caught in the middle!

Much research has been conducted on the effect of food colourings and excess sugar intake on the behaviour of children. Attention Deficit Disorder (ADD) and Attention Deficit and Hyperactive Disorder (ADHD) is widely "diagnosed". Are these just naughty children that need taking in hand, or are we really looking at a mind-altering diet? Studies, largely in the United States, which have examined sugar intake amongst inmates in young offenders' institutes, suggest that there is indeed a connection. My friend, Lisbeth, who has taught for many years, can confirm that since the banning of sweets and sugary drinks in her school, the children's behaviour has improved. A study, published in the *British Journal of Psychiatry*, claims to be the first to examine the long-term effects of childhood diet and adult violence.[4] Those given excess sweets and chocolate every day are not only badly behaved during childhood but tend to develop into aggressive adults. It is also possible, that the more demanding children are given sweets to quieten them.

In effect, Lewis' mother and her estranged husband had unwittingly performed their own challenge tests. In time, Lewis learned that his behaviour changed after eating these foods and when I visited six months later, to his great credit, he was self-regulating himself.

"I'm not really happy when I behave like that," he confessed.

The danger here is that if so many children are being "labelled" as ADD or ADHD, there is the possibility of "medicalising" a parenting problem. To make a true diagnosis, it is essential that a thorough multi-disciplinary assessment is made. This can take time and needs to be carried out in a variety of environments. Although research in the UK suggests that only a small percentage of children with ADHD respond to changes in diet, a reduction in sweets and sugar-containing foods can only be beneficial, not least on dental health and body fat. What is more worrying is recently released information under the Freedom of Information Act, suggesting that thousands of children are being prescribed anti-depressants and "calming drugs", such as *Ritalin*.[5] Prescription drugs used to

---

[4] Moore, S et al. 2000. Confectionery consumption in childhood and adult violence. *British Journal of Psychiatry*. 195, 366-367

[5] Paton, G. 2010. Spending on ADHD drugs 'soars by two-thirds'. *The Daily Telegraph*. May 11th Available at:
http://www.telegraph.co.uk/education/educationnews/7710885/Spending-on-ADHD-drugs-soars-by-two-thirds.html

treat ADHD rose by a third in two years. Further research also suggests that younger children, because of their birth dates, may be mistakenly diagnosed with ADHD, because they are simply less mature.[6] Babies born in July and August are most likely to face an ADHD diagnosis and could be prescribed medication unnecessarily.

[6] Moore,M. 2010. Summer babies 'more likely to be diagnosed with ADHD'. *The Daily Telegraph.* August 18th

ALL IN THE MIND

"Qualis sit animus, ipse animus nescit"
(The mind itself does not know what the mind is)

Cicero

It has been said that one in four of us will have some form of mental illness at some stage in our life. Hmm…scary thought!

While working as a still relatively young (and immature) community dietitian in Woodlandshire, I had had no contact with mental illness or learning disabilities of any kind. When a local Adult Training Centre (ATC) heard that I was in post, they made contact and asked would I supervise a slimming group that the trainees and their parents had requested.

I made my first visit with some trepidation, having no idea what to expect. Many of the trainees had Down's syndrome while others suffered from the effect of brain-damage at birth, or cerebral palsy. What a friendly and loving welcome I had! These *"little clowns of God"*, as the author Morris West affectionately dubbed them, hugged me and I hugged them back.[1] They were the keenest and most motivated slimmers I ever came across and were eager to tell me on each of my visits how well they were doing.

After my initial alarm, I looked forward to my visits with pleasure and was most impressed by the way in which the centre was run. Trainees were happy in their tasks, which were

---

[1] West, M. 1981. *The Clowns of God.* Hodder and Stoughton (Reprint Edition)

187

described as "piece work": electrical components were fitted together, the system having been fragmented into easy sequential steps, especially for them. They were paid a nominal sum, worked from 10.00am–4.00pm, had transport arranged to and from the centre and obviously took pride in their work. The manager was very popular, innovative, highly respected and ran a tight but happy ship. Sadly, I have a feeling that these council-run ATCs no longer exist in that particular format.

There are several drugs and medications that are used to treat mental illness, which can have a direct effect on appetite and weight gain. I used to have running battles with the psychiatrist who referred these patients and in the end, the patient and I had to come to some kind of compromise as to what was more important – mental health or body size. But as every overweight person knows, being overweight and wanting to be thinner can in itself be truly depressing. Talk about being between the devil and the deep blue sea! It was suggested in the '80s that patients who had "healthy eating" instruction and advice *before* they were prescribed certain psychiatric drugs were less likely to gain weight. People with early symptoms of depression and psychosis *should* have nutrition assessment and advice, as they often experience unintentional weight loss, as part of their condition. Depression often takes the form of not bothering about anything; this includes not preparing a meal, not eating and not drinking. A vicious downward spiral can develop with the effect of poor nutrition and dehydration compounding an already wobbly mental state.

Jean had manic depression or, as the Americans refer to it, bipolar disorder. She was essentially a jolly lady in her 50s and was taking lithium salts, which then was a standard treatment. The side effects can cause tremors as well as upsetting thyroid function. Further, thirst increases, digestion can be disturbed and weight gain is common. Monitoring is paramount to ensure that the dosage level is right for each patient. Overdosing can be fatal. Because of this fine line, dietary advice for weight loss is very minimal. A sudden decrease in body weight would have a knock-on effect on the blood levels of lithium and could be dangerous, as could a restriction of fluid intake and/or salt (sodium).

I used to visit Jean at home. She had gained a lot of weight and my role was to encourage her to lose it. Frankly, I think I did little in the way of giving dietary advice and therefore failed miserably in my objective. Jean seemed to enjoy talking and I shared her ups and downs. Her "ups" would take the form of shopping till she dropped and till her husband put a stop on her bankcard. But he couldn't stop her incessant talking. Her "downs" meant that she stayed in bed all day with the bedroom curtains drawn – sometimes I would arrive for our appointment at 4.30pm and she had only just managed to rouse herself from her bed, still in her nightdress. Much to her distress, the thirst caused by the lithium and the consequent fluid intake resulted in her wetting the bed once or twice in her sleep. I would reflect on the strain that this illness put on her family. Understandably, there were family rows, but several years after I had retired, I bumped into her near to where I live. Things had improved markedly, though she was still a large lady.

Some of the patients I was asked to see in the psychiatric wing were so fogged with their medication that I doubted whether they could hear or understand what I was trying to suggest. They would gaze at me vacantly, their tremors obvious, making futile attempts to concentrate. Ideally, I would return another day when they were more *compos mentis* but often, this wasn't possible owing to the number of referrals and the constraints of the working day. One just hoped that a smattering of advice had fallen on fertile ground. How saddening it was to enter that wing of the hospital, which, incidentally, was under the management of the community Trust. It is a world of The Lost and Forlorn with pathetic and tragic histories. One lady was referred to me because she had coeliac disease (and therefore needed a special diet) but she was on the ward because she developed strange personality changes, which included masturbating in front of her daughter. How embarrassing and demeaning that would be, if she realised what she was doing.

There are several locked doors, through which one has to enter and be checked in by staff, some of whom show scars, bruises and sticking plasters from attack by violent patients. Patients loiter in the corridors, leaning against the wall, staring into space. Some give no reaction to one's greeting, while others approach and simply stare in silence, which can be a little unnerving. Others are glimpsed through the open doors of their rooms, gazing vapidly or rocking gently and rhythmically. A few may be shouting, screaming and swearing needing to be calmed or restrained.

The staff tell you that the patient you are seeking is in the smoking room. Opening this door is entering another world. There is a thick, blue-grey haze through which one fumbles and peers myopically, feebly bleating out the name one has been given. Eventually, someone responds and I wait while they finish their cigarette and can then extract them from the murky atmosphere to find somewhere that is less carcinogenic to talk. Even though I am not a smoker myself, shame on those "do-gooders" who want to stop even psychiatric patients (or terminally ill patients in a hospice) from having a much needed and much enjoyed cigarette. It is about the only activity which gives them pleasure. This is especially galling when inmates in prison can enjoy such a luxury.

Once they were home, follow-up visits were often requested and because such patients are demanding, in the sense that they need a lot of support and time, I got to know them quite well. Two ladies come to mind. Sandra had had a very severe bout of depression. One day, she got into her car and drove and drove, until the petrol ran out and she had no idea whatsoever of where she was. By the time that she was referred to me, she had already spent 12 weeks in the psychiatric wing at Borderland and had gained a massive amount of weight. She was an intelligent and fun-loving woman and lucky to have a loving and very supportive husband and two daughters. Slowly but surely, she was managing to get her life back together again.

Emma also had severe depression and lived in an attractive village in Borderland. In addition, she suffered from agoraphobia – and had a large dog, a Curly Coated Retriever. The dog only got walked when her husband came home after work but it frustrated her that she couldn't take him out on her own. Sadly, her husband didn't understand her illness and did not provide the solace and encouragement that she craved. After I got to know her a little, I tentatively suggested that she might like to walk together with my dog. "We could walk and talk. The dogs will be fine," I urged. This worked well and during the course of our chats, she told me that she had always wanted to learn T'ai Chi. "Hmm," I thought, my scheming little mind getting poised for action, "Sandra's husband teaches T'ai Chi!" The maverick in me got to work and I proposed to each separately and tentatively that they might enjoy meeting up and having a walk with the dogs.

They agreed readily. It was a lovely summer and we made a date. We were all scared in case one got panicky. So we set some ground rules before we set off, just in case. It turned out well and it was only later that I thought what a dumb thing to do! I had no training in psychology. I hadn't asked permission from my manager (who probably would have locked me up pronto!) and I wasn't sure that my insurance would have covered me should some disaster have befallen us. As it was, the two ladies became firm friends and provided each other with much needed empathy and reassurance. Emma had a few T'ai Chi lessons, which she enjoyed, and I was lucky!

Halfway houses are community NHS-run homes for mentally ill patients who have left hospital but who need further support and adjustment before returning to their former lives, if that is possible. They are run very much on a family basis, although the "family" tends to be rather extended!

Derek was in his 40s but looked older. Bearded and very thin, he had had schizophrenia for many years and had had intermittent treatment. I was asked to see him because he was losing weight and not eating properly. He had been hearing voices and seeing visions but his medication had been tailored so that, although he could still hear his voices, they were restricted so that he did not feel compelled to act on them. In answer to my question as to why he was "allowed to hear them still", the care staff replied: "Well...they have been such a large part of his world for so long, that if we took them away completely by increasing his medication, he would just break up. He would feel that he has lost everything in his life. That would be the last straw for him".

In spite of attempting to encourage Derek to eat more food, he preferred to have the specialised nutritional supplements, which we could ask the GP to prescribe. Derek was delighted with these "treats" and began to improve his nutrition.

It wasn't often that I was referred patients who were potential suicides and I probably would have run a mile if I had been. Dr Webb wrote to ask if I would see a Mr Harvey. He had been unwell, had had some psychiatric treatment in hospital but lived alone and was finding it difficult to eat properly. He was a pleasant man in his late 30s, living in the usual kind of chaos that was beginning to be familiar to me with such patients. Obsessive Compulsion Disorder (OCD) is common in mentally ill patients and often takes the form of hoarding. Any attempt to move any objects causes great distress. Mr Harvey felt that he should have some of the special supplements that are available for patients who are not eating properly, or who are losing a lot of weight. I tried to steer him away from this, as they are not ideal and not a substitute for normal food. He then calmly explained that he had tried to commit suicide in the past.

"Oh Golly," I thought. I tried to keep my tone light-hearted and neutral.

"And what about now?" I ventured, "Do you still feel suicidal?"

"Yes, I do," he countered, without hesitation.

"OK – let me write to Dr Webb and we'll see what he can do."

The Power of the Pen never ceases to amaze me! Within receipt of my letter the next day, Dr Webb organised everything and we had a Happy Bunny in the shape of Mr Harvey. He was working his way contentedly through a box of nutrition supplements and was seeing a community psychiatric nurse (CPN) for regular support.

One of the hazards of working locally is that patients tend to recognise you in the street or in the supermarket, usually while you are tossing up whether it is worth buying that large bar of chocolate.

Although Annie had been referred simply "to lose weight", she wasn't long in the clinic room before it was obvious that she had some mild but definite mental health problems. Her progress was not good. After several follow-up appointments, she would recognise me standing at the supermarket checkout and draw attention to both of us by shouting at the top of her voice.

"HELLO! YOU'RE THE DIETITIAN, AREN'T YOU? I HAVEN'T LOST ANY WEIGHT YET!"

Heads turned in our direction. I wanted to sink into a large hole in the floor. She was well-known in the little local supermarket and staff would greet her by name. After I had left Borderland, I still used to see her and, to my shame, would sometimes change direction if it looked as if our paths would cross! I was sad to see that by this time she had indeed lost weight – too much – and was always dragging a shopping trolley along the street, often in tears. She had told me that she was getting married and I wondered how this had worked out, or whether in fact this was just another of her wishful thoughts. Another occasion for muttering to myself, "There by the grace of God go I."

DYING TO EAT

What is the matter with Mary Jane?
She's crying with all her might and main
And she won't eat her dinner – rice pudding again –
What is the matter with Mary Jane?

A.A. Milne, "When We Were Very Young"

"Hello Miss Farmer – we have a new lady for you on the ward. Her name is Lucia and she wants to ask you questions about her diet."

My heart sank. It was a Friday afternoon. I was winding down.

The nurse asking me to call was a psychiatric nurse working in the wing attached to the main hospital, which dealt with mental illnesses.

Lucia had had anorexia nervosa for years and, although now just 30 years old, had managed her life remarkably well, until now. She was recently married and as I got to know her it seemed that this was the trigger that tipped her over the edge. She started drinking. A Lot.

At under six stone (38kg), it doesn't take much imagination to figure out how this would affect her. She got blind drunk very easily. And it was finding her in a "bit of a state" that made her husband bring her to A and E, after which she was admitted to the mental health wing.

Had she not started on this slippery slope, sliding down the gin-laced flume into the whirlpool of a life of bursting bubbles, she would possibly have managed her anorexia reasonably well and continued contentedly with her, albeit somewhat higgledy-piggledy, personal world. She was a sweet girl, with a gentle, loving nature and had worked as a carer. But initial impressions belied the manipulative characteristic, typical of such patients. As we got to know Lucia, she drove the staff alternately mad with frustration at her obstinacy and full of concern for her health, mental, emotional and physical. Professionals are not supposed to get involved but the intensive care and attention that her condition warranted fuelled these see-sawing emotions.

She was weighed regularly. Pretending that she needed the lavatory beforehand, she would nip off to her room or the kitchen and gulp down one or two pints of water to make up the weight. Staff would have to check her pockets to ensure they weren't full of loose change. Her room would have to be spot-checked to find hidden food – under her pillow; inside her pillow- case; under the mattress or inside the mattress protector; nestling in the pot plant; on top of the curtain rail – you name it, she would find a hiding place!

She was made to join her fellow patients in the dining room – the idea being that she would be encouraged to eat, by seeing the others do so, plus it was a way of monitoring whether she did eat or not. Lucia didn't like this and opted for the alternative: to have a member of staff sit just outside the open door of her room while she ate and for two-three hours afterwards, to ensure that she did not vomit up her meal.

The mental anguish, torture and extremes of denial and behaviours that Lucia and others like her go through is hard to imagine.

Causes of anorexia nervosa are many and various and the whole spectrum of eating disorders can morph from one to the other. Sometimes it is based on an inability to accept the fact that the girl-child is growing into a woman. (It tends to be girls rather than boys who are affected, though the incidence of boys is on the increase). I heard a sad story of a young girl who was lucky enough to have her own pony. As she grew and developed, she began to outgrow her beloved steed. Her parents could not afford to buy her another so, in her child-like way, she reckoned that she had better stop growing. To do that, she had to stop eating.

Nowadays, much of the blame has been put on the culture to be overly thin, not slim. "Size Zero" has become the aim for young models and wannabes. Airbrushed models "glamorise" anorexia, says the Royal College of Psychiatrists recently.[1] Backed up by a study in Cambridge, it calls for warning symbols on digitally altered fashion photographs and to have ultra-thin models banned. Children, who are as young as ten feel under pressure to have a "perfect body". What is even more worrying is the fact that children as young as three years also old worry about their weight. Where has happy-go-lucky childhood gone?

It is thought that more than 160,000 people in Britain suffer from anorexia and the associated warped body image that develops. Worse, the numbers seem to be rising by around 11 per cent each year.

Put one of these girls (or boys) in front of the mirror and ask them what they see. They will tell you that they see a fat person – in spite of the fact that they are literally skin and bone.

The NHS Information Centre suggests that one in three Hospital admissions for eating disorders involves a child, with those aged 15-19 years old being the largest group.[2]

[1] Collins, N. 2010. Psychiatrists call for end to 'glamorising' of eating disorders. *The Daily Telegraph*. February 22nd. Available online at:
http://www.telegraph.co.uk/health/healthnews/7291425/Psychiatrists-call-for-end-to-glamorising-of-eating-disorders.html
[2] NHS Information Centre Statistics and Data Collection Publications, 2010. *Rise in children treated for eating disorders*. October 13th. Available online at:
http://www.ic.nhs.uk/news-and-events/news/on-in-three-hospital-stays-for-eating-disorders-are-among-children-say-new-figures.

High achievers – yes, highly intelligent girls and boys – who are also perfectionists, are especially susceptible. Anorexia is a serious mental illness and needs to be treated as such. It is psychological in origin and seems to be closely bound with a need for some control in life. Eventually, the anorexia itself can take over and itself begins to be the controlling influence. *"The problem with this illness is that it damages the brain,"* says Professor Janet Treasure, Director of the Eating Disorders Service at the Maudsley and Kings College Hospitals.[3] Sufferers go to extreme measures to ensure that they don't get "fat". In addition to limiting their intake of food and lying to their families about it, they will induce vomiting and/or take laxatives just to make sure that their bodies retain as little food as possible. Dentists often diagnose anorexia, due to the acid reaction of gastric contents on the teeth. Salivary glands tend to enlarge as well, giving an altered facial appearance. Sufferers feel the cold and often wear thick clothing, even in summer. This also helps to disguise their painfully thin bodies.

The disease affects the bones, the circulation and the heart, hair growth and skin. It can cause anaemia, loss of menstruation and libido, depression, mood swings and bowel problems. It can run in families and former anorexic women who are lucky enough to have children (once a very low body weight is achieved, menstruation stops) need to be careful how they feed their babies and introduce them to solid food, without imposing any of their latent feelings. Obsessive Compulsive Disorder (OCD) is also quite common and anorexics often develop rituals over eating and mealtimes.

The sooner it is diagnosed and treated the better. It is incredibly difficult to treat successfully, takes a lot of clinical energy and time and demands input from the whole family.

[3] Jardine, C. 2010. Healing that must begin at home. "Feature article". *The Daily Telegraph*. September 29th

During this time, families walk on eggshells and tensions are taut. It does not always have a happy outcome and even former patients feel that their condition may always be lurking in the background.

There are ethical issues too: stubborn refusal to eat can mean that patients could be sectioned under the Mental Health Act and then "force-fed" by means of a tube. This smacks of the Dark Ages and is only used as a very last resort.

Many years ago, Glaxo, as the pharmaceutical company was then (now Glaxo-Smith-Kline) made a film, detailing the true story of a young girl in her teens, who noticed that everyone admired her mother and her mother's figure. Friends would constantly say, "Doesn't your mother look marvellous? Isn't she beautifully slim?" In her distorted mind, being slim seemed to be the way to be admired, to make friends and to be successful.

The film follows her downhill journey towards being "slim and successful". We see her swallow pints of salt water to induce vomiting. Then the vomiting becomes automatic. She gets thinner and thinner. Her mother takes her to the GP who is unsympathetic. Eventually, she finds someone who understands, who wins her trust and is able to start her on treatment.

What complex beings we are! And how an attitude to food can be so significant and warped in some of us. Lucky are those who just accept and are happy in their own bodies, enjoying what they eat, neither starving themselves, nor over-eating, refusing to let food take over their lives.

Lucia was the first patient with full-blown anorexia nervosa that I had been asked to see. Often, if patients like her are lucky, they are referred to specialist units, which have a team of psychologists and psychiatrists, who are well versed in the tricks of the trade. Lucia wasn't so lucky and while the staff did the best that they could within the confines of their knowledge and experience – the occupational therapist was especially skilled in Cognitive Behavioural Therapy (CBT) – her care wasn't as fine-tuned as it should have been. Her treatment plans varied from being quite harsh and punitive to wheedling and "negotiating".

You might wonder where the dietitian fits into all of this. My own view, rightly or wrongly, is that it is important for the patient's mind-set to be attended to first, before any thoughts of encouraging further eating and trying foods hitherto shunned, especially bearing in mind that Lucia had had years of experience with her condition – more than I had! Further, food and health benefits need to be clarified, as opposed to food purely as a source of calories and weight gain. Lucia and others like her are not going to change overnight. I rang colleagues at The Maudsley Hospital in London for some advice; they were much more knowledgeable than I.

"Tell her she will DIE, if she doesn't start eating," they said bluntly.

I did. Lucia wasn't impressed. It had precious little effect. Perhaps by that time, that is what she wanted to do. After some weeks, I began to win her trust and we worked out an eating plan together, starting with miniscule amounts of foods and building up gradually.

Ward rounds, as they were called, were painful occasions. Each Tuesday morning, the consultant psychiatrist, his registrar and a retinue of medics, nurses, occupational therapists and, if appropriate, myself, would gather in a tiny office in the psychiatric wing. Each of the patients would be discussed in turn and in detail, their medication and care plan reviewed and how they were improving – or not. After that, the patient was then called in.

There was often no courteous or friendly greeting. Eye contact was at a minimum and usually there was barely room for another chair. It was obvious that the patient knew that they had been talked about – warts and all. In my view, the whole thing was excruciating and intimidating. The consultant reviewed the events of the previous week and, in Lucia's case, this was mostly about her weight; about her attempts to disguise any weight loss; about hiding food; vomiting and so on. Her responses to the consultant's questions were minimal and barely audible.

I would be asked to estimate her calorie intake and her calorie need. Occasionally, I would dumb this down a bit, as I didn't want to frighten Lucia as to how much food she really should be eating. As I got to know her better, we would talk about all kinds of things: her love of animals; her work; her family and her husband, eventually leading round again to the question of food. As she progressed, she was rewarded. She was allowed home to spend a day or a weekend with her husband but each time this occurred, a pattern began to emerge: she would end up in A and E "drunk as a skunk". In addition, after a visit by him on the ward, she somehow managed to escape from the building and, like lightning, would run down to the shop opposite the hospital and buy a bottle of gin. Where she got the energy from to do this was a marvel in itself. She would stop off at the cafeteria, buy a small carton of juice, throw it out and top up with the neat gin. We were always amazed at how fast her tiny frame could scamper!

Eventually, we noticed that her husband's reaction to these episodes was not as we would expect. He seemed almost glad that she was re-admitted. Later, Lucia confided to me that she did not like his sexual advances and that she felt out of control. All she really wanted was a cuddle but he always mis-read the signs and wanted to go further. Her reaction? Blot it out with gin.

I did not know enough of Lucia's past to know if she had been abused as a child but it made me wonder. On one of these leave periods I visited her at home, as she did not live very far away from me. Her husband was not there and she seemed happy and relaxed as we walked the dog round the village together. It was an opportunity to see her personality off the ward but, like many of her anorexic fellow-sufferers, she was a good actress! She stayed on the mental health ward on and off for nearly two years. Sadly, her story does not end on a cheerful note and she committed suicide on one of her visits home. I always felt that, had she not started drinking and had her anorexic condition not been picked up, she might have managed her life perhaps not ideally but adequately, as she had done for many years previously.

Christine's story was altogether much happier.

The referral letter from her doctor said that the 11 year-old had been losing weight and her parents were worried. Re-reading the letter before her appointment, I felt more and more that there were hidden extras in this request. I tossed and turned the night before the outpatient clinic worrying over how to tackle this.

Morning came and with it, Christine's turn. Her body language indicated strongly that she would far rather be anywhere but in a dietetic clinic. Calling her in from the waiting area, I quietly suggested to her parents that they wait outside to start with. This went down like a lead balloon but I held firm. Eventually, after about 15 minutes, Christine started to open up. She and her friend had started an exercise regime. They enjoyed it and found they were losing weight. Then they found that they could lose more if they cut down on their food intake as well. She admitted that it had got out of hand but didn't quite know what to do. We promised each other that we wouldn't tell her parents anything she didn't want them to know, unless I felt it was pertinent and important. One of these was that her parents watched her as she ate and appeared to silently monitor her. And of course, there were the food rows.

After 40 minutes – oh yes, and other patients getting *very* impatient, I called her parents in. They were not in the best of moods but the immediate effect of their presence on Christine astonished and alarmed me. She went deathly white. She stopped making eye contact and went back to monosyllabic answers. We made an agreement with her parents as promised but alarm bells rang loudly in my head. I feebly suggested that if things hadn't changed in a couple of weeks, that it might be best if Christine was referred to the specialist eating disorders clinic run by Dr Pinner.

Another night of tossing and turning. Next day, I rang Christine's mother.

"I think we might bring that referral forward, if you don't mind," I suggested. "Would it be all right with you if I wrote to Dr Pinner today?"

To my relief, she agreed, though somewhat reluctantly. Within a few days, an appointment came through for Christine and her parents. Dr Pinner wrote to me later, agreeing that Christine was heading towards an anorexic state but that she and her parents were responding positively to the family therapy. He kept me informed over the course of her treatment, which I really appreciated. Eventually, she was discharged and was doing well.

In this day and age where physical appearance and eternal youth are uppermost in people's minds, fuelled by fashion magazines and the enviable figures and appearances of film stars, it is easy for attitudes to become skewed and to forget what really matters. Having said that, many people are so immersed in how they look that it becomes an obsession and can affect their mental health. Talk to those plastic surgeons whose daily bread is earned by altering people's faces and bodies to their own design and they will defend the use of their skills by saying that the patient's mental health is at risk, or, in the case of models, their career is at stake. We aim towards the impossible dream. We can't all look like Yasmin Le Bon or George Clooney!

What *is* more important is our health, a quiet acceptance of what we can't change and a sunny outlook on life. Happy are those who are comfortable in their own skins.

THE WIND OF CHANGE IN THE CORRIDORS OF MEDICINE

"...For 'tis sport to have the enginer
Hoist with his own petar..."

William Shakespeare, "Hamlet"

Possibly one of the greatest changes over the last 40-odd years is the relationship between the medical profession and dietitians.

To their credit, dietitians have proved that they do have brains, a good understanding of physiology and of the medical conditions that relate to food. They are not just sweet, slim young girls who attempt by gentle persuasion to encourage overweight people to lose a few pounds.

Three or four decades ago, for example, a doctor would "prescribe" a daily allowance of so many grams of carbohydrate and calories for a diabetic. These would then be translated by the dietitian for the patient into food and meal times which was synchronised with the medication. Gradually, more responsibility was given to the dietitian so that, latterly, referral letters sometimes only gave a set of symptoms, often with no diagnosis, especially when food allergies or intolerances were suspected. It was realised that it was best to let the dietitian and the patient sort it out themselves. Dietitians were thus credited with enough knowledge to not only put forward a possible diagnosis, but also to recommend appropriate foods and make possible suggestions for medications that might help.

One of the exciting things about medicine and nutrition is that new research sprouts novel, exciting and stimulating findings about how our bodies work, how they react to our changing environment and how innovative cures and therapies help individuals battle with serious, and not so serious, diseases and discomforts. As the enlightened boffins in their white coats share their discoveries in the dawn of each new age, it can also be a case for being hoist by one's own petard, which incidentally is rather relevant to nutrition. A petard is an explosive device used in medieval warfare but the word *peter* is French for breaking wind. So being blown up by one's own fart takes on a whole different meaning!

But I digress.

The speed at which new findings reach our research journals means that previously held tenets at worst lose credibility and at best cause utter confusion and frustrations. Take alcohol for example. Recent research has suggested that moderate amounts prevent Alzheimer's disease and heart disease. The antioxidant, resveratrol, in red wine, purple/red fruits and peanuts, has been claimed to fight cancer as well as protecting the heart and the brain.[1] Then we are told that it causes memory problems, then back again to its preventative properties. Such puzzles are enough to make one take to drink! Which, incidentally, is what a number of health care workers do to keep sane in a mad world. Coming home after a long day at work, a glass of wine was just what I and, I later discovered, many of my colleagues needed, to give us the energy to cook a meal, walk the dog and clear up, before tackling the never ending paperwork from the day's visits and clinics, to say nothing of the "stats" to be entered on the palmtop computer before bedtime. My husband was seriously thinking of suing the NHS as he was sure I was becoming a lush. Luckily, I left the NHS in time and it never

---

[1] Devlin, K. 2009. Wine, veg and little meat 'a recipe for long life'. *The Daily Telegraph*. June 24th. Available at: http://www/telegraph.co.uk/health/healthnews/5611459/Wine-veg-and-little-meat-a-recipe-for-long-life.html

came to that. Nor did I become a lush. I guess there is still time for that!

Looking back over several years, how drastically some diet advice has changed and what goes around, comes around. At the risk of sounding like a Grumpy Old Woman, what is slightly irritating is that what is sometimes claimed as "new" has its origins steeped in history.

A high fat (ketogenic) diet, for example, was first used to treat epilepsy in 1921 in patients who do not respond well to anti-seizure medication. Several lines of "new" research recently have reported modified versions of this to treat children, with a particular form of epilepsy.[2] Another report suggests that the reason fat people find it so hard to lose weight is because they have more fat cells than normal weight people.[3] It has been well-known for some years that there is a genetic component in the development of obesity. The late Professor Sheila Bingham and others referred to the possibility that more fat cells are formed if babies and children are overfed during critical periods of growth, thus predisposing the resulting adult to a lifetime of struggles with weight control.[4] Further, we learn that diabetes in children is more likely to develop during the winter months, suggesting that there is a link with infectious diseases.[5] The main culprit is still thought to be the Coxsackie B virus, a fact that has been known for at least 20 years if not more. Whilst I

[2] Unnamed author. 2010. High Fat Diets Effectively Treat Absence Epilepsy. *Medical News Today Online*. August 27th. Available at:
http://www.medicalnewstoday.com/printerfriendlynews.php?newsid=199112
[3] Highfield, R. 2008. The reason fat people find it hard to lose weight is found. *The Daily Telegraph*. May 4th
[4] Bingham, S. 1987. *Everyman Companion to Food and Nutrition*. Dent.
[5] Devlin, K. 2009. Children 'more likely to develop diabetes in winter than in summer'. *The Daily Telegraph*. August 24th. Available at:
http://www.telegraph.co. uk/health/healthnews/6068858/Children-more-likely-to-develop-diabetes-in-winter-than-in-summer.html

am sure that such research is conducted in earnest and with enthusiasm, it seems strange to claim some projects as "novel". Those of us who are now retired from the health professions are having a laugh. We shake our grey curls, our dewlaps quiver and we adjust our dowager humps in disbelief at "the younger generation", as we opine, "But we used to do that years ago!"

The Atkins diet has again come under scrutiny. It has received great acclaim in recent years (as did Professor John Yudkin's low carbohydrate diet of the 1960s) as a weight-loss diet. Also like Yudkin's advice, it flies in the face of conventional and current wisdom and recent scientific research for avoiding heart attacks and stroke. Studies from Harvard University suggest that the high fat content of this diet *could* lead to atherosclerosis (hardening and clogging of the arteries due to a build up of plaque), which in turn can lead to heart and arterial disease.[6] Kidneys may also be affected. Further research suggests that those following the Atkins diet are more likely to suffer from depression, when compared with other slimmers on low fat/low carbohydrate diets. If that wasn't enough, a link has been shown with high protein diets and Alzheimer's disease.

Omega-3 fish oils, derived from "fatty fish" such as herring, mackerel and salmon, are advocated as being "good for the heart and the brain". They certainly are helpful as "natural" anti-inflammatories for those with joint problems, especially if taken in high concentrations, when they act a bit like WD40! Cod liver oil is a good source of Omega-3s but this also contains the fat-soluble vitamins A and D, which can be stored in the body. Taking this long-term is not advisable, especially if other sources of these vitamins are also taken as a supplement, as they

---

[6] Alleyne, R. 2009. Atkins-type diets may increase risk of heart disease. *The Daily Telegraph*, August 25th

can become toxic over time. Other supplements of Omega-3s without vitamins A and D are available.

The late Professor Hugh Sinclair, who died in 1990, was a great advocate of the right nutrition for good health. In 1956, he wrote a landmark letter to *The Lancet* suggesting that many of today's illnesses, notably coronary heart disease, lung cancer and leukaemia, were, in part, due to deficiencies of "essential fatty acids" (EFA), particularly those that are derived from fish oils (now referred to as "Omega-3s").[7] In 1976, he joined an expedition to Greenland and put his theory to the test by consuming an Inuit diet, consisting solely of seal meat, fish (including shellfish) and water for 100 days. Analysis of his blood afterwards showed a dramatic reduction of platelet "stickiness" (this is a contributory factor in the formation of blood clots) and thus reduced the incidence of thrombosis. The effect was spectacular: he described how easily he bled following a simple scratch, while pruning his roses and suffered spontaneous nose-bleeds.

Probably the most dramatic change in nutritional and medical advice is that for gastric ulcers, when Drs Barry Marshall and Robin Warren in Australia discovered in 1982 that the bug, *Helicobacter pylori,* was a causative factor. Oddly enough, Dr John Lykoudis was treating his patients in Greece with antibiotics for their gastric ulcers in 1958, long before it was realised that a bacterium was responsible. Up until this medical epiphany, patients attempted to keep their symptoms at bay by drastic alteration of their diets. White fish, chicken, refined starchy foods and milk were the mainstay. It doesn't take an Einstein to appreciate that long-term dependency on these foods ensures a deficiency of iron, zinc and vitamin C – essential nutrients for

---

[7] Hugh Macdonald Sinclair. Available at:
  http://en.wikipedia.org/wiki/Hugh_Macdonald_Sinclair#Letter_to_The_Lancet

healing. Conventional wisdom and long-held beliefs were hard to overcome.

Dr Barry took matters into his own hands, or more precisely into his own mouth, in a theatrical demonstration to convince his medical colleagues, by ingesting a culture of *Helicobacter pylori* extracted from a patient. Within days, he was doubled up with gastric pain and all the classic symptoms of ulceration. The doctors were finally convinced. Diet is now no longer a primary treatment for these patients; a course of antibiotics and bismuth salts and they can once again enjoy their spicy foods, coffee and oranges, should they so wish. In 2005, these two doctors deservedly received the Nobel Prize for Physiology or Medicine in recognition of this work, which they continue to do.

Dietary advice for kidney disease has also undergone radical changes. In the 1960s, patients had to be advised on highly complicated diets, ensuring that levels of protein, sodium and potassium were within amounts that could be dealt with by the failing kidneys. These diets were highly unpalatable and unsatisfactory for the patient and involved a lot of ingenuity and undesirable and complicated arithmetic for the dietitians, especially when sodium and potassium had to be converted into milligrams from millimoles and vice versa. Designing an appetising menu, which conformed to these prescriptions was a real struggle. Because protein was limited, dessert recipes were devised using cream and water as a substitute for milk, or manufactured products, such as "coffee-whitener". Many renal dietitians spent hours perfecting them. Then, with the advent of renal dialysis and kidney transplants, patients, their families (and dietitians!) were released from such dietary ordeals. All breathed a collective sigh of relief. Although dialysis is not ideal for the patient, as it is uncomfortable and means being hooked up to a machine for several hours a week, it is essential to rid the blood of the metabolites that would otherwise rise unchecked and become toxic. *And* it means that patients can eat more or less normally. Ideally, such patients should all have transplants but their availability is another story. Exciting research suggests that a dialysis machine may be made small enough, so that it could be worn "as a belt" and give extra freedom to these patients.

Great changes over the years have also been witnessed regarding dietary control for diabetics. Because of the role of insulin in carbohydrate metabolism (and, we now know, of fat metabolism as well), the emphasis used always to be on the carbohydrate (starch and sugar) content of the diet, which was severely restricted. To help patients identify and regulate this, a system of "red and black lines" was designed in 1932 by the eminent physician, Dr R.D. Lawrence (a co-founder of the British Diabetic Association, as it was then, now Diabetes UK). Foods containing starch and sugar such as bread, cereals, potatoes, parsnips and many fruits made up the "black list", while most protein foods (meats, fish, egg and cheese) formed the basis of the "red list". Milk and vegetarian options for protein, such as beans, were tricky, as they contain both protein and carbohydrate and therefore appeared in both lists. Daily "rations" of food were prescribed by the diabetologist. One ration comprised one black line (equivalent to 10 grams of carbohydrate) and one red line of food (equivalent to 7.5 grams of protein and around 9 grams of fat).

It was complicated. It needed getting used to and involved weighing foods, which was a nuisance. Having said that, I met several elderly diabetics in the outpatient clinic who were quite happy to continue with this system and, providing they could control their diabetes, they were left alone to follow their "lines". Later, this was made simpler by advising patients on "handy measures" of food, each of which was equivalent to ten grams of carbohydrate. Examples would be: one eating apple; one small slice of bread; two plain biscuits; one-third pint of milk (190ml) and so on, so that the patient could make up his daily intake to the required prescription of total carbohydrate. This could vary from say, 80-100 grams to 200 grams a day, depending on the age of the patient, activity levels, body weight, medication and whether they were on insulin. Being on insulin also meant that carbohydrate foods had to be taken at specific times of the day, according to the type of insulin – long-acting or short-acting, or a combination of both. Once insulin is injected, you can't take it out again. It has to be balanced by food. And the reason that it has to be injected is because, as a protein, it would get digested if taken by mouth. (However, research suggests that soon, insulin may be available in the form of a bubblegum, in which the insulin is protected from digestive juices by microscopic capsules).

In the '70s and early '80s, fat intake was unlimited as was protein. Some years ago, it was realised how irresponsible this was. It is now appreciated that insulin is involved in fat metabolism and, obviously, too much fat can make you fat. Obesity itself has a bearing on insulin production and there is a definite connection between diabetes and heart disease. Patients were finding the carbohydrate restrictions very difficult and were usually not compliant anyway. So it all changed again!

By the 1980s, measured portions of carbohydrate disappeared. Its intake was actively encouraged, provided it was of the "slow release" kind (e.g. porridge oats, wholemeal bread, brown rice and pulses). Dietary fat was discouraged, especially from saturated sources, and guidelines mirrored those for "healthy eating" as a "preventive medicine" for the general population, which include cutting down on salt and alcohol, having regular meals and taking exercise. Later, carbohydrates were divided into a hierarchy of their glycaemic index (GI), depending on how slowly or quickly they were absorbed into the bloodstream after digestion. The GI diet quickly became adopted as a slimming regime for non-diabetics as well. Small amounts of sugar and sweet foods even began to be incorporated into the general diabetic diet – BUT there are caveats: they need to be eaten after the main meal, when they would be slowly absorbed with the rest of the food and not cause a sudden rise in blood sugar (glucose). The patient also needs to be aware of dental hygiene and not be overweight.

Currently, it would appear, we are back to "Carbohydrate Counting", especially for those who are managed by insulin and/or are overweight – much the same as we were 20 years ago. A splendid example of what goes around comes around!

Dose Adjustment for Normal Eating (DAFNE), originating 25 years ago in Germany, allows insulin-dependent diabetics to adjust their dose of insulin to their carbohydrate intake.[8] In turn, this depends on knowing what that carbohydrate intake is.

In 2009, Diabetes UK celebrated 75 years since its inception. This amazingly successful charity was initiated by the well-known author, H.G. Wells, who wrote his famous letter to *The Times* in February 1934, suggesting the formation of a permanent association for diabetics, which would give them mutual aid and assistance towards leading as near normal lives as possible and would promote study and research.[9] The Association now has over 170,000 members, supporting people with diabetes and their families and is heavily involved in research and education. H.G. Wells would be proud!

And why all this fuss about diet anyway? Anyone who has seen the marvellous film *"Being There"*, starring Peter Sellers and Shirley MacLaine, may remember that Peter Sellers' character, "Chance", always gave the same answer to any moral

[8] DAFNE. Available at: http://www.dafne.uk/com/
[9] Wells, H.G. 1934. Letter to *The Times*. February 15th. Can be viewed at: http://www.diabetes.org.uk/About_us-/Who_we_are/History/The-founding-of-Diabetes-UK/

or ethical question, "It's like a garden..." His simple brand of wisdom was interpreted by his benefactors, as allegorical. It's not such a bad parallel in this instance either. The microscopic blood capillaries and nerve endings that nourish and sensitise our organs are incredibly fragile structures. Allow blood glucose levels to rise above the optimum and it's like over-watering or adding too much fertiliser to a delicate plant – it withers and dies. And the organs that they had been sustaining, suffer. The retina of the eye, the kidneys and the extremities are the first to feel the pinch.

Retinopathy, nephropathy and neuropathy eventually result in blindness, kidney disease and gangrene respectively. Not nice. And that is the simple reason, dear diabetics, as to why your doctor and dietitian berate you in the attempt to keep your blood glucose within acceptable levels. That finger prick is the gateway to good health!

Truly scary are current figures released by Diabetes UK, that not only are thousands of child diabetics suffering life-threatening complications, but that 100 people a week are having limbs amputated. Further, increasing numbers of younger people (teenagers) are developing Type 2 diabetes. Early diagnosis is obviously key but many fail to spot the signs. The rise in diabetic complications also makes one question diabetic therapies and patient compliance. With luck, future insulin-dependent diabetics may be able to have insulin pumps, which give much better control.

When the British Egg Marketing Board (now The Eggs Authority) launched its 1957 advertisements with the help of the comedian Tony Hancock, no one could have appreciated the longevity of the popular catch phrase "*Go to work on an egg!*" Eggs came off rationing in 1953 and in the same year of the advertisements, the British Lion Mark was introduced. In the 1960s nutrition and medical research was beginning to link high cholesterol blood levels with increasing incidence of heart attacks and, because eggs have a high cholesterol content in the fat of the yolk, their fate, as one of the nation's favourite, highly digestible, easy to eat and easy to cook foods was doomed.

A few mavericks like myself, appreciated that the highly nutritious value of eggs far outweighed their value in the diet as a whole. In the past, dietitians were instructed to urge heart-attack candidates to eat no more than three eggs per week in total. Their fate was further doomed when Edwina ("Eggwina") Curry, as Minister for Health in 1988, pronounced that most eggs are infected with *Salmonella*, which can cause food poisoning. Gone were the breakfast eggs, softly boiled so one could dunk "soldiers" of bread or toast; gone were the lightly scrambled eggs, so sought after by invalids; gone were the egg-nogs so enjoyed as a pre-Christmas dinner drink by elderly maiden aunts; out went the chocolate soufflés which were the final masterpiece for a dinner party at home. In came rock-hard boiled eggs that were tough on elderly dentition and digestions.

By the 1990s, a glimmer of light dawned. Perhaps eggs aren't so bad after all? Let's look at the saturated fat content of the diet in its relation to cholesterol levels and heart disease and BINGO! Together with Delia Smith's help in teaching people how to actually boil an egg and the improved safety precautions against *Salmonella* meant that by the 2000s, they were back on the menu again and in pole position. Their nutritional benefits are appreciated and they are enjoyed and eaten with relish. And this is backed up by scientists who claim that "the egg should be considered a super food" by boosting health and helping to tackle obesity.[10]

It is at this point that I love to recall an editorial in the highly respected medical journal, *The Lancet*, which recounted a simulated conversation between "Mr Everyman and his GP." [11]

---

[10] Unnamed author. 2010. No title. "News in Brief". *The Daily Telegraph*. March 9th

It was written in the early 1970s and much of it is relevant today.

EVERYMAN SPEAKS TO HIS DOCTOR
ABOUT WHAT TO HAVE FOR BREAKFAST

"Well, Doctor, what about cereals with milk and sugar, followed by toast and marmalade?"

"But surely, you know that these things are fattening and, that to be overweight is to be on the road to an early death?"

"Bacon and eggs, then?"

"What! Daily? Heavens no! Do you want to raise your cholesterol level, which carries the statistically proved risk of a coronary heart attack? And, by the way, look out that you don't use too much Worcester Sauce, with whatever you do have, unless you are prepared to suffer serious damage to your kidneys."

"Perhaps fish would be safer?"

"Fish? You must be singularly ill informed. Owing to poisonous effluents, both sea and river fish are now contaminated with mercury and arsenic and may poison you. The US Food and Drug Administration suggest that fish can be eaten but not more than once a week and, provided that you avoid tuna fish and sword fish altogether."

"Fresh fruit is surely all right?"

"Only if you wash it very thoroughly before eating. It has been demonstrated that birds have dropped dead after pecking at fruit which has been sprayed with insecticides."

"Well, maybe the safest thing would be to give up eating anything at breakfast and settle for a good strong cup of coffee."

"Ah, that is where you are dangerously wrong. It has

[11] Editorial, circa 1972. *The Lancet* (Full reference unknown).

been shown that anyone who drinks one cup of coffee a day is running an increased risk of cancer of the bladder. Those who drink more, of course, incur a greater risk. Coffee, my dear Sir, is definitely out."

At this point, Everyman tried a wan little joke. He should have known better.

"I suppose I'd come to no harm, if I just had a glass of water and lemon juice for my breakfast?"

"That depends on whether the water is soft or hard."

Everyman felt on solid ground at last.

"We're all right there, Doctor. We have a water softener."

"More fool you: don't you read the papers? A Medical Research Council Unit has just issued a report strongly supporting the theory that the use of soft water is related to the increase of coronary deaths. Scrap your softener man. It may be a killer."

Poor Everyman, slightly unnerved by this conversation, reaches out for a cigarette, but remembers just in time that this is the royal road to lung cancer, bronchitis and heart disease.

Yes, Yes: scientific research must not be shackled. If these things are dangerous to health, we had better be told so. Agreed, agreed. But should not someone tell these eager beavers of researchers that the atmosphere of anxiety and misgiving that is being created about almost everything that we put into our mouths has its own profound effect upon our health?

It is strange that we hear so little about the effects of anxiety. For, in the long run, it is anxiety, not tobacco, coffee, or soft water, that is the hidden destroyer in the contemporary world. Anxiety treacherously opens the door to every kind of accident and physical disease, cripples efficiency and murders happiness. In wartime, it was an indictable offence to "spread alarm and despondency" - even if the facts were true. It was recognised then that human survival depended on morale. It still does.

I do not know the answer to this dilemma: but I do know that medical researchers should open their eyes to the danger of activating anxiety, this insidious cancer of the human mind, this grey enemy of life - and should devote at least a part of their research to the aim of reducing, rather than increasing it.

And good news for chocoholics. The Aztecs got it right! So much "healthy eating" information often advises us that the foods we really like are killing us, so one of the most welcome pieces of research comes from several studies on the connection between the humble cocoa bean and good health. It is claimed that it could help not only to protect us against heart attack but that the survival rates of chocolate-eating heart attack patients are higher. Further, it appears chocolate can guard against heart failure, high blood pressure and cancer, due to its antioxidant properties. Best of all, it contains the neurotransmitters, dopamine and serotonin, which make us feel good. A superfood indeed! There is a caution however: dark chocolate, which has a high content of cocoa solids is better in this respect than the milk variety. And one should not forget that it can make you put on weight if you overdo it!

And now, we can all go nutty - unless, of course, these cause an allergy! Nuts, hitherto spurned due to their high calorie value, can come out of their shells and have been pushed to the top of the league. Walnuts, almonds, pistachios, pecans, macadamias and peanuts especially are said to be good for both heart and brain. Unsalted versions would be best. That traditional stand-by for vegetarians - the trusty, dependable, stolid nut roast -

can take its place on the dinner-table with pride. Further, eating nuts may reduce the risk of heart disease in women with Type 2 diabetes.

Allergies and food intolerances now take up a mass of dietetic and medical time. In the 1960s, it was rare to find even one patient with a severe allergy amongst the outpatient list. Anaphylactic shock caused by eating peanuts, or worse, being in an environment where peanuts had been, was unheard of. Now, allergies and food intolerances probably account for at least a quarter of patient referrals to a dietetic department, some of which are discussed under "Little People".

The concept of allergy was originally introduced in 1906, by Clemens von Pirquet, a Viennese paediatrician. Further understanding and clarification of some of the biochemical mechanisms involved came with the discovery of immunoglobulins, notably IgE class (proteins involved in antibody production) by Dr "Kimi" Ishizaka in Japan in 1960.

It is well-known that there is usually a family connection but this does not explain the rapid increase in incidence over the last few years. Various theories abound, such as dietary changes; agricultural advances; changes in hygiene practices; increased exposure to potential allergens and reduced exposure (of children) to bacterial and viral infections. Recent attention has been paid to the types and content of bacteria in the gut and it is thought that these have an effect on immunoglobulin balance and regulation. In children, common allergens include cows' milk, eggs, wheat, soya bean and peanuts. In adults, allergic reactions to seafoods, especially shellfish, and nuts, such as walnuts, Brazil nuts and hazelnuts can occur. Because science is still unclear, and orthodox medical allergy specialists are few and far between, patients are often mesmerised and drawn towards pseudo-scientific organisations that offer help and advice.

219

Ideally, if a patient suspects a food allergy – and keeping a diary of food eaten and any reactions is useful here – he/she should see their GP initially and hopefully then be referred to a specialist doctor and/or dietitian. The danger in self-diagnosing is that patients can put themselves (or more seriously, their children) on very restricted diets and end up truly malnourished. The survey, recently published by Portsmouth University, has already been referred to in the chapter, "Little People". Catering for those with allergies is at the least an added nuisance for other people and at most, a worry for school caterers. Perhaps we worry too much? There are some who go so far as to suggest that to have a food "allergy" sets the child apart from his/her peers and makes them "special". For those who actually do suffer and especially for those whose allergy is severe enough to cause anaphylactic shock, immunotherapy is the new approach, being pioneered at Addenbrookes Hospital in Cambridge.[12] Oddly enough, babies who are born in the autumn are at a greater risk of developing allergies, than summer babies. This is thought to be due to a greater exposure to pollen during their foetal development.

The idea of "functional foods" is a relatively new concept. Also called "nutraceuticals", these are essentially foods, which are fortified or naturally enhanced, and are thought to have extra health-promoting and/or disease-preventative characteristics, in addition to their nutrient profile.[13] The term was coined by a Dr Stephen De Felice in the late 1980s, though this notion is not entirely new; adding iodine to salt in the early 1900s was successful in reducing the incidence of goitre.

[12] Alleyne, R. 2010. Doctor says new technique can cure all food allergies. *The Daily Telegraph*. February 22nd
[13] Buttriss, J. and Saltmarsh, M. Editors. 2000. *Functional Foods: Claims and Evidence*. Royal Society of Chemistry

"Phytochemicals" is the term given to plant-based chemicals with these features. Further, the suggestion is that, if enough of the food is eaten, it begins to have a pharmacological effect and acts like a drug. Some experts suggest that single nutrients also begin to take on these qualities. Between 1988 and 1995, for example, the Japanese insisted that calcium was a functional food.

The primary aim of a functional food or ingredient is to promote health and well being. But how does one measure "good health" scientifically? It is not necessarily the absence of disease. The range of products and claims made for treating various conditions and diseases with functional foods is vast. Examples include antioxidants, such as flavenoids and phenols found in tea and some fruits, which are said to neutralise free radicals, maintaining cellular integrity, thus slowing the ageing process; phytoestrogens, found in soya, which benefit menopausal women and are thought to prevent cardio-vascular disease; prebiotics, such as fructooligosaccharides (complex sugars found in onions, garlic, leeks for example) and probiotics, such as lactobacilli and bifido bacteria, found in yoghurt and specially formulated drinks, both of which make for a healthy gut; plant sterols (or stanols), found in nuts, legumes, seeds and processed wood pulp from pine trees which are said to lower cholesterol. (These are found in "fortified" foods such as margarine spreads and special, yoghurt-style drinks). We have already mentioned Omega-3 oils, found in oily fish, avocado pears, nuts and seeds, which are said to be good for heart and brain health, for joints and the immune system.

The term "probiotics" is on many people's lips – literally and verbally. These non-pathogenic bacteria seem to play a significant role in the treatment of a range of gastro-intestinal conditions, not least as a protection against diarrhoea resulting from antibiotic therapy and from *Clostridium Difficile* (*C. Diff*) infection. They have been found to be more effective than standard oral rehydration. Some cases of ulcerative colitis respond well and probiotic use has been extended to treat all manner of embarrassing conditions in the nether regions. But, warns Catherine Collins, chief dietitian at St. George's Hospital, London, their use needs to be tailored to the condition.[14] There isn't necessarily a "one-size fits all" and very recently, the European Food Safety Authority has ruled that there is no real scientific proof that they boost the immune system or treat digestive problems.[15] Unsurprisingly, the probiotics industry is united in fighting back.

The difference between *prebiotics* and *probiotics* is that the former encourage the growth of "good gut bacteria" specific to each individual. Probiotics, on the other hand, are "ready-made" and in this respect, could have limited use. Critics of these further suggest that the digestive enzymes in the stomach would break them down before they had a chance to have any effect. The manufacturers advise that there is "safety in numbers" and that the products contain more than enough to off-set this eventuality.

There are other nutraceuticals, many of which are not that new – some were identified in the 1920s – but it is only relatively recently that their health benefits have been recognised. As you can imagine, this concept is heavily marketed and this is where one has to do a bit more investigation, so as not to be led astray by clever publicity. If in doubt, ask your dietitian!

[14] Collins, C. 2007. Probiotics in Dietetic Practice. *Dietetics Today*, May, 40-43
[15] Lawrence, F. 2010. Probiotic health claims ruled unproven. *Guardian.co.uk*. October 19th. Available at: Guardian.co.uk/society/2010/oct/19/efsa-rules-probiotic-health-claims-unproven

TUBES AND TWIDDLY BITS

Guard us, guide us, keep us, feed us
For we have no help but thee.

James Edmeston, "Lead us Heavenly Father"

"Hey! It's red! Hooray!"

I was observing a nurse who was encouraging a patient to swallow a Ryles tube so that he could be fed through it. The tube was thick, made of rubber and was about the diameter of a string of spaghetti. It was inserted via the nose and after much gagging and swallowing, one hoped that it eventually reached its target – the stomach. To test that it was in the correct place, a small amount of stomach content was drawn up and tested on litmus paper. Turning red indicated the presence of acid – in this case, hydrochloric acid, an essential component to digestion. On reflecting about feeding patients via tubes for this chapter, I cast my mind back to these early days and to our physiology practical lessons at college, when we had to self-administer exactly the same tubes, in order to carry out various tests on gastric function. (See "How It All Started").

This was 1970. Down in the hospital kitchen, Julia, the chief dietitian, assembled a concoction of ingredients in a large jug, which held the feed required for 24 hours. In the spirit of "bucket chemistry", she literally chucked in the following:

Complan made up with full-cream milk; *Marmite*; orange juice (whereupon the contents promptly curdled); a couple of raw eggs (Edwina Currie – don't look now!); black treacle and corn oil. Back on the ward, the amount of feed required was measured out from the jug and placed in a special flask, connected by rubber tubes to the Ryles tube. A clip on the tubing governed the rate of drips into the stomach. Some years later, the large jug was replaced by waxed cartons, fastened at the top with a slide-on clip, which was markedly unreliable. Like the jug, the cartons were often placed on the bottom of the hot trolley to be taken up to the ward with lunch and left in the warm ward kitchen. Enough to make one's hair curl these days, it is utterly extraordinary that no patient ended up with *Salmonella* or any other food borne infection!

I still have a practical nursing book, which was published in 1959, on my bookshelves.[1] One of the actual recipes for a tube-feed is as follows:

Fine oatmeal; milk (full cream); eggs; butter; puréed vegetables; golden syrup; Marmite; salt; vitamin C supplement (or fruit juice); iron supplement in solution; halibut liver oil; beef scrapings.

"Beef scrapings"? These sound like leftovers! In common with many nursing procedures in those days, the equipment needed to administer the feed included a mackintosh (or rubber sheeting) and a stainless steel receiver. There is a clue here. It sounds as if it could be messy! How archaic that seems now. By today's standards, these old-fashioned methods were pretty crude, inexact and, quite likely, decidedly unsafe.

Nowadays, the process is highly scientific. Such feeds are manufactured by specialist companies under strict regulations, hygiene and quality control. Enormous care is taken to minimise infection. Feeds and their containers are sterile, as are the giving-sets (the twiddly bits that connect the formula to the patient's feeding-tube). The feeding-tubes themselves are polyurethane

---

[1] Gration, H.M. and Holland, D.L. 1959. *The Practice of Nursing. 6th Edition.* Faber and Faber.

and much, much thinner than the original Ryles tubes. They are therefore easier to pass into the oesophagus, via the nose or, in some instances, directly into the stomach or small intestine, using an endoscope. The variety of liquid formulas is huge and carefully designed to take care of different nutritional requirements.

I have just re-read an article about a "day in the life of a critical-care dietitian".[2] She is in charge of feeding really, really ill and vulnerable patients. Their lives hover between this world and the next. Some are awaiting transplants. Organs of others are shutting down and all need constant biochemical monitoring, with the enteral feeds (or parenteral in cases of intestinal failure) needing to be appropriately adapted and matched. This girl is highly skilled and knows all about the variety and diversity of tube-feeding formulas.

Giving-sets are used only once for each administration and the rate of feed is regulated and monitored by electronic gismos, which can be portable, thus allowing greater freedom for the patient.

At Borderland, tube-feeds were the bane of our lives, especially as a large teaching hospital, which was outside our area but to which patients were often referred, seemed to make a habit of inserting the feeding-tubes on a Friday afternoon, thus sending the patient home that evening with just enough feed to last for the weekend. They seemed to take special delight in 'phoning chirpily with the news, "We've another patient for you."

"Where does the patient live?" we would ask, hoping they had got it wrong and it wasn't our area.

"Oh...she's yours all right! I'll fax the details through for you."

Groan...groan from us. A few choice words to express our

---

[2] Anonymous, 2007. A day in the life of a critical care dietitian. *Dietetics Today*. British Dietetic Association. May, 38-39

feelings and then into rapid action as I have described in the chapter on "Territorial Boundaries and the NHS".

Margaret was one such patient. She had cancer in her cheek and oesophagus, which had required drastic and invasive surgery. I visited her at her lovely home which was in the countryside and that was her problem.

She lived on the borders of three counties. Her "PEG" (Percutaneous Endoscopic Gastrostomy – a feeding-tube that is inserted directly into the stomach) had been inserted in one. Her GP, Dr McGregor, was in the other and we were based in the third. Our locality manager refused to pay for her feed. The GP rang her with a polite request and the insistence that our authority was liable. She disagreed. The GP then rang me. I agreed to do some ferreting about, rattle some cages and spent hours making telephone calls. Still, there was no one willing to accept the cost for Margaret's treatment. Dr McGregor eventually saw red and in his exasperation and frustration uncharacteristically swore down the 'phone. "Do you want my patient to fucking DIE?" Naturally enough, more than a few feathers were ruffled. They took umbrage and reprimanded him for his language. Eventually, I telephoned the Family Practitioner Committee and the Area Health Authority. Yes, Margaret *was* registered with Borderland Family Practitioner Committee and therefore our lot should stump up.

Eventually and grudgingly, they capitulated. They had no choice.

Later, I was visiting Margaret again and decided to call into Dr McGregor's surgery. Until then, we had only spoken on the 'phone. I was intrigued to meet the man who took on the management in such splendid cavalier style. It was a hot summer's day. He was charm itself.

"Yes...yes...come in...how nice to meet you...you've been to see Margaret? That poor woman... She is doing remarkably well in spite of everything... Cup of tea? Or something cooler?"

He ushered me into his consulting room and it was then I noticed that as well as wearing shorts, he was also bare-footed. I liked him immediately!

We reflected on our struggles against the system and unashamedly giggled and collectively ranted at the expense of managers in general.

To feed or not to feed a patient by artificial means is an eternal and soul-searching question. It is one that bothers the patient, the relatives, doctors and nurses alike. Once the option has been determined to insert a feeding-tube, it becomes a "medical intervention" and then enters that fascinating and intriguing, but often disturbing veritable minefield: the realm of medical ethics. A can of worms is indeed opened. It goes without saying that many patients who suffer from stroke, head injury or neurological disease, such as motor neurone disease or multiple sclerosis, would die if they were not fed artificially. Likewise, if patients have lost the ability to feed themselves or swallow due to other causes, or if it would be highly dangerous for them to do so. For such decisions to be made, note is taken of the patient's wishes, the diagnosis and prognosis, the medical evidence and the assessment made by the speech and language therapist (SALT), who can tell whether food and liquids would go down the "wrong way". If this happened, the patient could either die of choking or end up with a severe respiratory infection.

Ethical question number one: Do we allow this patient to die of starvation, while he/she is in our care?

Answer: "No"

It is worth highlighting that any romantic ideas of dying from starvation and dehydration suggesting that the patient "just gets weaker and slips away" are far from the truth; it is not pleasant and can be painful and extremely distressing for all. One could argue that it constitutes a form of abuse and neglect.

Such patients can last for weeks. They can feel hungry and be in pain, to say nothing of increasing the risks of bedsores and infections. Death from starvation and dehydration becomes a case for the coroner.

Question 2: And if you do not feed, do you then not give their medication either? Or hydrate them subcutaneously?

Answer: It depends. It is obvious that each patient needs to be vetted on individual merits, depending on their medical condition, their possible prognosis, their age, their mental capacity and so on.

In brief, there are four general principles of medical ethics, which form the basis of such decisions: *autonomy* (respecting a patient's wishes and facilitating their own decision-making); *justice* (an impartial and fair approach, without prejudice); *beneficence* (doing the best for the patient) and *non-maleficence* (not doing the patient any harm). These are basic and simple definitions and further reading is helpful.[3] In some cases these principles can appear to be contradictory.[4][5]

Artificially feeding a patient can, but not always, provide a health benefit to that patient, which is not necessarily the same as curing the underlying disease process, but it can in some instances make them stronger. It is not an appropriate goal of medicine to prolong life *at all costs*, with no regard to its quality or the burdens of treatment. And the family's wishes may not always be "in the best interests of the patient". Abhorrent as it may be to consider, there are occasional cases where a family is only too keen for their relative to die, so that they may inherit. And the sooner the better, thank you!

Antonio was 90 and was from a close-knit Italian family who

[3] Rai, G.S. 2004. Editor. *Medical Ethics and the Elderly*. Radcliffe Medical Press
[4] English, V. 2001. *Withholding and Withdrawing Life-Prolonging Medical Treatment*. 2nd Edition. BMJ Books and Wiley Blackwell..
[5] Hope, T. 2004. *Medical Ethics: A Very Short Introduction*. Oxford University Press

had settled in the county town of Borderland. He had suffered a severe stroke. A feeding-tube was inserted, while he was in hospital. Eventually he was allowed home and his son gave up his job to care for his father. His father recovered some of his speech and was able to joke and laugh again. In time, he was able to take "baby pasta" and sieved tomato sauce, lovingly prepared by his son, and did so well that eventually he was able to eat more or less normally. The feeding-tube was removed and he had several years of good quality life, before he died.

Valerie, a former headmistress in her 50s, had Pick's disease, which is a rare and aggressive type of dementia that attacks relatively younger people. She couldn't remember how to eat or drink and her loving, uncomplaining husband, family members and friends would take many hours feeding her with suitably puréed food that she could just about manage, to the extent that as soon as she finished one meal, it was time for the next. Valerie got thinner and thinner and her condition was deteriorating fast.

We had a family conference at Valerie's home with the GP, the speech and language therapist, the nutrition nurse at the hospital who was in charge of artificial feeding, and myself. Not only was there the issue of Valerie becoming severely malnourished, she was now having difficulty swallowing her own saliva. Anyone who has owned a dog with a soft mouth and heavy jowls, or seen the film *Turner and Hooch* will know that, on standing, saliva thickens up like custard! Friends of ours had a St Bernard; he loved to rest his heavy head on the arms of the armchair or on one's lap. Many hours were spent scraping off the resulting congealed and dried saliva!

We produce about three litres of saliva a day and swallow it happily without thinking about it. For someone who has "forgotten" how to swallow or is unable to for various reasons, this thickens up and can cause choking. Such patients need suction and are loaned machines to do this.

It was eventually decided that we should refer Valerie for a PEG, though I could see that her husband still looked uncomfortable. The alternatives looked worryingly bleak. On the day of the minor operation, I accompanied Valerie and her husband to the Endoscopy Suite at the hospital and observed the proceedings.

Valerie was laid on an examination couch with one surgeon at her middle and another at her head. A television monitor was in place, so that as one surgeon passed an endoscopy tube through her mouth, it could be seen in the oesophagus, worming its way to the correct position in the stomach. Eventually, the surgeons were happy that it was in the right place and the other surgeon could make the hole (stoma) in Valerie's stomach, so that the feeding-tube could be pulled through. The ("sleeve") top part of the tube was then withdrawn. The other end poked out through the hole in her tummy and it is here that the giving-set is later attached in order to commence feeding.

Although Valerie was sedated, as the hole was punctured in her abdomen, she curled up, winced and her face screwed up. I had a bad feeling about this. The first few days at home seemed to go well and then there were problems. It seemed that another part of her tummy had also been punctured when the hole was made and she was bleeding internally. She was taken back to theatre to mend it. Valerie never did do very well. The Pick's disease advanced rapidly and she died soon afterwards. I felt that her husband never really forgave us for our intervention and I still feel very sad about that episode. On the other hand, none of us in the team felt that we could have left things as they were.

Belle had had Motor Neurone Disease (MND) for several years and already had a PEG before I met her. She was still able to walk about, dress herself with help and, although she could not talk, the animated and bright conversations that we had using pen and paper were amazing and always enjoyable. She loved clothes and would show me her latest catalogues. We would discuss materials and patterns, after the "business" side of the visit had been attended to. Dribbling saliva was her main concern and she had a ready supply of kitchen roll to mop up her mouth. Her husband, Maurice, a retired engineer, transferred his meticulous work ethos to managing the feeding and keeping the house all ship-shape in Bristol fashion. The house, in a village to the north of the county, was spotless. There was always a tea tray ready for me with exquisite china cups and an embroidered tray-cloth. He was a true star! I visited them regularly, to ensure Belle was maintaining her weight and to iron out any little associated problems, but I also wanted to keep an eye on Maurice – I was worried about him – *he* was getting thinner! Somewhat making a joke if it, I would insist that he, too, got on the scales.

So often the focus of care is on the patient – but what about the carer? Who cares for them? In the end, one is keeping a weather eye on the whole family.

Belle was "hooked up" to her liquid feed, during the night, so as not to disturb their days. Other than that, she and Maurice enjoyed life within the limitations of the PEG. They had many little outings and, thanks to the district nurse who put them in touch with a charity that organised holidays for patients with feeding difficulties, they had a much-needed holiday at a hotel in Bournemouth. Eventually, Belle died of a heart attack one night in her husband's arms. It happened in her sleep and was quite peaceful. I still visited Maurice for a while afterwards, as he picked up the pieces after Belle's death.

Practical problems with tube-feeding vary with each patient as one might expect: one needs to ensure that they are as upright as possible, when "hooked up" to the feeding machine, that the rate of feed is comfortable and adequate. Some prefer a steady rate of drips; "bolus feeds" work well for others and do, in fact, better mimic normal feeding patterns. Good mouth-care is essential. For those who are able to swallow a little safely, small amounts of liquid such as fresh pineapple juice, frozen into cubes to suck, provide relief from dry mouth and sticky saliva. Flavoured lip balm alleviates dry and cracked lips. Too dry a mouth can promote the growth of the yeast infection, *Candida*, which can be very sore and distressing.

One patient who came into my sphere had extra needs that required some interesting research. Ray had porphyria – a rare condition caused by the absence of certain enzymes that deal with porphyrins, which are precursors to the production of haem (the iron-containing component of oxygen-carrying haemoglobin in the blood). This disease was dramatised in the film, *The Madness of King George*, starring the wonderful Nigel Hawthorne in the title role. But Ray had also had a stroke and was being tube-fed. My searches took me to Kings' College Hospital in Denmark Hill, London and thence to the University of Glasgow, where a helpful professor advised me how to tinker with Ray's diet. It was extremely important that he had enough carbohydrate – more than in the standard formula – so we had to rig up an extra bottle of another proprietary formula that was just sugars. Nausea is a constant companion for the porphyria patient but can be alleviated to some extent with being fed little and often. Anaesthetics and medicines could cause Ray problems, as could any dehydration due to vomiting or diarrhoea. In spite of my ignorance on this complex disease, Ray did amazingly well until he had another stroke.

Some variations in tube-feed formula were more bizarre. Mr Hughes was being tube-fed but was also an alcoholic. He requested that some of his feed be his favourite tipple, *Guinness*. Somehow, we managed to accommodate him and his local pub happily supplied him with several pints of "the black stuff" daily!

Autonomy in making decisions about tube-feeding was made starkly crystal clear to me by Joyce.

Joyce had had MND for many years. She was registered blind and had had Still's disease as a child, which is characterised by inflamed and painful joints, leaving her with pronounced walking difficulties. She also had leg ulcers, arthritis and heart failure. Her medication list made her look like Pill-Popper of the Year. She was a dear lady, of extremely sound mind. She kept herself busy in the nursing home doing crochet-work and, unable to speak, communicated to everyone with her "light-writer" – a sort of typewriter that illuminated what she wrote on a screen, followed by an electronic voice-over. When she was fit and well, she used to work for the Association for the Blind. When I was asked to see her, eating and drinking were now becoming problematic. Due to the advancement of her MND, Joyce's swallow was becoming unsafe and she was well aware of the risks. She hated her food being puréed but knew that she couldn't manage it otherwise. Similarly, her drinks had to be thickened with a special thickener, to avoid choking on them. This is particularly unpleasant and there is no sensation of thirst being quenched.

Because of these problems, she preferred to take her meals and drinks in her room, becoming embarrassed if others were present. Being unable to swallow her own saliva meant that she dribbled a lot: another source of acute distress. She was losing weight fast; in two months, this plummeted by over 20lbs (10kg). The staff in the nursing home and I were sure that she was clinically depressed but hesitated to add to her already overwhelming medication list with an antidepressant. Who wouldn't be depressed in her place? It was also possible that one of her heart drugs was causing her to feel nauseated. Two weeks later, the staff called again; there had been no improvement. Could I visit again?

By this time, the issue of inserting a PEG had been raised by her GP, in view of her poor intake of food and fluids. Joyce and I had a chat, sitting side by side on the edge of her bed, so that I could read her light-writer. It went something like this:

"My Doctor told me that I would choke or starve if I did not have tube-feeding."

"Yes – that's right." I said. "What do you think?"

"The tube would prolong my life."

"Mmm…"

(Tears) *"What life?"*

"Indeed – what life?" I thought.

I didn't verbalise this unhappy notion but tried to be upbeat. I attempted to encourage her to think more about the possibility of having tube-feeding and wondered if she had had counselling from the Motor Neurone Disease Association.

"They are too far away in Norwich."

There were further anxieties that bothered Joyce. Her brother had told her that she would have to use her capital and possibly sell her house to stay on in the nursing home. She found it difficult to talk to him as he lived in Wales. Her best friend, who was a regular visitor, had been accused by him of "being interfering" and with not having Joyce's interests at heart. She started to weep again. I felt quite helpless. I couldn't think of anything to say that might be comforting, useful or encouraging. I put my arm round her shoulders and told her that I thought she was very brave. I asked had anyone told her that before. She shook her head and then wrote,

"Thank you for listening."

She wasn't the only one fighting back the tears.

It is at this point that ethical concerns were raised. Joyce was of sound mind and determined that she did not want artificial feeding. She wanted to die and as far as she was concerned, as soon as possible. As professionals, one has a duty of care towards patients and cannot actively and knowingly starve them to death, though if one is honest, this does happen sometimes unintentionally. Joyce knew the options open to her and chose to continue as she was. She died about two weeks after I last saw her. I just hoped that her death was peaceful and that she died from the complications of the disease that had plagued her for so many years, rather than from lack of food and fluid.

There are times when one has to accept that the patient, like the proverbial customer, "knows best" and the kindest thing is to go along with their wishes, easing their chosen path appropriately, ensuring their comfort as best one can. The professional cannot always "sort it out" but this is not necessarily a failure in one's duty. "Care" takes many forms: Tender Loving Care (TLC) may be just what is needed at the time.

PROLONGING LIFE OR TENDER LOVING CARE?

One to watch and one to pray,
And two to bear my soul away.

Thomas Ady, "Matthew, Mark, Luke and John"

Jill came into the office, where some of us were catching up on paperwork, and dumped her notes unceremoniously and noisily on a desk.

"I can't *believe* it!" she exclaimed, exasperated.

"Whaaat...?"

We looked up from our letters, referral notes, patients' notes, mileage claims, expenses and general paper-based mayhem, to say nothing of scribbled messages to answer 'phone calls, make visits and contact others.

Mileage claims were a special headache for me but if we didn't do them, we didn't get our expenses. Simple as that! There were acceptable numbers of miles for certain routine journeys – I was often caught out, as I preferred "the scenic route". A trip meter was helpful but even then, in the early days, each starting point, destination and venue had to be listed on the forms, together with the reason for the visit, and the miles in both vertical and horizontal directions. They were supposed to add up to the same. Try as I would, I could *never* manage to make them match up and would helplessly ask Bridget, our receptionist, for help. She was an arithmetical wizard and would immediately spot my error, without resort to pen, paper or calculator. "There you are!" she would say, pointing out the missing ten miles after a mere glance at my messy scribbles and rubbings out.

I had just returned from a catering meeting at Tranquillity Hospital. These were held monthly and were opportunities for the healthcare staff to comment on the food and the service, for the caterer to explain changes in the menus – it was the era of Lloyd Grossman and "Celebrity Chefs' Dishes" – and for me to coordinate, throw in a few nuggets of nutritional information and write the minutes. As usual, my desk overflowed with unread Trust documents (full of gobbledegook), requests to give talks and training, letters to patients to arrange home visits, others pending and a bundle of new referrals to triage for the outpatients' clinic (two weeks for the severely ill and malnourished and for newly-diagnosed diabetics; two-to-four weeks for allergies and Irritable Bowel Syndrome etc; and more than four weeks for the obese). I had an easy rule. If I hadn't heard from the referring person or the patients themselves after a few weeks and their paperwork was already slipping off my desk, it usually meant that they probably did not need us. They had either got better on their own, or died. On A Good Day, the rest actually got filed.

I was so engrossed in my paperwork, I was startled when the 'phone rang.

"Miss Farmer?"

"Yees…?"

"Are you visiting me this afternoon?"

Oh! No! I was so taken up with the paperwork, that I had failed to see I had indeed marked a home visit in my diary. I had no excuse, except my addled brain.

"Oh! Mrs du Fait. I am really, really sorry – it slipped my mind…er…what would you like to do? Would you like to make another date?"

Luckily this lady was housebound and very kind and understanding. We made another date and I promised that I would be there. I put the 'phone down feeling very stupid.

"Why do these care staff even *think* of asking us to visit when their patient is totally moribund, utterly decrepit and at death's door?" Jill continued. She was becoming increasingly upset.

"Of *course* this woman isn't eating," she fumed, her cheeks reddening and her blood pressure visibly rising. "She's bloody DYING! They need a funeral director, not a sodding dietitian!"

In her distress, Jill's language got the better of her. We didn't often swear that badly but occasionally when things got on top of us, it helped!

Jill then burst into tears. Tears of frustration, rage and fatigue.

"It's really too much," she sobbed. "And I've still got my stats to do. I'm already late with them – I.T. have been on at me about them…" She dabbed her eyes and blew her nose noisily. "And I've *still* got two home visits to fit in," she whimpered. "AND I need to be home to pick up Alison from school."

We made sympathetic noises. We understood all too well. It was especially difficult for women in the NHS to fit in the demands of the job and be a good Mum. I made her a cup of tea and offered to do her home visits for her. She started to calm down and fortified by her tea, handed me her referral letters and began to tackle putting data into her palmtop.

In the world of palliative care, The Grim Reaper is often not very far away and the pearly gates may be inching open to welcome the newcomer. In spite of feeling like death or just wanting it all to end, there are occasions when patients might be tempted to try small amounts of appetising and comforting food, but there are also times when they just simply can't face anything; even to think of food or drink makes them retch and vomit.

Unbelievably, in spite of this, a dietitian may sometimes be called upon to give advice and encourage someone to eat and drink. Often, the care staff or nurses feel that they should make the referral so that *they* feel better about the situation. If this doesn't happen or one doesn't fulfil these expectations, it is possible to feel that one has failed in one's professional duty.

Most people who work in the care professions do these jobs because they *want* to care; to look after people; to make a difference; to relieve pain and suffering and so on. What causes most "grief" and frustration is not being able to help as much as they would like, especially in the area of palliative care, and not being able to "turn off" at the end of the working day. Things like paperwork, taking work home and the feeling that one never finishes all one's tasks top the list. Adding to this is the fact that, sadly, within the NHS, there is a "self-blame" culture. If you can't cope, it's Your Fault. As professional carers, we are expected to offer help that is based on expert and sound knowledge. We have to appear to be strong, successful and in control. It feels inappropriate to admit one's limitations, vulnerability and ignorance. It *is* important to off-load, though the ears of family members and colleagues are perhaps not the best to choose. Clinical supervision is there to help those in the NHS but again, this rather depends on one's supervisor! I was lucky in asking a staff nurse on the rehabilitation ward and, when she retired, I approached the nurse in charge of the hospice, both of whom were practical, down to earth and highly experienced. I became good friends with both.

It *is* normal for staff to struggle at times. It is *not* normal to feel that it is our fault. Staff need TLC sometimes too! Awareness of problems and solutions need to be addressed within the organisation.

Part of my work as a community dietitian in "Elderly Care" involved visiting patients in the local hospice. Kitty had been in the hospice for a few days and was feeling very rough. She had ovarian cancer and it had spread rapidly through her body. The nurses were worried as she wasn't eating and had asked me to see her. In their minds: "patient not eating – ask for the dietitian – she'll sort it out."

It was obvious when I popped my head round her door that Kitty was in a bad way and suffering. She had a vomit bowl on her lap, which contained some vile green stuff and she looked wretched. I introduced myself and explained who I was. No response. Her head remained fixed downwards. She was utterly dejected. I wouldn't want to talk to anyone if I was in her condition either, let alone about food. It was one of those days that I had taken my Golden Retriever with me. The staff and patients welcomed her visits warmly although it was all very unofficial.

"The patients love seeing her – and so do the staff," Matron told me. "Do bring her."

Rather diffidently, I continued.

"Kitty, I've brought my dog to see you…is that OK?" Kitty's head came up from her misery. She managed a weak smile and stretched out her arms.

"Oh! A dog! How *wonderful*! Please let me stroke her." Molly came forward and laid her head on Kitty's knee. I was amazed at the instinctive way that Molly seemed to know how rotten Kitty felt. Her normal approach was on the lines of "Well? Where are the biscuits then?" But not today. Kitty explained how much she missed her dogs at home. We indulged in "doggy talk" and didn't mention food at all. Kitty looked visibly cheered and began to relax. I thought, "To hell with dietetics!" It seemed it was the best thing that had happened to her since she had come to the hospice. She died two days later.

One of the best feelings one can have at the end of a working day in this kind of environment is that warm glow resulting from having actually helped someone – eased their pain; calmed their worries and fears; answered their questions satisfactorily and given good, well-grounded advice. It does not always turn out like that and, as one reflects on the day's events on the journey home or at bedtime, as one inevitably does, there are days when one knows one could have done something better or differently.

Had I not had the dog with me that day, I would not have been able to offer Kitty any solace or comfort and would have felt a professional failure. As it was, it turned out to be the best for both of us, though perhaps not in the way that was in my job description.

I was also asked to see George there a few days later. He had diabetes and was riddled with cancer, which had started in his oesophagus. He was very ill and confused. He did not know where he was or why he was there. He was drinking only clear fluids, refusing all other food and drink and yet he was referred for "dietetic advice". I visited soon after he was referred and it was apparent that George had not long to go before his number would be called and he would be summoned up above. We started chatting. He was very confused. Talking food was gingerly attempted but it was obviously out of the question. I held his hand and he suddenly realised that my dog was with me.

"What a lovely dog!" he said.

"Say 'Hello'," I said, turning the dog so that she was within reach. He put his hand on her soft coat and suddenly, smiles wreathed his face, where previously there had been distress, tension and confusion. He visibly became calm.

"What a lovely girl," he repeated over and over, as he scrunched up her coat and felt her warmth and silkiness. He died the next day.

It is amazing what solace and comfort a pet dog or cat can bring to those in distress. Much research backs this up and the charity "Pets as Therapy" (PAT) take this seriously, training volunteers to visit care homes, hospitals, special schools, hospices and stroke-units with their dog, cat or even a rabbit.

Sometimes it *can* be appropriate to consider improving nutrition and hydration of a patient who is terminally ill. Advantages include increased survival rates, less toxicity to chemotherapy and improved response to treatment. Some patients actually feel better and stronger. Improved appetite is helped by good mouth care, attractively presented food of the right kind, medications such as steroids and/or appetite stimulants and, if appropriate, an apéritif. (Some hospices mix alcoholic drinks with the liquid nutritional supplements to increase their calorie value and make them more appetising!) Dry mouth, caused by poor food and fluid intake and medications, can be improved by encouraging frequent drinks, sucking sweets, ice-lollies and sorbets, glycerine-based mouth washes or using artificial saliva drops. However, not all terminally ill patients either want this approach or respond well. Questions arise and have to be answered such as: "Is my patient hungry?" "Does he/she want to live?" "Is it the patient's family that want him/her to have extra nutrition, rather than the patient?"

There appears to be no evidence that extra nutrition for these patients prolongs life, nor, on the other hand, that it prolongs the dying phase. Views on this thorny subject often differ between the hospital, the patient, the family and the palliative-care team in the hospice. It is important to know what the patient wants and whether he/she is competent to make these important decisions.

Food, love and care are inextricably interlinked. How often did one have a sweet as a child after a tumble "to make it better"? Food has many emotional connotations and is associated with love, affection and comfort. Conversely, it can also be misused and abused so that it can become a controlling influence. At one end of the scale, one sees indulgent parents offering sweets as bribes or consolation; children pester their parents for sweets and snacks. Or they become "fussy-eaters", when perhaps all they really want is a cuddle, some attention, a game or simply time with their parents. Food represents a physical and enjoyable way of expressing celebrations, love and friendship. In the Western world, not to eat (or drink!) is to deny one of life's pleasures. Sufferers of anorexia nervosa, for example, use food as a controlling influence over themselves and others *par excellence*. When we are talking about caring for a loved one, or for a patient in hospital and he/she refuses to eat, the food-provider or carer can understandably feel rebuffed and take the slight personally. On the other hand, food and eating can sometimes be the only way in which the patient remains in control. He or she may not be able to control physical actions, their disease process or their medication, but food and eating may be one way in which small battles can be won and an iota of dignity retained.

For the patient to eat and start to gain weight is viewed as a barometer of "doing well" and "getting better" and it makes the carer feel good too. Not eating and weight loss are downward signs of getting sicker and nearing death. The carer can feel a failure. It is frightening. We go into "denial-mode". We don't want to "go there" and sometimes our reactions to that are to try and force food on our poor, sick patient and "make him/her better".

My mother had heart failure towards the end of her life. It wasn't until I observed her trying her best to eat and to swallow just to please me, that I realised how difficult it was for her, due to the effect of her inability to breathe properly. She described the feelings in her chest as "little birds' wings fluttering". When one thinks about it, the act of swallowing involves momentarily shutting off the airway to avoid food going "down the wrong way". If one is struggling to breathe, as with heart failure, or advanced respiratory disease, this is a tricky thing to do.

I would see my beloved mother rolling the food round and

round in her mouth in an attempt to swallow, until I had to leave and go into the kitchen, voicing a few choice words under my breath. It drove me mad! But she couldn't help it and it was sad to watch. Sips of cold water and "double-swallow" – tips from a friendly speech and language therapist – helped enormously. Her appetite was virtually nil; part of this was due to her general discomfort and may well have also been due to some of her medications. My brother and I took turns in sharing her care; we would lovingly prepare nutritious and easy-to-eat dishes, serving them daintily on her pretty china. Luckily, she liked old-fashioned dishes such as sweetbreads, savoury mousses, cheese soufflé and semolina. The portions were sparrow-like.

"Oh…!" she'd sigh, looking so worried and upset, "That's such a lot…I don't think I can manage all that."

"Well… just try a little," said the dietitian with a smile and the daughter would creep back to the kitchen to cry and to swear. I was a qualified professional. This is what I do! I was falling into the pit myself. I just did not want this to be a food fight.

With our own healthy appetites when we are well, it is hard to imagine the profound changes, mental and physical, which occur in our patient or loved one, when they are seriously ill. Chewing and swallowing are surprisingly energy-demanding. Nor should we allow our own food preferences to influence what we offer. A nurse offering her patient puréed food won't have much success if she says, "Do you want some of this slop?"

Bert was also a patient in the hospice, enjoying some respite care. He had lung cancer and was beginning to fail. His appetite was poor but he managed small amounts of food bravely, if only to please the staff. On one of my visits, his wife was present. She leaned forward to her husband and said, "Now then, Bertie-Boy! When we get you home, we'll jolly well make sure that you eat."

"Oops!" I thought. I caught his eye; he looked trapped. It's now or never, I thought, so I gently (and I hope, tactfully) explained the patient/carer conflict that can occur and suggested that we three work out together what Bert would prefer. Empathy with our patient is essential; we need to know what he/she wants at this stage of a serious illness and/or advanced years, not what we think he/she *should* have. And we should not forget that utter fatigue and low mood are well-known enemies to appetite in the very ill and frail. We also need help and guidance from other professionals and should not be too proud to ask. Caring is exhausting and we need to be aware that our own feelings and fatigue don't override our actions. Recognising the pitfalls that can occur is half the battle and we are then more ready to deal with them, if they have been aired. Love is a powerful emotion; when caring for someone, it is his or her needs that need to be considered – not our own. We need to give that love unconditionally, unselfishly and with insight.

Peter was a Methodist minister who had bowel cancer and had been referred to us by the Macmillan nurse, at his request. In his "previous life", he had been a quantity surveyor and had taken to the Methodist Church later on. I visited him and his wife, Janet, at their attractive home. He was charming and very brave. He knew that he was dying. His main anxiety and aim were to regain some strength, so that he could finish decorating the little house that he and his wife had bought. As he pointed out, the manse, in which they lived, belonged to the Church. He could not bear the thought of his wife being homeless after his death.

As well as general advice about allowing himself some rest periods; foods and snacks that might help, mouth-care and the fact that some of his medications caused a change in taste, we aired the problems of possible feelings of rejection between

245

Peter and Janet, should he be unable to eat food that she had made. Janet very sensibly had prepared herself for this and wisely agreed not to spend too much time "slaving over a hot stove". Fighting over food issues simply had not occurred to her, due to their wonderful understanding of each other.

Patients and their families can be incredibly generous and kind, which is even more poignant, when in the face of their own distress and sorrow. After Peter died, I received such a nice note from Janet. What a wonderful couple they were! In her grief, she had time to write to the staff that had looked after her beloved husband to thank them for their care.

"I feel so tired and I'm losing weight again," wailed Ida. She sounded fretful, anxious and frightened. This telephone call was one that I was half expecting but did not want to hear.

Ida had oesophageal cancer and I first met her at the local hospice. She had asked to see a dietitian and to start with, my advice went down well and she was beginning to feel stronger. Now, things were on a downward slope. Mention "cancer" and people immediately are on the alert: the death knell sounds in their minds; voices become grave and hushed; visions of people in acute pain, struggling to breathe, pale and ill, flood the mind's eye. But people forget that many cancers can now be cured with brilliant advances in modern medicine. Even so, oesophageal cancer is still one of the trickier ones.

The growth in Ida's food pipe (oesophagus), which runs from the back of the mouth down to the stomach, prevented her from eating and swallowing normally. Not only had the food pipe lost its elasticity but it was also getting narrower. Most people know the feeling when they have taken rather too large a mouthful and several swallows are needed, as well as sips of water, to get the wretched thing down. For Ida, it was not so much biting off more than she could chew, but biting off more than she could swallow. As the growth got bigger, Ida found it increasingly difficult to take normal meals. If she tried to eat too much, she got "heartburn"; food was regurgitated which was distressing, and made her throat sore from the acidity. She was losing weight, which might be a blessing for some but for Ida this meant that she was getting sicker. It has been estimated that a cancer growth uses up about 40 per cent or more of an individual's calorie requirement. Cancer is greedy, so weight loss is hardly surprising.

Some oesophageal cancers respond well to surgery but sometimes, patient comfort may be compromised and the means defeat the end. To cut out the growth, much of the food pipe has to be removed, which means that the stomach (on the bottom end of the pipe) is hitched up much higher in the chest when it is re-connected, which also means that one feels full very quickly after eating. Instead, in an effort to reduce symptoms, some patients have a "stent" inserted. This consists of a plastic tube, the diameter of which is no more than that of a *Bic* biro, which helps to keep the food pipe open (or "patent"). It doesn't take much imagination to realise that you could not squeeze a good-sized mouthful of roast beef and Yorkshire pud down that! Food needs to be suitably mashed or puréed.

At 83 years old, Ida was an attractive and bubbly person. To meet her initially was a surprise; she looked so well! She took great care in her appearance and had always thought that she was healthy and ate well. So, when one hears that oesophageal cancer tends to be associated with unhealthy lifestyles, like smoking and drinking too much, this was a bitter and unfair blow. She was determined that her cancer was not going to interfere with her life; she continued to cook, to entertain and enjoy her friends. She even held a "Goodbye Party" for them and for the professionals who had helped her, before she got too weak and ill.

Her diet by the time that I saw her was perhaps bizarre and, for some, absolute heaven! It consisted of chocolate cake, avocado pear, prawns and wafer-thin ham. Her portion-sizes were miniscule. No one was going to get fat on those! Characteristically, as happens with this kind of condition, she was finding that all her energy went into preparing her food and then, just as she sat down to eat it, waves of exhaustion enveloped her and she just couldn't manage it. To eat and enjoy decent and varied food became an overwhelming and almost obsessive desire but she was also, quite understandably, very frightened of choking. Her vision was becoming blurred and fatigue was her greatest enemy. She also felt nauseated much of the time.

I visited her at home, when we discussed all of this. It was just possible that the symptoms of blurred vision and utter weariness could be a side effect of the special "antacid" that she had been prescribed but they could also be due to the cancer. We decided on a plan to ensure that she rested properly during the day, but that also would increase the calorie intake of the foods that she was used to and enjoyed, albeit some of them mashed suitably to baby-food consistency. She got in touch with the splendid Oesophageal Patients' Association and I prescribed some palatable nutrition supplements.[1] She found that sipping cold fizzy drinks between mouthfuls prevented blockage of the stent. Some cancer-fighting drugs cause an unpleasant and metallic taste in the mouth. Avoiding red meats, cooking in "Pyrex" dishes rather than metal containers and using plastic cutlery help to rectify this.

Three weeks later and Ida was feeling much better; she had more energy and although she had not put on any weight, she had not lost any more, which delighted her! However, a few months afterwards, Ida's health deteriorated significantly. She had been very frightened once, when the stent blocked and

---

[1] The Oesophageal Patients' Association. Information available online at:
http://www.opa.org/uk/pages/patient_support.html

finally, the cancer took over. Although she died in hospital soon afterwards, it was not without a fight.

Arthur had come from the local hospital for rehabilitation after suffering a severe stroke but he also had quite severe dementia. He arrived at Tranquillity Hospital with a PEG already *in situ* (in position). He had no idea what was going on or where he was. His confusion was pitiful and the nurses found it distressing too. Several times, he managed to pull the feeding-tube out from his stomach. In spite of his dementia, was he trying to tell us something? Each time, it was replaced and bandaged firmly in place. Again and again, he managed to free it. Then the entry hole in his stomach for the tube became infected. Arthur became extremely unwell. Late one night, after trying to comfort him, one of the staff nurses took matters into her own hands; she removed the tube and dressed his wound. He was cared for lovingly and given fluids subcutaneously until he died peacefully some days later.

This episode was extremely disturbing for the nurses, who questioned Arthur's care plan and the fact that he had had a feeding-tube inserted in the first place by the hospital, to the extent that I organised a discussion forum one afternoon for them. Present were the consultant geriatrician, the visiting GP, the hospice chaplain and myself. We debated legal aspects; living wills; the sanctity of life; quality of life; initial decisions made on treatment – what is in the patient's "best interests"? And, of course, the ever-present fact of litigation. None of us wanted to be accused by relatives of starving a patient to death. Apart from airing our feelings, it was agreed that there should be more communication with the Acute Hospital in such cases.

A salutary letter comes from a Mrs Thornton who describes how her mother, aged 88 years, had a mild stroke. Hospital staff tried to persuade the family that "it would be kinder to let Mum go" and that she would slip away gently, if not fed or hydrated.[2] The family insisted that the old lady have a PEG. She made a good recovery and had a further three years of active life. One just never knows! Chatting to friends recently, they were concerned that the husband's mother was being "kept alive artificially" because the staff in the care home were feeding her liquid nutritional supplements. She was having 900 calories a day for six months – barely the minimum for survival. But this lady could swallow and nutrition is an essential part of care. Had she been subjected to tube-feeding (which wasn't appropriate anyway), that would have been on a different (medical) level. Even the word "artificial" can vary in meaning. Some would say it is "assistive", not artificial, as there is nothing "artificial" about the food and fluids provided. This lady rallied and is still alive at 96.

There have been many headlines recently in the newspapers regarding the dilemmas posed on preserving life "at all costs" – or not, i.e. should patients receive "medical assistance to die"? *We Don't Need Doctors to Speed us to our Graves; When Doctors must Consult Patients; Law Change Would Let 650 Die with Dignity; Everyone should have a good death*…and so on. Death and dying isn't so simple anymore. The competent wishes of the patient and the need for legal and ethical principles to be upheld require clarification. To my simple mind, a "one-size-fits-all" law for these cases is nigh impossible. Each needs to be assessed individually and in depth.

Latterly, requests have been made to the NHS to re-examine the *Liverpool Care Pathway*, which has been described as a useful template to guide professionals in delivering ideal care to those

[2] Thornton, J. 2009. Deciding whether a patient is dying and should no longer be given food or water. "Letters to The Editor". *The Daily Telegraph*, September 4th. Available at: http://www.telegraph.co.uk/comment/letters/6132817/Deciding-whether-a-patient-is-dying-and-should-no-longer-be-given-food-or-water.html

who are dying and giving support to their relatives. Designed by the Specialist Team in Palliative Care at Liverpool Hospital and the Marie Curie Hospice, it was recognised as a model of best practice by the NHS Beacon Programme in 2001 and recommended as a model by the National Institute for Clinical Excellence (NICE) in 2004.[3] More than 300 hospitals, 130 hospices and 560 care homes currently use it. It has been suggested that it is now used right across the NHS but recently, doubts have been raised that patients have been inappropriately assigned to it, especially if they are elderly and very sick. Just because they "tick all the boxes", such patients may not actually be ready to die. But being on the pathway, which can involve them being over-sedated, together with the removal of fluids and medication, can be a sure way to hasten their demise. Nor does it allow for the wonders of Mother Nature, who inexplicably sometimes defies death.[4] At best, this seems to be a "recipe for care"; at worst, a Procrustean bed. It has been accepted that medical and nursing staff need more training on care of the dying and interpreting the pathway. Hopefully, this will allay the fears of vulnerable people being hastened to an untimely and premature death. (As an aside, macabre comfort may be taken from the findings that "Britain is the best place in which to die" as it tops the Quality of Death Index, compared with 39 other nations).[5]

Advance Directives and Living Wills are not the answer in

[3] The Marie Curie Palliative Care Institute, 2009. *The Liverpool Care Pathway for the Dying Patient (LCP)*. December. Available online at:
http://www.liv.ac.uk/mcpcil/liverpool-care-pathway/

[4] Pemberton, M. 2009. Liverpool Care Pathway: The decision to withdraw treatment from a patient is an incredibly complex one. "Finger on the Pulse", *The Daily Telegraph*. September 7th. Available online at:
http://www.telegraph.co.uk/health/healthadvice/maxpemberton/6139668/Liverpool-Care-Pathway-The-decision-to-withdraw-treatment-from-a-patient-is-an-incredibly-complex-one.html

[5] Unnamed author. 2010. Why the best place to die is Britain. *The Daily Telegraph*. July 15th

every case either. I heard of a woman, who was suffering from terminal cancer, who had written her requests, which included refusal to have artificial feeding. At the last minute, she changed her mind and asked to be fed. Sadly, the damage to her digestive system was already done and she died.

As such uncomfortable, disturbing, high-level and esoteric discussions take place, scientific research goes on apace. Recent research from Addenbrookes Hospital, Cambridge, shows that some "vegetative patients" can communicate. Magnetic Resonance Imaging (MRI), which records blood flow through the brain, indicates which bits of grey matter are "switched on".[6] The implications of unlocking the "inner voice" of such patients, who are able to give "Yes"/"No" answers to direct questions, are obviously profound. In the light of such pathways of care – or should we say, death – these are bewildering and extremely distressing....

Since these extraordinary findings, there have been several cases published. Two recent examples, similar, yet disparate, come to mind.

Richard Rudd was severely injured in a motorbike accident in October 2009.[7] He had told his parents before his crash that should he ever have to be on life support and need 24-hour care, he did not want to live. The months passed and eventually, everyone felt the time had come to turn off the machine. At almost the eleventh hour, doctors discovered that not only could Richard blink and move his eyes right and left to order, but that he could, by this method, answer direct questions. One of these was " Do you want your treatment to continue?" Richard answered "Yes".

[6] Monti, M.M. et al. 2010. Wilful modulation of brain activity in disorders of consciousness. *New England Journal of Medicine*, 362, 579-89

[7] Harrison, D. 2010. Parents of coma blink patient Richard Rudd speak of emotional turmoil. *The Daily Telegraph*. July 18th. Available online at: http://www.telegraph.co.uk/health/7896432/Parents-of-coma-blink-patient-Richard-Rudd-speak-of-emotional-turmoil.html

Tony Nicklinson is also on life support and 24-hour care. He has "locked-in syndrome", following a stroke.[8] Like Richard, his only method of communicating is by blinking and nodding. In contrast, he wants his wife to end his life but does not want her to be on a charge of murder.

Such cases are harrowing, deeply tragic and heart breaking. They highlight not only the advances of medicine but also the emotional costs that come with them.

Forecasting death is indeed an inexact science. Nor is it an art. Sometimes, when all but essential medications are stopped, "dying patients" mysteriously improve. There is a balance between active medical treatment, which might prolong life (but also possible suffering) and withdrawing or withholding it, which in turn, might also prolong misery. Much thought and consultation with others is essential. Cachexia, or muscle wasting, is a common accessory to cancer and directly accounts for 25 per cent of all deaths. An antibody has been discovered which blocks this process and it is hoped that survival rates will now improve. The more robust the body, the more able it is to withstand the disease and benefit from treatments.

Further, we should not forget the psychiatric well being of our patient. Indulging in sexual activity seems a strange and possibly inappropriate topic to suggest for a severely ill patient but in some instances, if both partners can manage and are willing, The Palliative Care Team encourages it, as it provides release of pain, great comfort and a further certainty of being loved.

The modern hospice movement evolved throughout the 1960s, initiated by Dr Cicely Saunders. She opened St. Christopher's Hospice in London in 1967. Her work has been a huge inspiration in creating a new and better way of caring for dying

[8] Alleyne, R. 2010. Locked in syndrome man asks High Court for right to die. *The Daily Telegraph.* July 19th

people. In her work, she saw and described dying patients suffering from pain and loneliness. She felt that skilled nursing and medical care could improve these conditions and that not only the patient, but also the whole family could benefit from this in a climate of safety.

"One must take the time and the trouble to deal with every case as an individual one," she wrote.[9] Wherever such patients are, they need *"skilled and specialised nursing"*. She further noted, *"As the body becomes weaker, so the spirit becomes stronger."*

It was she who introduced the idea of *Total Pain*: the physical, emotional, social and spiritual dimensions of extreme anguish. Continuous control of physical pain, as well as awareness of *Total Pain* are the main features of the hospice idea. Another important concept in the hospice movement is that of a "a good death".

As well as medical and scientific advances, changes in society have a strong impact on health care, as well as on how we die. Some, like Dorothy Turner, took matters into their own hands by making an appointment with *Dignitas*, ending their days with solemn dignity. Diane Pretty was not so "lucky" in that respect, having lost her legal case to end her life, and she died naturally from Motor Neurone Disease in a hospice. Terri Schiavo's feeding-tube was removed and then reinserted twice (after decisions by the courts) and she died of starvation and dehydration two weeks after the second instance. In 1993, Tony Bland's demise (the 17-year old victim of the Hillsborough Stadium disaster) became a landmark case. He had been in a persistent vegetative state (PVS) from 1989 to 1993, when his parents and the NHS hospital trust sought permission from the High Court to withdraw his artificial feeding and hydration.[10] He died nine days later. Many are concerned that such cases

[9] Cicely Saunders 2006. *Selected Writings 1958-2004.* Oxford University Press.
[10] Smartt, U. 2202, Updated 2007. *Euthanasia and the law.* BBC News. February 21st. Available online at:
http://news.bbc.co.uk/1/hi/health/2600923.stm

advance the laws around euthanasia to the point where the sick, disabled or elderly are despatched on the grounds that their lives have no value. Much has been written in the press recently about the Suicide Law and "assisted suicide", with fears that euthanasia may be sneakily introduced to Britain via the backdoor; that vulnerable, elderly and frail people may feel pressured to end their days prematurely, thus discontinuing the burden they place on family; bullied into assisted suicide or worse, that families may take the opportunity to end the lives of elderly relatives who have become an encumbrance. The "Right to Die" should not become "A Duty to Die".

And with that lurking beneath the surface, albeit based on the highest of principles, it is felt that patients may be abandoned, that they may not receive good medical practice or palliative care and that the very essence of their lives – such as they are – could be disregarded. Laws are set in stone, rigid and hard-edged. There is no room for compassion. We need legal, medical and ethical guidance. Some would say that a blanket law has no place over this issue. *"...we really have to be rather less regimented about who qualifies for palliative care and who does not. The idea that only irreversible conditions qualify for holistic relief of suffering and pain is patently absurd and cruel,"* writes George Pitcher, following the story of an elderly man who was misdiagnosed with pancreatic cancer.[11] Once again, human intervention over the natural laws of Nature seems set on a course of self-destruction.

It is causing "mutiny in the ranks" too. Doctors, nurses and other health professionals are starting a campaign to change the law on the right to die, challenging the views of the British Medical Association and the Royal College of Physicians.[12]

---

[11] Pitcher, G. 2009. How could they treat an old soldier like this? "Comment". *The Daily Telegraph*. December 10th

[12] Unnamed author. 2010. Doctors campaign for assisted suicide. *The Daily Telegraph* October 3th

Oh! What a tangled web we weave, with medical ethics and the selfish desires of man. Oh, that we could rest in peace – *requiescat in pace.*

I have often been asked about my work with elderly people and especially those with severe dementia, whether it's all worth it, how one justifies it and copes. Doing one's rounds in the care homes does expose some disturbing and distressing sights. Some are so thin, that their legs are about the same diameter as my arm – and they are pretty thin; some are curled up in the foetal position, shutting themselves off from their surroundings; some sit and rock incessantly or scream and shout, while others moan constantly; some sit silently gazing vacantly into space and others engage in surreal conversations. They need feeding, washing, changes of bedding and incontinence pads, company and a sense of being needed and loved. Most have no idea where they are or why. Do they even know *who* they are? *We* have no clues as to what is in their minds. At the end of the day, these are still people who need looking after, now being unable to care for themselves. Although their "personhood", as we know it, has gone, what is left is a living being – the subconscious animal existence, which needs shelter, food and fluids, warmth and affection.

Many argue that you wouldn't let a pet dog, cat or horse suffer like that. We have that exceptional power to put them gently out of their misery with the final visit to the vet. We play with words; we say "putting them to sleep", "euthanasing" them, "putting them out of their misery", "sending them to a better place". Anyone who has taken their beloved, elderly and suffering pet to the vet can identify with "that look in his eye" – which first says, "I've had enough" and then, "I know what is happening – I know what you are going to do to me..." We don't use words like "killing", "murder" or "manslaughter". Moralising and theorising about euthanasia when it is "up close and uncomfortable" is a very different ball-game from generalisations.

Should one think about hastening the death of a loved one, especially one that has severe dementia, how does it happen? Is it an impulsive action or planned? And what if, on that day, there is a spark in their eyes, which tells you they know what you are going to do? Or, if that day is a "Good Day", when the clouds lift momentarily from their minds? Do you hesitate? Who knows what guides one to carry out such a desperate action? Is it out of love and compassion from a higher level that those of us outside the situation don't understand? Times are changing but they are scary and pose more questions than answers. We should not forget the enormous advances that have been made in palliative care and pain control. Ideally, all who need such care should be able to have it but the desire to die is not always just about that, as the above cases illustrate.

I wouldn't want to have killed my mother, nor do I think she would have wanted me to. "I don't want to gate-crash on the other side, without a proper invitation," she would say. Apart from which, she had a strong ethical and religious background. I was lucky not to have to be put in such a position – and so was she. She did not have dementia or terminal cancer; she knew that she did not have much longer on this earth and suffered with heart failure for only a short period, before Nature ended her life with a severe heart attack.

Some retired GPs are circumnavigating this ethical can of worms by offering patients tips on how to starve themselves to death. In this way, they cannot be said to "medically assist someone to die". This is painful and cruel. Who would want their loved to one to suffer in this way?

"Living Wills" can help to guide doctors and nurses in such situations. In spite of being made in advance (sometimes called "Advance Directives") and logged in the patient's notes, they were not legally binding until October 2007, and must comply with the guidelines as set out in the Mental Capacity Act of 2005.[13] This Act has also prompted the General Medical Council to review advice to doctors on end-of-life care. Will they be prosecuted if they carry out their patients' wishes and assist them to die? Or, will they be struck off, if they do not respect the wishes of those patients who are refusing treatment towards the end of their lives? Understandably, doctors are asking for further clarification. Conversely, doctors can overrule those who have indicated that they *do* want treatment up until their last moments, provided the medical opinion is that it would not only be futile but also cause more of a burden, outweigh any advantages and lead to unacceptable discomfort and distress.

Talk about a rock and a hard place! They are damned if they do and damned if they don't. At the end of the day, once ethical principles have been upheld, one can only do what is thought to be best for each patient, according to his/her wishes at the time, with the current knowledge and expertise to hand.

It is not within the bounds of this book to explore the rights and wrongs of euthanasia or when to feed artificially or not, nor am I the least bit qualified to do so, but the above stories are enough to illustrate the gaping chasm between those heart-searching questions. What does the patient want? Is he/she competent? What is the level of pain and distress? What is the best and current medical advice? It is impossible to even imagine the excruciating anguish, sorrow and utter desperation that lead one to thoughts, decisions and actions, such as giving permission to doctors to unplug the machines. Nor have these comments included some of the tragic cases of severely disabled babies and children. Modern science has its own backlash; in an earlier era, such extremely premature babies simply wouldn't have

[13] Department of Health. 2005. *The Mental Capacity Act.* Available at: www.legislation.gov.uk/ukpga/2005/9/contents

survived. We are more than lucky if we are spared from such decisions.

Death is indeed something most people fear, not least the rocky road to that final destination, which may be paved with pain, loneliness and depression. There is no dress-rehearsal and no one to pop back and say, "It's OK; nothing to worry about; it's a doddle; a piece of cake; don't be frightened." No saying either, "Sorry, I've changed my mind…"

Lucky are those for whom Mother Nature takes a kindly hand. My father-in-law was 93, had all his marbles, was still living in his own home with help from family and Social Services and was still driving his ancient VW Polo. He enjoyed reading, his Probus Club and his television. He had a fall in the bathroom, banged his head and died two days later in hospital, due to a brain haemorrhage.

In Diana Athill's *Somewhere Towards the End* she describes her own feelings towards "the end", as indeed it must come for all of us but it is the nature and fear of that pathway to absolute finality that most concerns her.[14] Most of her family members, like my father-in-law, had sudden deaths without preceding incapacities or disabilities; her Uncle, for example, fell off his horse stone dead, while out enjoying the hunt! Lucky are those who achieve old age in a calm and untroubled way, gently relinquishing physical failures without indignities, until an irrevocable detonation in operational function, like a burst water pipe or a break in a main fuse. For those who believe in the power of prayer, I am willing to bet that this is at the top of the Wish List for most of us!

It's a strange and surreal thought that we all have about the last moments of someone's life. We want them to be peaceful, calm, pleasant, without pain and for the dying to know that

[14] Athill, D., 2008. *Somewhere Towards the End*. Granta Books.

they are loved and cared for but it is those of us who are left behind who have those memories – not the dead. It is good to think that *our* last moments with them are as comfortable and comforting as possible. Dying is such a private thing and for some, very frightening. To "shuffle off one's mortal coil" alone, in agonising pain, or as a result of violence, is heartbreaking in the extreme.

And, once someone is dead, people say all sorts of nice things about them. When I'm at a funeral, I often wonder if the deceased knew that their family and friends loved and admired them so much. Conversely, do those left behind know that the deceased thought the world of them too? Wouldn't it be better to let our nearest and dearest know how much we love them before it's all too late?

AGE SHALL NOT WITHER THEM
OR PUT ANOTHER WAY

"Age does not matter unless you're a cheese"

Helen Hayes

What's the use of worrying?
It never was worthwhile.
So, pack up your troubles in your old kit-bag,
And smile, smile, smile.

George Asaf (George H. Powell)

A wealth of urban legend surrounds the following poem but it is generally held that when an old lady died in the geriatric ward of a hospital in Scotland, it appeared that she had left nothing of value. The nurse who packed up her possessions found it.[1] The quality so impressed the staff that copies were published and distributed widely, including the Christmas edition of *Beacon House News*, a magazine of the Northern Ireland Mental Health Association. This was the lady's bequest for posterity. The authorship is attributed to Phyllis McCormack, herself a nurse, working with old people. It was first published in Chris Searle's poetry anthology, *Elders*, (Reality Press, 1973).

---

[1] McCormack, P. 1966. *Try to Remember.* Copyright unknown. Available online at: http://www.maturetimes.co.uk/node/4279.

COLD TEA AND TEARS

"TRY TO REMEMBER"

What do you see, nurse? What do you see?
What are you thinking when you look at me?
A crabbit old woman, not very wise
Uncertain of habit with faraway eyes

Who dribbles her food and makes no reply;
Then you say in a loud voice, "I do wish you'd try."
Who seems not to notice the things that you do,
And forever is losing a stocking or shoe.
Unresisting or not, lets you do as you will;
With bathing or feeding, the long day to fill.
Is that what you're thinking, is that what you see?
Then open your eyes nurse, you're not looking at me.

I'll tell you who I am, as I sit here so still,
As I move at your bidding, as I eat at your will.
I'm a small child of ten... with a father and mother,
And brothers and sisters who love one another.

A girl of sixteen with wings on her feet;
Dreaming that soon, a lover she'll meet.
A bride soon at twenty...my heart gives a leap;
Remembering the vows that I promised to keep.

At twenty-five, I have young of my own, who need me to build
A secure and happy home.
A woman of thirty. My young now grow fast,
Bound together with ties, that forever should last.

At forty, my young ones have grown up and gone
But my man is beside me to see I don't mourn.
At fifty, once more...babies play 'round my knees;
Again we know children, my loved ones and me.

Dark days are upon me, my husband is dead…
I look at the future and shudder with dread.
For my young are all rearing young of their own,
And I think of the years and the love I have known.

I'm an old woman now, Nature is cruel,
'Tis her jest to make old age look like a fool.
The body, it crumples, grace and vigour depart,
There is now a stone, where once I had a heart.

But inside this old carcass, a young girl still dwells,
And now and again, my battered heart swells.
I remember the joys, I remember the pain,
And I'm loving and living life over again.

I think of the years…all too few, gone too fast,
And accept the stark fact that nothing can last.
So open your eyes nurses, open and see…
Not a "Crabbit Old Woman", look closer… see "Me".

Attributed to: Phyllis McCormack

There has been much written about caring for elderly persons in the press recently – and with good reason. Elderly care is a huge problem that will not go away and which is destined to continue, as we all live longer. Staff in care homes have been blamed for not carrying out their duties according to "best practice" and in some instances these accusations are justified. As I write this, BBC Panorama aired a programme about the standards of caring for elderly and vulnerable people in their own homes.[2] Secret filming showed incidences that made one's hair curl. It was very

---

[2] BBC Panorama. 2009. *Britain's Homecare Scandal.* Screened BBC One, April 9th. Available at: http://news.bbc.co.uk/panorama/ hi/front_page/newsid_7990000/ 990682.stm

worrying indeed. Further reports show staff in care homes failing in their duties and being unable to cope, resulting in the need to close the homes. Such decisions are not taken lightly: moving elderly residents, some of whom may also have dementia, causes great upset and confusion. Many go downhill rapidly as a result. Personal anecdotes and official reports abound regarding poor standards of care both in homes and in hospitals, particularly relating to feeding residents (or not) and keeping them clean and dry. (See also "Territorial Boundaries in the NHS"). Worse, is the finding that a large proportion of residents in care homes may have been given the incorrect medication, while more than 100,000 were feared to have been abused.

It should be remembered that we are dealing with a section of the population who, in general, don't like to make a fuss, are accepting of "the ways things are" and who don't want to be a nuisance. We need to anticipate their needs, because they often won't (or can't) tell us.

The Department of Health National Minimum Standards and Care Homes Regulations from the Care Standards Act 2000 were updated in 2005. There are several of these, which are particularly relevant to the provision of meals and feeding of residents. Now, these standards are under the aegis of the Care Quality Commission (CQC), an independent health and social care regulator, which came into being in April 2009.[3]

In spite of these, misuse and misunderstanding of what constitutes "basic care" still widely occurs and worse, abuse, while those on the receiving end suffer in silence with few to champion their cause.

I had a friend who just missed celebrating her 100th birthday. She had severe arthritis and had had a mild stroke. She was in a care home for just a short while before she died. I asked her how

[3] Care Quality Commission. Available at: http://www.cqc.org.uk

she managed to get to the lavatory and her reply was: "I can't. They just tell us to do it where we are."

I had a similar story from another lady, who was visiting an elderly friend in hospital. Neither of these ladies was actually incontinent. They just needed some assistance, which, basically was refused.

A friend's mother was in hospital following a fall. She was 90 years old, deaf and blind. She could neither hear nor see anyone approaching with her meals and drinks and no one indicated to her that they were on her table. As it was untouched, the staff took it away. There appeared to be no records as to whether she had eaten or not. When questioning the staff about this, the family got short shrift. Ultimately, the old lady developed pneumonia and died. Whether this was from malnutrition and unwitting resulting starvation and dehydration, or from her illness, could be debatable.

Another friend's mother is in a care home, as her needs have increased and she has mild dementia. It is one of the "nicer" homes but one morning recently my friend observed that her mother's hands were caked in poo. She had had an accident; faeces had seeped under her nails and she had already eaten her toast for breakfast! Her pills were still sitting on the chair beside her; no one had checked to see if she had taken them. Latterly, with the recent cutbacks, it is deemed by this home, that residents who have catheters may not have incontinence pads as well. Not all catheters are leak-proof. My friend found her mother ice-cold in a wet bed, where she had been all night. Fuming, she shot off to the local chemist and bought every incontinence pad off their shelves, together with the receipt. One morning, her mother was found not wearing her bra and on another, had no blouse underneath her jacket. She was told, "There weren't any clean ones" but in fact there were five in her wardrobe.

Now that I am retired, I visit a local care home with my dog, as one of the Pets as Therapy (PAT) volunteers. I have come to know several of the residents well. They are worried – and so am I. There have been several changes of managers – to date, four or five in the past year. My "informants" tell me "This is a sinking ship" and "There is something very wrong going on". They tell me that they can't eat the food. It is not appetising; it is cold; the portions are small; sometimes it is burnt; the meat is tough; many of the meals are bought in pre-prepared and there are strange combinations of foods in the menus, like gravy with fried fish. Several of them are visibly thinner. One of the ladies has false teeth that swim alarmingly around her mouth when she speaks – highly indicative of major weight loss. Her neighbour looks positively anaemic. Where possible, several of them supplement their food with a trip to the local Tesco Express. One has a small refrigerator in his room and the staff microwave his ready-meals for him. At fees which start at £550 per week, this is scandalous!

I have made some enquiries and have been told that "the doctor visits and assess the residents regularly." When I asked my "moles" about this, they told me, "We never see a doctor unless we ask."

I contacted the CQC and was subjected to a patronising monologue. The dietitian in me is angry. I have no status and feel thwarted. I am just a little old lady who brings her dog in! I am now on "a mission" to see what I can do. Currently, there is no manager and a neighbouring matron is "Acting".

It has to be said that people in care are not *always* the sweet little old ladies and gents that we would love to adopt as a surrogate granny, auntie or uncle. Some of them can be extremely bad tempered and stubborn. Often, this is because of pain, frustration, anger or dementia. They can bite and spit, throw food, shout, swear, scream and resent being cleaned up when they have made a mess. But that is no excuse for not looking after them as best one can, nor should one forget that there is an accountability of care. It is also salutary to remember that giving up one's own home and having to depend on others for help with basic necessities, such as washing, dressing, feeding and being taken to the lavatory, is a huge unwelcome step that many are forced to take.

In my role as a PAT visitor, I made the error once of asking such a resident if she'd like to see the dog. Her response was to growl and spit with amazing accuracy from her high vantage point, being propped up in her chair. After that I kept well out of range!

Just being old and the need to be cared for does not mean that one automatically loses one's faculties, one's mind or control of bodily functions. Nor should one be treated like a child, or worse, as if one did not exist. It is easy to forget that old people were once young, active, vivacious, sexy, beautiful, brave, full of fun, intelligent, clever, had many talents and survived the war. They enjoyed wearing fashionable clothes, had their hair done and tottered in unsuitable shoes. They had careers, lovers, wives and husbands, bore children and enjoyed grandchildren.

The playwright, Tamsin Oglesby, was inspired to write her darkly comic play, *Really Old, Like Forty-Five*, after visiting her mother-in-law in a nursing home. *"Our attitude towards the elderly has changed radically in recent years"*, she wrote in an article. They are referred to as being *"a 'burden'; they create a 'burden of care'"*. Such language *"strips old people of their humanity and value...our culture fetishises youth, but has little respect for the old."* [4]

On a routine visit to a care home, I was observing the lunch being served. As she struggled to the dining room with her two sticks, one incredibly bent and twisted lady turned to me, with a quavery voice.

"I used to be a hockey champion, you know. I played for

[4] Oglesby, T. 2010. Elderly people are not a burden to be dumped. "Comment", *The Daily Telegraph*. February 3rd

England..."

It was hard to imagine. I discovered that another resident was a former tennis champion. One day, a carer supported a balloon on a string from the ceiling, so that she could bat it about. The sparkle in her eyes and her smiles were a joy to behold! Her incredibly thin and twisted body, gnarled, bent hands, swollen knees and the skin stretched taut over her face belied her youthful talents.

The Primary Care Trust (PCT) where I used to work provided a dietetic service to around 50 care homes in an area that was approximately 1600 square miles, covering a dense city area, as well as villages and open countryside. The number of residents that filled these homes totalled around 1600...and counting. My own experience in visiting these homes (there were about 40 on my case load, varying in size from six residents to nearly 100), enabled me to have a "bird's eye" view. One of the tasks within our dietetic service was to visit the homes at mealtimes. This could be a real eye opener.

Gladys was in her late 80s and had been in care for several years after suffering a profound stroke. She could only tolerate puréed food and this had to be neither too hot nor too cold. If the temperature wasn't right, she was promptly sick. On the day that I visited, there was a new member of staff. She checked with the senior carer whether Gladys' food was the right temperature.

"Ah...let me see," said Delia.

She put her bare finger in the food and licked it.

"Yes, that's fine, dear. Do you want to feed her now?"

I could not believe what I saw. The student who was with me that day openly goggled. We did not dare make eye contact with each other for fear of what might inadvertently and inappropriately be said. Our written report to the manager, which was sent later, was more professional!

At another home, residents were helped to their tables at lunchtime. Everyone had their special place at table and shuffled into the dining room. One tiny little soul had difficulty getting to her table as everyone else was already seated. A male member of staff lifted her bodily and carried her high over the heads of the others to her table. She waved grandly and with royal aplomb to those below, as she sailed over their heads.

Those who are known as "messy eaters" are given adult-sized bibs and, with the best will in the world, these look patronising and demeaning. Some were torn at the seam, so that food debris accumulated within the gaps. They didn't always start off clean either. Spaghetti Bolognese is perhaps not an ideal choice of dish. We can all get messy with that! And there are those whose innately anti-social and shambolic eating habits are a positive turn-off for delicate appetites. Some of those who have lost weight in the home where I visit, tell me that their appetite goes immediately they see "Big Martin" start to tuck into his trough with over-enthusiastic gusto. It goes without saying that such residents are best seated separately.

Sometimes sufficient attention would not be given to those seated in wheelchairs; they were either too far away from the table to reach either their plate or their mouth easily or were slumped down in their chairs, so that they were not sitting upright. Try chewing, drinking and swallowing in a semi-reclining position yourself. It is not easy! And as for taking soup with a spoon…!

Those who needed to be spoon-fed, often had to share a carer. I witnessed one alternating between three residents, which made feeding an unpleasant chore for all and not socially interactive or enjoyable as it should, or could be, if on a one-to-one basis.

Often the floor would be sticky – someone had been playing with the sugar! Tables would not be set tidily, nor with matching cutlery. Flowers would look nice on the tables but there could be a danger of a resident with dementia mistaking them for food and enjoying a meal of daffodils. Hot food should be hot and on warm plates. Cold food should also be at the right temperature. Sad to say, this was not always the case.

This is the beginning of a catalogue of disasters. Anyone who has visited a relative in a poorly run and badly managed care home will recognise some of these shortcomings.

Getting older *per se* can bring about changes in eating, not least due to loss of dentition. There are alterations in appetite and taste, ability to chew and a reduced flow of saliva. Dementia can further compound these problems by its affect on the feeding centres in the brain, affecting not only appetite and taste sensations but also the ability to recognise food and the need to eat and drink. More details on feeding patients who suffer with dementia have been discussed in the chapter, "Did I Have Lunch?" Food refusal is also quite common; is this part of the dementia or a part of the individual grappling with some kind of residual control? Exacerbating the problem is the fact that, in some way, the dementia itself increases the need for calories. The ever-present familiar enemies, malnutrition and dehydration accompanied by the risk of urinary tract infections (UTIs), lurk in the shadows around the corner, hovering ominously in the wings, hungry for new victims. It is not often appreciated that lack of sufficient fluid is, in itself, a cause of mental confusion. Attention needs to be paid to offering fluids and food of the right consistency frequently. "Little and often" is best. And, if the residents drink more fluid, they need to be taken to the lavatory or have their incontinence pads changed more frequently. Old-fashioned "nursery-foods" give familiarity, are reminiscent of the past and give comfort. Useful aids such as plate-warmers for "slow eaters", special feeder cups or special cutlery can be available from the occupational therapist and can make huge differences in facilitating independence. Providing food and fluids for someone is absolutely basic to care and of paramount importance to physical and mental well being. Eating and drinking are, quite simply, necessities of life. If we don't do that we die.

In my experience, the smaller homes, especially if they were family-owned, were usually better run and had suitable and exciting menus. Alcohol in the form of sherry, whisky or wine was often offered at the main meal. They were cleaner and residents better cared for. In homes that were less efficiently run, changes in management were frequent.

Celebrities like Michael Parkinson, in his role as "Dignity Ambassador", are using their status to speak out and urge us to report poor care.[5] It doesn't always have to be like this.

There is a wealth of NVQ courses related to care and in some care homes staff are actively encouraged to take these, with a salary rise as an incentive on completion of each level. However, care home managers are often unable to release their staff for training courses due to their short supply. Further, staff are constantly in a state of flux and any training needs to be a "rolling programme", probably "in house".

Many of the carers in our care homes are not British and older people find it difficult to understand strong foreign accents and limited spoken English. Dare I add that it is not unusual for some older people to be outright racist and that can, understandably, cause problems with staffing. I have witnessed a resident in a care home being verbally abusive to a carer who was black. Fortunately, the latter was a very understanding lady. Euphemisms for embarrassing ailments are not understood, nor are the nuances and understatements, so characteristic of

[5] Smith, R. 2010. Sir Michael Parkinson: Blow the whistle on poor treatment of the elderly. "Feature article". *The Daily Telegraph*, January 12th Available at: http://www.telegraph.co.uk/health/healthnews/6968185/Sir-Michael-Parkinson-Blow-the-whistle-on-poor-treatment-of-elderly.html

the English language and the "Older Generation".

How irritating it is to be called "Love" or even "Darlin'" by assistants in shops or elsewhere, just because one is showing some grey hairs! I have to confess to bristling slightly myself, when thus addressed! Recently, the Nursing and Midwifery Council have had to remind nurses that the patients in their care should be addressed appropriately and not as "Lovie", "Ducks", Sweetie" or "Dearie".[6] Such terms of endearment may come gradually as long-stay patients and residents in care homes come to know their carers well, or when things get particularly traumatic. On these occasions, such a term can have a calming effect but an "assumed intimacy" masquerades as "care" when it is actually over familiar. The new "Dignity Nurse Role" in elderly wards and in care homes means that the elderly are not allowed to be called "bed-blockers, bumbling old folk, wrinklies, crud or crumble" any more. Probably only medical people find that funny. Except my dear old departed Mum. She would have cracked! She had a healthy irreverence for old age. (This report also reminds the nurses that their patients, especially the older ones, need adequate nutrition and fluids and may need help with these). Those who lose control of bodily functions, need assistance with all the personal intimacies that healthy people take for granted. Some, who, because of their dementia, lose what are essential inhibitions, occasionally reverting to instinctive "animal" reactions and behaviours, which is highly undignified. I have observed one lady forget her surroundings in her care home and, feeling the "call of Nature", start to undress and attend to it in the day-room.

My friend's 92 year old mother has a catheter, as she is unable to control passing urine. At Easter, Granny came to stay, together with my friend's son and granddaughters, aged three

---

[6] The Nursing and Midwifery Council. 2009. *Care and Respect Every Time*. March 17th. Available at: http://www.dhcarenetworks.org.uk.News/NewsItem/?cid=5221

and one years. These little girls constantly have respiratory infections that they pick up from nursery and can exhale with a single sneeze, enough "snot" to cover anyone within a couple of yards. Granny's catheter leaked, dribbling over the carpet; the baby was being toilet-trained and emptied her full potty on the floor; her sister was sick all over the carpet and the washing machine packed up! Dignity? You must be joking!

Advancing years do not do us any favours, but all people young and old deserve our respect, especially when we are in a position of trust. There is a general fear of getting "old". It depends which side of the mirror you are! Looking at one's reflection, one is saddened at the loss of youthful looks, by the extra wrinkles and sagging jaws, but then is that what other people *really* see? We have become obsessed with how we look and with how we perceive others who view us. There are so many media articles and programmes about achieving the "right looks" and figure. It used to be "making the best of oneself" but now, if one doesn't look like the models do, then one is destined for the scrap heap, which can, in many cases, lead to real depressive illness. Some may find that their perception of an ageing body is grotesque and repellent, because it represents being a burden, becoming severely ill and in pain, losing our marbles, our control and our independence – not necessarily the ageing process alone. *Botox*, collagen implants and plastic surgery are only skin deep. Ageing still carries on underneath. Physical youth is not "eternal"! But on another level, is that not a demonstration of how shallow we have become? Of how important it becomes as to what other people think of us? Of not seeing beyond the physical appearance so that we can appreciate personality, wit, charm, and intelligence and the young at heart?

Giving full-time care to someone who is frail, disabled, vulnerable, ill or simply advanced in years can be highly rewarding. It can also be physically, emotionally and mentally exhausting, frustrating and stressful.

Caring for someone doesn't just mean doing the odd bit of dusting and making a sandwich for lunch. It can include personal care; cleaning; shopping; washing and ironing; the preparation and serving of appropriate food; sometimes, assisting the person to eat and drink, as well as keeping them company, chatting with and amusing them, or simply just "being there". For those who care at home, it often means not being able to go out on a whim, enjoy a meal in a restaurant or go to the cinema or theatre.

There are an estimated six million carers in the UK today. Many of them start to care for a relative by default and unwittingly find themselves doing more and more until, without realising it, they become a full-time carer, whether they want to or not. These unsung heroes and heroines who devote their lives to look after a loved one at home, be they a spouse or other family member, experience highly emotional stresses as well as physical ones.

Carers at Breaking Point screams a headline to mark the start of the annual Carers' Week (2009).[7] These are the unpaid carers who give up their time, their jobs and their lives to look after a family member full time, thus saving the NHS an estimated £87 billion a year. Many of them have attempted suicide to escape the constant stress and strain that their total unselfishness imposes upon them. Add to that the total frustration they experience, in attempting to get help or any kind of benefit. Although the Labour government promised £150 million (a doubling of the current amount) so that carers could have respite, a report by Crossroads and The Princess Royal Trust, tells us that this did not materialise.[8]

---

[7] Unnamed author. 2009. Carers reaching 'breaking point'. *The Daily Telegraph*. June 8th

Angela Rippon, the well-known television presenter, who, at the time of writing was caring for her elderly mother, has appealed for easier access to respite for carers, most of whom work 24/7, 365 days of the year.[9] Not only is respite care hard to attain, but there are times when a carer is either too proud or is simply unaware of its existence to consider it or accept it. My cousin has cared for his wife who is disabled, from a long-ago road traffic accident but who now has multiple sclerosis (MS) as well. He desperately could do with some help but as things have gone on for so long, he feels that by accepting it, he is failing in his duties and becoming weak.

So who cares for the carers?

Caring is hard work. It is a lifetime dedication. It does not allow you time for yourself. It can be a struggle at times. It is understandable to feel resentful occasionally, especially when time for oneself is so limited. This can mean rushed or missed meals, wearing any old clothes and just skating over the carpet with the hoover. And that can be a good day! It is normal to struggle and feel inadequate at times. It is *not* right to feel that it is your fault.

If you are a carer, be flexible, use help that is offered, do not blame yourself for feeling inadequate, network with others, use opportunities for support and attempt to find solutions. There is help out there; don't be afraid or too proud to use it. And one should not forget the many, many young children who care for a disabled parent.

We are living longer. Some are lucky enough to be healthy in their old age. Official forecasts from the Office for National

[8] Donnelly, L. 2010. Millions of pounds promised for carers has been diverted to plug NHS debts. *The Daily Telegraph*. March 8th

[9] Unnamed author. 2009. Angela Rippon criticises 'bureaucratic nightmare facing dementia carers'. *The Daily Telegraph*. June 12th. Available at: http://www.telegraph. co.uk/news/uknews/5514801/Angela-Rippon-criticises-bureacratic-nightmare-facing-dementia-carers.html

Statistics tell us that those aged over 110 – "supercentenerians" – will rise rapidly over the next 25 years, but recent surveys (ONS) suggest that there are more Over-60s in the population than Under 16s. The number of people aged 85 and over has grown more than five-fold over the past 50 years. There is already heavy pressure on finances for health-care, housing and community care for the elderly. Scary, huh?

And if that wasn't enough, scientists are developing a "super-pill" that could keep us going past our 100th birthday by reducing the risks of heart disease, diabetes and stroke! Rock on?

And if you *do* end up in a care home, whatever you do don't let the resident cat curl up beside you! "Oscar" of a nursing home in Providence, Rhode Island, has become famous – or infamous? – for his uncanny ability to detect when someone is about to die.[10] Five years of records show that he has rarely made a mistake! Surprisingly, friends and relatives find this a comfort; he can be at the bedside of their relative when they can't be.

---

[10] Leonard, T. 2010. Cat predicts 50 deaths in RI nursing home. *The Daily Telegraph*, February 1st

IT'S DODGY TO BE TOO THIN IN OLD AGE

L'appétit vient en mangeant
The appetite grows by eating

François Rabelais, "Gargantua"

I am at a party. There are people there that I don't know very well. The inevitable question arises. "Do you work? What do you do?" I reflect on this strange pigeon-holing that small talk brings.

"Well…" I hesitate, knowing from past experiences that people tend to equate dietitians with slimming and what the response is likely to be.

"I am actually retired now but used to work as a community dietitian with the NHS."

"Oooh! That's interesting…" A surreptitious glance at my shape – thanks to my parents' genes, I am slim. "You can help me then. I've been trying to lose weight for years…what do you think of the Peanut and Orange diet?"

I was right! Why…I berate myself…did I not pretend to be a lollipop lady again? I got away with that once before and was very convincing but then, everyone was rather inebriated at the time.

"Er…" I start, but am then given an unsolicited diet history and am rescued by my hostess just in the nick of time.

Everyone knows that overweight and obesity is a growing epidemic with serious medical and psychological overtones. "Going on a diet" is a national pastime for many. One cannot walk down the street, do one's Sainsbury's shop, go to the hairdressers or even the theatre, without overhearing about somebody's personal battles with their weight or the fat content of various products on the shelves and the "wicked food manufacturers" who encourage us to buy them. Dietitians aim to be helpful with such patients and steer an empathic course between being a "bossy-boots", giving didactic advice and gentle counselling, based on proven nutritional science and common sense, enabling the patient to come up with his/her own solutions.

However, the dangers of *under*nutrition, especially in the later years of life, tend not to be subject for conversation at dinner parties, coffee mornings or in the launderette, so it may come as some surprise to hear that in the last three years of my working life, I actually spent a lot of time encouraging older people to eat more and to gain weight. Much has been written about the need for proper care and good nutrition for older people in residential care and in hospitals recently. This is nothing new. More than 150 years ago, even Florence Nightingale knew that good nutrition would not only prevent illness but was essential to healing.[1] She wrote:

"Every careful observer of the sick will agree in this: that thousands of patients are annually starved in the midst of plenty, for want of attention to the way which makes it possible for them to take food…I would say to the nurse 'Have a rule of thought about your patient's diet. Remember how much he has had and how much he ought to have today'".

Reports dating back to 1979 (DHSS) identified that approximately three per cent of the elderly population were clinically malnourished and that, if they became ill and were hospitalised, this became worse. We go to hospital to get better,

---

[1] Nightingale, F. 1859. *Notes on Nursing: What It Is, and What It Is Not.* Chap. VI, p.45. Self-published.

don't we? Umm...well...one would hope so but more recently, it was estimated that over 40 per cent of the elderly in hospital or in care were malnourished.[2]

The long-running "Dignity for the Elderly Campaign", sponsored by *The Daily Mail*, together with official figures obtained by the Conservative party, suggest that deaths of older people in care homes have risen by 16 per cent since Labour came to power in 1997.[3, 4] Around 20 per cent of patients in hospital are underweight and the Nutrition Action Plan Delivery Board claim that since 1997, nearly 50,000 patients have died in our hospitals due to malnutrition.[5] Malnutrition and illness go hand in hand.

The National Institute for Clinical Excellence (NICE) and the National Collaborating Centre for Acute Care reported in 2005 that malnutrition costs the NHS £7.3 billion annually, while obesity treatment is around half of that at £3.5 billion. That same year, a survey by the British Association for Parenteral and Enteral Nutrition (BAPEN) suggested that more than three million people are at risk of malnutrition.[6] More up to date figures from BAPEN and other surveys tell us that these figures are rising year on year.[7, 8] The cost of treating diseases associated

[2] Stratton, R.J. , Elia, M. 2000. How much undernutrition is there in British hospitals? *British Journal of Nutrition*, 84; 257-279

[3]. Brogan, B. 2007. Minister admits: our elderly are being starved. *Mail Online.* http://www.dailymail.co.uk/news/article-430420/Minister-admits-elderly-starved.html

[4] Unnamed author. 2009. Malnutrition deaths in care homes and hospitals up 16pc. "News Bulletin", *The Daily Telegraph.* April 8th

[5] Devlin, K. 2010. Malnutrition is linked to 50,000 hospital deaths. *The Daily Telegraph,* February 26th

[6] Unnamed author. 2009. 3m Britons face malnutrition, says study. BAPEN survey. *The Daily Telegraph.* February, 10th

[7] BAPEN. 2010. Available at: http:// www.bapen.org.uk/ res_press_rel_2010conf5.html Press release. Issued November1st

[8] BBC News, 2011. BAPEN Survey, March: *Third of patients admitted 'at risk of malnutrition'.* March 16th . Available at: http://www.bbc.co.uk/news/health-127481114

with this could now be estimated at £13 billion a year. This problem will not go away, unless everyone in care is involved. Good, decent, nutritious and tasty food are the keystones of rehabilitation after illness, the way to prevent further illness and infections and essential to better health all round.

Nutrition *is* everybody's business, whether one is a doctor, a carer or a hospital ward domestic. A wealth of posh reports is fine but for the people in the care industry, are these a help or an itch that continue to needle? People become malnourished for a host of reasons and those working in care need to be sensitive and aware of these. Sometimes, it is as basic as not liking the food that is presented. It has been known that a resident is vegetarian but the care staff have not been informed of this, or that a person couldn't eat her food for the simple reason that she didn't have her dentures in. Loneliness, depression, pain, infirmity and medications all play their part.

Current health and nutrition messages urge us to cut down on fat, sugar, salt and alcohol in our daily diets, to increase our consumption of fruit and vegetables and have plenty of high fibre carbohydrate (starchy) foods unless, of course, you are following the Atkins diet – but that is another story! Once one is caring for someone who is frail and vulnerable and who has been ill, the goal posts change dramatically and one is only grateful to find something that tempts the appetite. It is sometimes difficult to get this principle across not only to carers, but to older people as well.

It is often hard for those with small appetites to eat enough in order to provide themselves with sufficient calories and this is where the nutrition messages need to be changed. Too much high fibre is bulky and filling; this is fine if attempting to lose weight but not if appetites are poor and need tempting.

NHS hospitals have always been the butt of complaints about food and sometimes, one is hard put to match the dishes on the plate with the menu descriptions. Some have suggested that prisoners – or even pigs – are better fed. In 2000, the Labour government enlisted the skills of Lloyd Grossman to pep up the menus. "Celebrity Chef" dishes featured regularly. More recently, a government adviser on nutrition, Professor Tim Lang, called for a culinary shake-up in hospital menus, with the focus on reducing the numbers of patients with malnutrition, especially those who are elderly.[9] Now it appears that it is Heston Blumenthal's turn to entice these patients back to eating and drinking enough. What Jamie Oliver has done for schools, Mr Blumenthal hopes to do for hospitals. Snail porridge, sardine sorbet and bacon-and-egg ice cream for anyone? In collaboration with the NHS and Reading University, it is hoped that his secret to success will be to tickle the taste buds of the elderly by injecting and enhancing the flavours of familiar foods. It seems such a pity that the former government felt the need to call on "celebrities" to get them out of a hole, when there are perfectly skilled and trained caterers and dietitians already on the NHS payroll.

Chefs, whether of "celebrity" status or not, can dream up enticing and appetising dishes and menus until they are red in the face but the ultimate test then is how they are cooked, re-heated, plated and served and hopefully enjoyed by the intended consumers, the patients.

In the 1960s, it was always the ward sister who served the meals. With a mixture of tradition, drama and routine, she would put on a spotlessly clean, starched apron, roll up her sleeves and pull on special long white cuffs to keep them away from the food. She knew her patients' needs and would plate up accordingly and as attractively as possible, giving appropriate instructions to the nurses, who were "waitressing" and assisting with feeding.

---

[9] Unnamed author. 2010. Hospital food should have to meet 'legally binding standards'. *The Daily Telegraph*. March 31st

As around ten million hospital meals are binned each day, perhaps we *do* need someone of Mr Blumenthal's calibre to put things right and ensure that patients are actually fed and served decent and tempting food. This information comes hot on the heels of the finding that the numbers of patients who leave hospital with malnutrition are rising.[10]

In 2000, the Luton and Dunstable Hospital reported on a huge project, titled *"Eating Matters"*. Some money became available through a hospital charity and a staff nurse set to work to involve *everyone* in the hospital from the chief executive down. It was extremely hard work but a total success. Extra training was given to catering and ward staff to encourage mouth-watering dishes that they knew their patients would like. Ward "waitresses" offered snacks between meals, such as savoury canapés, as well as baked goods in tiny portions. Patients were encouraged with: "Why don't you take two?" or "Would you like to try...?" Small, gnarled, bony fingers reached out tentatively. Rheumy eyes twinkled. Wrinkled faces cracked in shy smiles. This was a treat! The menus were updated and there was more choice.

Results? On the surgical wards, recovery rates improved; antibiotic use and the number of days in bed were reduced. The use of expensive "medicalised" nutrition supplements and drinks plummeted. Yes, the project *did* cost money but this was outweighed by the advantages. Sadly, after a couple of years, the money ran out and the scheme fizzled. What A Sad Day that was.

So why is undernutrition such a danger to the health of older people?

The lower the body weight, the less able we are to recover

---

[10] HESonline, Hospital Episode Statistics-Articles and Research-Statistics papers-Malnutrition. 2005-2011
www.hesonline.nhs.uk

from surgery and resist infections; skin can lose its integrity: wound healing is delayed and bedsores are more likely; muscles lose strength, resulting in decreased mobility – the "wobble factor" increases leading to a greater risk of falls. It should not be forgotten that the heart is itself a muscle – cardiac function can become impaired. Due to weakening chest muscles, breathing can become short, resulting in less oxygenation of the body and an increased risk of chest infections. The brain can become confused – one cannot think so clearly; mood can dip. The liver is unable to detoxify medications so efficiently and a frail body cannot fight underlying illness. Not eating can lead to depression, which itself can also lead to loss of appetite: a vicious circle indeed. Ultimately malnutrition leads to death.

A weight loss of ten per cent or more from the normal body weight suggests the beginning of a downward spiral and a decrease in functional abilities. When this happens, the aim should be:

To reduce further weight loss and/or maintain that level of body weight. (To achieve a return to "normal" or previous body weight may not necessarily be appropriate).

To maintain nutrition with a suitable choice of foods and possibly, with special, dietary supplements.

How food is presented cannot be overestimated; most of us "eat with our eyes". Tempting small appetites is a major part of care and that includes not only appetising food on the plate, that is nicely arranged, but with attractive (unchipped!) matching china and utensils and all the other attributes that help to get the gastric juices interested and flowing in anticipation of an enjoyable meal. (See "Age Shall not Wither Them").

It has been shown that older people in residential care eat with greater enthusiasm if they are at a table with others – assuming that good table manners are adhered to! Carers at home can either share a meal or simply be companionable by having something light to eat or drink with their patient/client.

A study from Ninewells Hospital in Dundee showed that, older people who had suffered hip fractures, could be encouraged to eat snacks of their choice between meal times, thus boosting their overall energy (calorie) intake and helping to speed up healing.[11]

So the next time that I am asked, "What job do you do?" I shall say, "I encourage people to get fatter!" (You're having a laugh aren't you?)

Visiting elderly care homes was a two-way process. I would advise, to the best of my ability, on individual residents and the menus. My colleagues and I offered training sessions on using and implementing a nutrition risk screening tool and would follow this up by visiting the homes, in order to witness the meals being served and further monitor the residents. In return, I would learn more about how the homes were run, and the role that other health professionals played, such as the physiotherapists, speech and language and occupational therapists. Sometimes, I got more than I bargained for. The following story is one of them.

"Gosh!" I breathed, exhaling slowly.

I was staring at a massive, jumbo-sized pair of old-fashioned (and I mean *really* old-fashioned) white, thick cotton bloomers. These came complete with elasticated long legs that reached practically to the knees and a pocket in the top of the leg for your hankie. Glamour pants these were not – more like passion-killers. Bridget Jones' Big Knickers are but thongs by comparison but, like a James Bond gismo, these doughty drawers contained a secret weapon.

I was visiting a care home in Calmershire and after checking on their weights and having a general review of the residents,

[11] Price, R. McMurdo, M. and Anderson, A., 2006. A Personalised Snack-Based Intervention for Hip Fracture Patients. *Journal of Human Nutrition and Dietetics,* April 19th Issue 2

Matron and I were discussing ways of preventing old people from hurting themselves, should they fall.

"They're called hip-protector knickers," explained Margaret, holding up a pair to show me the full works. "See these pads in the sides? They are made of a strong plastic – polypropylene – which allows the shock resulting from a fall to transfer to the soft tissues around the hip. In this way, they protect the hip bone from breaking."

I beetled home that evening and logged on to the Internet; there are at least 12 different companies that make this eye-boggling underwear. And, believe it or not, for *"Pant News Around the World"*, check out The *Pants Appreciation Society Newsletter.* (Yes! Really!)

With my mind still reeling from these revelations, I visited Judy, who is a falls-prevention service coordinator for the area. She gave me some facts about these not-so-naughty knicks.

"We found that older people in residential homes didn't like them at all, because they are difficult to get on and off and it hampered their ability to go to the lavatory unaided," explained Judy. "Occasionally we offer them to very thin individuals who are living independently at home, who have osteoporosis and who have already experienced a fracture. This gives them confidence to go outside and resume their quality of life."

She even gave me a pair to try and ensured that they were the right size and put on the correct way.

"Get this wrong," said Judy, "And you could end up with the hard pad in the wrong place and do more damage than good. You could actually concentrate the energy of a fall right onto the hip bone!"

In the best traditions of a researcher, I wore them for one whole day. Apart from the size (rather large!) they were surprisingly comfortable in a clinging, cycling-shorts sort of way and reminded me of the unattractive, baggy drawers, elasticated round the legs, that I had to wear at my convent boarding school. I needed a larger pair of trousers on that day but they were certainly nice and warm for cold weather. I wondered how acceptable they would be during a sweltering summer. I could appreciate that unpeeling them to go to the lavatory might pose a problem for someone whose hands were very arthritic or weak, especially if one was in a hurry. I also tried to lie down. Flat on my back, as if ready for my coffin, they were fine, but like most people, I curl up on my side to sleep. This was like lying on a rock, so I declined to wear them at night. And this perhaps is where their value might be limited. When elderly people need to get up in the night to go to the loo, they could be confused and are then more likely to fall.

Margaret made her staff wear them too. Their conclusions were the same as mine. So what did Margaret's residents think?

"One lady refused point-blank," she answered. "Otherwise, we never had any problems with those who did wear them. One lady who had suffered from previous falls was quite happy with them. Another of my residents, who had had a previous fracture, called them her 'Save-Me-Breaking-a-Leg Knickers' and although she didn't enjoy wearing them, was convinced enough by their protective value." On the other hand, Judy insisted that "her ladies" wear them all the time – 24/7.

There are all sorts of reasons why older people are more susceptible to fracture; one doesn't "bounce" quite as well as one used to! Older bones can get thinner simply due to age but also as a result of corticosteroid use (sometimes prescribed to treat arthritic and other inflammatory conditions), poor nutrition, alcohol abuse, a genetic predisposition to osteoporosis, poor mobility and some medications.

Hip fractures are a major cause of morbidity and mortality among the elderly and can occur at home, in care homes and, perhaps surprisingly, in hospitals. More than 200,000 accident-falls per year are reported in hospitals in England and Wales. These injuries place a major burden on individual Trusts and the NHS as a whole. They account for around 20 per cent of bed occupancy on orthopaedic wards, resulting in serious implications on elective surgery.[12] Studies suggest that those who are most compliant in wearing these "Hip-Hop Knicks" are those that need them most (due to having experienced a previous fall, having dementia or being physically unstable) but then in turn, these people generally have more nursing care anyway and maybe staff ensure that they are worn.

But they are only part of the fracture prevention story. Judy was convinced that they have their place, especially for those who are unsteady on their feet, and she told me about past and current trials, which compare effectiveness and the different types. "More research is really needed," she added.

Not everyone agrees that these knickers have even a small part to play. Dr David Torgeson of the York Trials Unit, which has been developed to conduct high quality, randomised, rigorous trials, and provide academic leadership and support to clinical trials, gave a definite thumbs-down.[13]

"My view is that they don't work," he told me. "Unfortunately I think they are ineffective and personally wouldn't recommend them to anyone."

The National Osteoporosis Society co-funded a large clinical trial carried out by the York Trials Unit and agreed that, because compliance in wearing the hip protectors is low, resources would be more efficiently spent on falls- prevention programmes.

There are further questions as to how the neck of the femur actually breaks. Could it be the fall itself, or a shearing of the femoral neck which causes the fall? Some patients have been known to report that they heard the "crack" *before* they fell.

Prevention is better than cure. One needs to look holistically at lifestyles, the environment, mobility, stability, diet, medications

[12] Mr Antonio Alonso, 2009. Orthopaedic Surgeon, Personal communication.
[13] Dr David Torgeson, 2009. York Trials Unit, Personal communication.

and exercises to improve balance. Drugs, such as alendronate, and vitamin D and calcium supplements to strengthen bone have been the mainstay of treating and preventing this crippling disease but latterly, research has suggested that these should not be prescribed on the basis of bone-density measurements alone and that long-term use can, in fact, make bone weaker. Further, it has been suggested that high-strength calcium supplements may increase the risk of heart attack. Happily, calcium from food does not appear to have the same effect.

So, although the jury is still out, "Hip-Hop Knicks" may be hot pants to you but these baggy bloomers just might save lives; they may reach parts other pants cannot. Just don't ask if your bum looks big in them!

TICK HERE FOR MALNUTRITION
SCREENING FOR NUTRITIONAL STATUS

Some hae meat and canna eat,
And some wad eat that want it,
But we hae meat and we can eat,
Sae the Lord be thankit.

Attributed to Robert Burns, "The Selkirk Grace"

"Hello – is that the dietitian?" said the voice on the 'phone.

"Yeees…speaking," I replied somewhat cagily, as I was attempting to get my thoughts in order and catch up on writing a report on a nursing home.

"Can you help? We have a lady – Mrs Green – who is not eating and drinking."

This was the manager of a local nursing home concerned for one of her residents.

"Is there any reason for that, that you can think of?" I query.

"Well no…" she replies, probably muttering under her breath, "That's why I'm 'phoning you, silly."

"Well…What does *she* say? Have you asked her about this? Do you think that she might be in pain? Constipated? Are her medications making her feel rough? Is she anxious or depressed? Does she have her own teeth? Is she offered food that she likes? Is she physically able to feed herself, or does she need a bit of help?"

I fired questions at her. There were more that I could have asked, such as whether this lady had any underlying physical illness that could affect her appetite, whether other residents upset her or whether she had dementia. Was she was drinking enough or were there unpleasant smells near her?

"Er...Oooh! Now you're asking...I'm not sure..."

"Have you weighed her regularly? Do you know when she was last weighed or what her weight is now?" I persisted.

"Erm...no...we haven't had time for that... "

I groaned inwardly, thinking I could get on my high horse and remind her snootily that regular weighing and recording are part of the Care Standards for care homes. (And, one would hope, that the weighing scales would be accurate and regularly serviced).

"Have you filled in the nutrition screening form?" I ask.

"No... what's that then?" she replied.

"OK then," I said, trying to sound bright and helpful, hoping that my inward sigh was not too audible. "I'll come out and see her as soon as I can."

We made a date in the diary for a few days' time and I wished that it was one that did not entail a 50-mile round trip. On the plus side, it was an opportunity to see how this home was being managed and to review the other residents.

"Eye-balling" someone for weight loss is not enough. It has been shown that a considerable amount of weight (around seven pounds/three-four kg) is lost before one is aware of the visual signs and, for someone who is already frail and ill, further weight loss can lead them into the danger zone.

Some kind of nutrition screening tool is therefore a MUST and, true to its name, there is one that has been produced by the Malnutrition Advisory Group (MAG) called just that: "MUST" – the Malnutrition Universal Screening Tool. This was first published in 2003 and identifies individuals who are at risk of malnutrition. In this context, "malnutrition" is taken to mean under-nourishment, though in theory, overweight and obese people can also considered to be "mal-nourished". It can be downloaded for free (in PDF format) from BAPEN, together with information on how to use it.[1]

MUST is especially intended for use by carers of elderly persons, whether they are in their own homes, a rehabilitation unit, hospital ward or in a care home. It is also likely that each Primary Care Trust (PCT) also has its own "home-grown" screening tool, which can probably be obtained by contacting the local Nutrition and Dietetic Services. Googling "Nutrition Screening Tools" also turns up a wealth of information on malnutrition and ageing.

The good thing about such a "tool" is that it helps to identify reasons why older people are losing weight and/or not eating, which hopefully can be rectified. For example, is this cause treatable, or is it related to illness? It can be completed by any member of the care staff (one does not have to be a registered nurse or dietitian to do it). It is quick and easy to use and non-invasive. Regular surveys by BAPEN (See "It's Dodgy to be Too Thin in Old Age") show that many older patients are already malnourished on admission to hospital, a care home or an elderly care mental health unit. Most of the hospitals which were surveyed reported that they had a screening policy but weighing patients was carried out in less than half, suggesting that malnutrition on admission is still under-recognised and/or not treated.

Where I worked, care home staff were also invited to regular training sessions by our department, in which we taught the importance of good nutrition, how to fill in the screening form and gave practical hints on putting its findings into action. (These sessions also included practical exercises, such as feeding each other; the importance of snacks and in-between meal extras; special needs for dementia sufferers and using the expertise of other therapists, such as SALTs and OTs). Visits were made

---

[1] www.bapen.org.uk/must_tool.html and www.easilearning.com/id15.html

monthly to the homes to review the residents with the staff and occasionally, as in the above scenario, individual residents were assessed and more detailed advice given.

WHAT A NUTRITION SCREENING TOOL SHOULD TELL YOU

- Any unintentional weight loss
- Dietary habits and meal patterns
- Appetite
- Physical ability to eat and drink
- Oral health status
- Fluid intake
- Illness or disease and medication
- Mental health status

Once the score is obtained, there should also be a guide, or care plan as to what kind of action might be appropriate in order to attempt to improve the client's nutritional status. The convent school that I went to had a motto: *Facta non Verba* ("Actions not Words") and this is so true for acting on the findings of nutrition screening tools. It should be remembered that, although much can be done to improve someone's nutritional status, it doesn't necessarily alter any disease process but it can make people feel better in themselves. With better nourishment, they can become stronger, better able to resist infections and practise their physiotherapy exercises.

"Do you think Mrs Green would benefit from some supplements, Mary?" the manager asked me.

"Well...let's see if we can improve things without first – I'll have a chat with her and let you know," I replied.

It was interesting how Philippa, the manager, immediately suggested these. Many dietitians, nurses and care staff alike feel that these are the definitive and easy answer in such cases.

"Nutritional supplements" fall into distinct categories. There are those that are promoted in the sports industry, which give serious sports lovers and competitors an instant boost of energy, as well as vitamins and minerals. There are old-fashioned types, such as *Complan* and *Build-Up*, which are powders that can be mixed with milk to give extra nutrition and are useful for the convalescent, or as an occasional meal replacement. These can be bought over the counter at most chemists and supermarkets. Finally, there are sophisticated formulas that are in powdered form (to be mixed with milk) or "ready-to-drink", which are available in little 200ml cartons. These are nutritionally complete and provide a complete meal-replacement. Sometimes referred to as "sip-feeds", these have been designated as medicines and are thus available on prescription "on medical grounds". They come under the category of "Borderline Substances", along with many other special foods, such as gluten-free foods and "elemental" or pre-digested foods. There is sometimes a fine line between a patient not eating because they are "a bit poorly", because of a primary or secondary medical condition, or because they are outright malnourished. Sip-feeds are horrendously expensive: one little carton (200ml), provides around 300 Calories and costs perhaps around £3.00.

Their palatability is questionable; some patients find that the milk-based ones are too cloying and rich, to the extent that they can be overwhelmingly nauseating. For such patients, the alternative would be one that is based on soya as the main protein source, or yoghurt and fresh-fruit flavoured. Even so, the bitterness of the formula can overcome any would-be gourmet delight. Manufacturers of these "supplements" strive to improve flavour and acceptability. Making these drinks very cold before drinking them helps, as does taking them via a straw, allowing for the sweet-detecting taste buds on the tip of the tongue to be by-passed. Sometimes it is recommended that they are frozen to make "ice cream" or a "sorbet", or they can be incorporated into sauces, desserts and baked goods. Tasting a variety of these supplements and trying them in different guises was one of the practical sessions in our training for care staff. Not surprisingly, responses varied from "Ugh! Yuck!" to "Mmm...yummy!" Even so, care staff's taste-buds may be different from that of their patients.

Studies on the subject of sip-feeds and their would-be benefits suggest that compliance is often low. It is not unknown for ward cleaners to find a sticky mess behind a patient's bed, or a wilting pot plant that has been "over nourished". Such misuse, abuse and wastage have enormous cost implications. Further, once these have been delivered to a hospital ward, care home or a patient's home, they cannot be returned to the manufacturer or to the dietitans' office, even if they are no longer required and are still within date and intact. A decision to prescribe them is therefore not made lightly. A rep. for one of these companies, that I used to know, used up his out-of-date supplies on his Clumber Spaniels. Needless to say, they looked decidedly rotund!

Further, their extended and/or irresponsible use in care homes implies that the NHS is subsidising a resident's food costs. The resident is still being charged for food, which is not being eaten. It is therefore desirable to encourage and tempt "poor eaters" with "proper", favourite foods as a first step. Most of us would probably prefer a slice of homemade Victoria Sponge, or scoop of ice cream compared with a drink in a carton. "What do you *really* fancy?" was often one of my first questions to such a patient, or "What is your favourite food?" and we would do our best to make that wish come true. We could accommodate one patient easily with a trip to the local supermarket: all he wanted was fresh, crusty, white bread, butter and jam, which he enjoyed for every meal. After a day or two, his appetite began to return.

Mrs Green and I had a chat and I showed the manager how to fill in the nutrition-screening checklist. Mrs Green knew that she should try to eat more but she said that she felt sick a lot of the time. I rang her doctor.

"Hmm...he agreed. "Perhaps we should run a blood test and see what her digoxin levels are (a drug prescribed for heart conditions, such as heart failure). If they are high, they will certainly make her feel nauseated."

If one looks in the British National Formulary (BNF), the pharmacist's bible, prescribing guidelines for elderly people are given in very small print at the beginning of the book but in practice, I often wondered if these were adhered to. The adult dose could be the same for a strapping gent of 11 stone (70kg), as for a "little sparrow" of six and a half stone (41kg). Not only that, but older people may metabolise drugs differently and, if they are less active, that also has a bearing on the drugs' efficacy and "half-life". Anaesthetic drugs, paediatric and veterinary medications are prescribed on the basis of body weight. This seems eminently sensible for older people too, as does reducing the possibility of adverse reactions and drug interactions, by limiting the range of medications.

With the blood tests back and her medications reduced, Mrs Green looked a lot brighter. Her appetite improved, she was able to take extra small snacks and milky drinks and didn't need the expensive supplements. It was agreed that she should be weighed fortnightly. A regular monthly weighing session was initiated for all of the residents and we made a date for an afternoon's training session for all the staff on identifying malnutrition risk and use of the tool. All in all, a satisfying afternoon's work!

DO SIT DOWN: CUP OF TEA?

Here thou, great Anna! Whom three realms obey,
Dost sometimes counsel take – and sometimes tea.

Alexander Pope, "The Rape of the Lock"

On the whole, home visits tend to be highly enjoyable. One gets to be thoroughly nosey, looking at how other people live, improve one's geography of the area and take time with the patient, without the interruption of angry patients banging on a clinic door, saying "Haven't you finished yet?" and "My appointment was at 3.00 – it's now 3.15!"

Obviously, they are quite time-consuming and expensive – not least because of the travel and consultation time and fuel involved. They are therefore not encouraged. Patients for whom home visits are a must are those who are severely ill or disabled and for whom travelling to an outpatient clinic would be nigh on impossible. My own feeling was that it was also best to see children at home; they got bored in the clinic and one could not always assess their general behaviour, or relationships with their parents and with food in that environment. I was constantly amazed at how pin-neat some of my elderly patients kept their homes. Hating housework myself, I was especially admiring of this. And then there were the others, where it was difficult to find somewhere to sit down, because of the debris covering every available surface.

Usually, I would try to arrange several in the same area and/or visit a care home nearby to make best use of the time but it didn't always work out, because of the urgent need for an early intervention. Running late and realising that I still had two or three visits to fit in before I could finish for the day was enough to make for a heavy heart, and so it was that I would wearily get back in the car and drive off to the next patient. But one's reserves of energy are a constant surprise and the minute one knocks on the door and there is a welcoming "Come in – the door's open," all fatigue is forgotten.

Some of the home visits to elderly patients were more social, than dietetic and the desired objective such as improved health and nutrition, could not always be achieved, whether due to the physical nature of disease, simple old age or non-compliance for one reason or another. This, frankly, was difficult to justify in terms of doing one's job properly, but I argued within myself that holistic care meant just that. A visit for some of these lonely souls meant more to them than textbook dietetic advice, especially if I brought my dog along as well, although this was strictly unofficial. Regular visits meant that one got to know one's patient and family well. This could back-fire occasionally.

The case of Belle and her husband, Maurice, was been described in the chapter on "Tubes and Twiddly Bits". When Belle died, many of us – district nurses, the Motor Neurone Disease nurse, the speech therapist and I – went to her funeral to support Maurice. How he would miss her! Like many spouses who care so selflessly, day-in-day-out, the death of their "patient" hits hard. It's as if they have lost their job as well as their loved one. The routine of care abruptly stops. Suddenly their time is their own and, not being in the habit of thinking about themselves, they don't know what to do with it. Luckily, Maurice had hobbies that he could take up again and a sister in Dorset to visit. I continued to visit him occasionally, when I was in his village; it seemed callous to dump him off my caseload, especially as I still had concerns about whether he was looking after himself. Unfortunately, I could feel that he was getting a bit too fond of me. This was trespassing outside the professional boundaries and needed careful handling!

Lydia was an eccentric old lady to say the least. She lived in a warden-controlled flat that was in a 1960s concrete jungle. The tortuous route to her flat was quite spooky and dark but I knew when I was getting close from the stale, acrid smell of tobacco smoke. Well into her 80s, Lydia was an avid chain-smoker, lighting one roll-up after another, with *Polo-Mint* chasers. A colleague had seen her previously and her case was then passed on to me. I was told she "was difficult". To say she was "a character" was an understatement. She told me that she had been a fashion designer and had worked in Paris. Whether or not this was true, I had no idea, but it sounded very romantic and exciting. She spoke with quite a strong French accent and at first, was quite forbidding and stern. She had been referred because there were concerns about her diet and her weight loss. We went through the usual procedures about her food intake – or lack of it – and it was obvious that, although she had a reasonable appetite and the staff brought her food, her arthritis meant that she couldn't actually access it easily. When I pointed this out, she extended a bony finger towards me: "You are very clever girl!" After that, we became friendly and she seemed anxious to maintain the contact.

She was extremely thin, with bird-like features. Her hair resembled a nest to match and I found out later, when she finally went to a nursing home, that it had not been brushed or washed for years. Occasionally she would smooth some Eau de Cologne through it in a casual deference to personal hygiene. She sat in her chair most of the day or lay in bed with the television on loud. The ceiling and walls of her room were brown from the nicotine staining and the staff were anxious to move her out but she would not budge. The room was crowded with old sticks of furniture, most of them covered with her possessions, old papers and books and so I used to perch on the commode. As she became more frail, she would not even attempt to use her bathroom or the commode but had a bucket by the bed, which contributed to the general *mal ordure*. She had a son who 'phoned and visited her occasionally but Lydia pointed out that she could not reach the 'phone from her bed. I promised that I would get her an extension lead. She was thrilled with this but I then spent sleepless nights imagining her tripping over it and it Would All Be My Fault. I am happy to say that she didn't. In spite of her eccentricities, I became quite fond of her and admired her individuality and her maverick attitude. She loved it when I brought my dog on a visit and would feed her *Polo Mints* galore.

At Christmas I sent her a card, which was a picture of the dog. It sat on her table in front of her, well into the following summer and, at each visit she would point to it, look at me and smile, not saying a word.

Eventually, her frailty meant that she had to leave her flat and be moved to a nursing home, where she had the famous bird's nest cut short and washed and her smoking habits had to be curtailed. She went downhill quickly and died soon afterwards.

It is not all members of staff who enjoy home visits. On one occasion, I had a younger dietitian with me. Kate was nervous of visiting people in their homes and of seeing critically ill or patients requiring palliative care, so she was glad of the company.

We were asked to visit Diana, who lived on the far outskirts of our patch. Diana, Dr Davies, the GP, explained in his letter, had had Multiple Sclerosis for several years, was cared for by her husband and was deteriorating fast.

"Oh," said my boss, who handed the letter on, as Diana lived in my patch, "I expect she just needs a few supplements

COLD TEA AND TEARS

and a bit of advice for her husband – fairly routine."

We made a date over the 'phone with Diana's husband, Tim. He opened the door.

"Oh yes...do come in...nice to see you. Cup of tea?"

We politely declined but sat in the kitchen and chatted a bit with him about Diana's diet.

"Well, I can only manage to get about two pints of milk down her each day and that's really difficult," he admitted sadly.

"And that's it, is it?" we asked, trying not to appear too judgemental.

"She cries if I try more. Perhaps you'd like to see her now? She's in the other room."

Nothing could have prepared us. Neither of us had seen anyone quite so emaciated as Diana. She looked worse than someone out of Belsen. It was the most pitiful sight. I thought Kate was going to faint. To her credit, she remained upright but looked very white.

Diana was also deathly white, with a green tinge. Her cheekbones were prominent, the skin was drawn taut across her face. Her eyes were just dark sockets – expressionless and staring. Her sparse hair stuck out in all directions, dry and without lustre. She wore a simple thin nightdress and through it one could see her skin hanging like gauze off her shrivelled body and cadaverous limbs. It was difficult to imagine the woman she once must have been. A living corpse indeed. I was aghast that she had only just been referred to us. I swallowed.

"Hello Diana..." We explained why we were there and that we had been chatting to Tim. She moaned in response and did not make eye contact.

"Do you mind if we weigh you? It means going in your hoist and we can fix this little gadget on which will give us your weight."

She and her husband agreed but the whole process caused

her so much pain and distress. With each rise of the hoist or movement to her body, she cried out like an injured wild animal. We could only make an intelligent guess in the end.

She was around four stone (25kg).

We made some tentative suggestions about improving her nutrition, explained that we would write to her doctor, shook hands with Tim and exited.

Back in the car, Kate couldn't stop herself and burst into tears. Tears of sadness and shock. I felt more anger than sorrow. Back in the office, we wrote to the GP and set things out as we saw them, recommending that she have a feeding-tube (PEG) put in place as soon as was decently possible. A couple of days later, I had a 'phone call.

"Miss Farmer? Dr Davies here. Er...I've just read your letter...do you think Diana will die if she doesn't have a PEG?" he asked, somewhat naively.

"Well...yes...she's really being starved...she is severely malnourished and dehydrated. All she has is two pints of milk a day...and that's semi-skimmed, not even full-cream. This is only just over 500 Calories..."

We discussed the pros and cons and the ethics of such treatment.

"I really don't think we can leave her like this," I added.

"Well," continued Dr Davies. "There are some other problems that you won't know about and I'd be grateful if you didn't take notes."

My pen had immediately twitched and I reached for some scrap paper.

"Her husband has cancer and not long to live. Diana doesn't know this and that is how he wants it. I don't want to give him more work to do in looking after her than he can manage."

I explained the support systems that were in place for patients with PEG feeding and suggested that perhaps if Diana's condition improved as a result of being properly nourished, it would help her husband psychologically as well as physically.

"OK..." Dr Davies made up his mind quickly. "Tell me what I have to do to start this rolling."

He must have made his case strongly, as the next thing we knew was that the nutrition nurse at the hospital had been notified and within a week, Diana was taken for insertion of a feeding-tube. The rep. from the company visited Tim and Diana immediately to show them how it all worked and the district nurse visited daily. A follow-up visit to Diana showed that she was doing well. Furthermore, her husband did not have the stress or expend a lot of energy in trying to feed her.

Irene had mental illness, which became even more apparent from my observations, when I visited her at home. She was referred to us because she was convinced that she had several food intolerances but she was also rather overweight. Her referral letter suggested that she had Irritable Bowel Syndrome. She was in her 50s and lived with her husband and a cat. Getting to the outpatient clinic at the community hospital was difficult for her and after several appointments there, I rather reluctantly agreed to her request to visit her at home.

One can always get an idea of what the inside of a house is going to be like by viewing the outside. The little front garden was unkempt, with old bits of wood lying around, a hangover from some more energetic DIY days, perhaps. Paint was peeling off the window frames and the door. The windows were grimy and on the inside, what were once white net curtains hung in drunken fashion, owing to a paucity of hooks in the right places.

It looked as if no one was in. I knocked and as the door creaked open, a head that I recognised appeared. A warm, stuffy smell with overtones of stale cooking odours reached my nostrils.

"Come in..." I followed. The lino-covered corridor which led to their sitting room squeaked on my shoes, as they momentarily stuck to the floor with each step; fat, sugar and other by-products of food – cat and human – appeared to be the cause. I eyed the kitchen as we passed by. It looked a dead ringer for some of those on the TV programme *"How Clean is Your House?"* Aggie and Kim would have had a field day! The sitting room was crammed full of furniture and a large Christmas tree. It was July and the Christmas decorations were still up, gathering dust. Papers and magazines were all piled up to the maximum height, after which they would surely topple over.

"Do sit down..." offered Irene. It would have been rude to ask, "Where?"

There was one hard chair on which her bearded, longhaired, ageing hippie-style husband sat. The settee was occupied with more papers and books. Irene squeezed in next to them and I shared the remaining chair with a rather fat black cat. It looked affronted and barely remembered its manners.

"Cup of tea?" offered Irene.

"Er...no thanks, I've just had one before I came out to you," I lied.

It may sound snobbish but the thought of actually touching, let alone ingesting anything coming out of that kitchen filled me with abhorrence.

"How are things?" I started.

"I'm still getting awful cramps," complained Irene, "And I think I'm now allergic to citric acid. Here...look..." She had indeed done an amazing amount of research, obtaining as many booklets on health supplements, intolerances, allergies, herbal and homeopathic treatments as she could lay hands on. For most of this she had physically trawled the high streets for health-food shops, bookshops and libraries.

"See all those foods and juices and things that contain citric acid," she continued, showing me her spoils. "Even my pills from the doctor have it in!"

"What makes you think this is the problem?" To be honest,

I'd never heard of this before but tried to keep an open mind. I was also angry that there is so much "information" that is often not based on sound science but on anecdotal evidence – and some of that is pretty scarce – that vulnerable people like Irene gobble up in their gullibility and frustration at not having the answer to their health problems.

"Well…I read some stuff on the Internet and it all seemed to fit."

"So…erm…you seem to know so much about this, what would you like me to do?"

"Well…if you could make me up a diet without all this stuff in then I'd be well away and laughing, wouldn't I?" Indeed she would!

I wasn't even sure that citric acid really was her problem and it was tricky to distinguish to what her symptoms were due. As time went on, her weight problem receded in importance and I felt totally and utterly out of my depth. I wanted to help her but discussion with my colleagues got me nowhere. They passed her off as "a basket case" and suggested I discharge her from my caseload. As it happened, I was going to leave the Trust soon anyway and suggested to Irene that she would have another dietitian to advise her. She actually looked quite bothered by this; perhaps she felt that we had "clicked".

To salve my conscience and because it was obvious that she needed help, I suggested to her GP that a community psychiatric nurse (CPN) be assigned to her. At least she could air her grievances that way and hopefully get some guidance.

Debbie had Huntington's disease, or Chorea, as it is sometimes known. She was very young, in her late 20s, and very severely affected.

It is a genetic disorder, the symptoms of which don't often occur until the individual is in his/her 40s or 50s but Debbie was one of the rarities. The effects of the disease in the brain cause uncontrolled, jerky, rapid movements – sometimes dubbed St Vitus' Dance – and because of this, calorie needs are high. However, getting sufficient of these can be a problem, especially when chewing and swallowing are also affected.

Debbie had a devoted band of carers. She loved her "ciggies" and they would light a cigarette for her and place it intermittently between her lips, so that she could have a "drag". She could not speak but managed to communicate her needs through little grunts and squeaks. As the carers got to know her, they were amazingly adept at interpreting these.

My role was to try and check Debbie's weight regularly, to ensure that she was getting enough calories and that the foods offered were of a suitable consistency, so that she did not choke. Some of the research suggests that calorie needs could be as high as 6,000 daily and that symptoms could be improved, if these could be met. The practicalities of this in Debbie's case were nigh on impossible. In spite of the fact that the disease affects mental ability and memory, Debbie was insistent and quite clear that she did not want an artificial feeding- tube.

When I first met Debbie at her house and had fought my way through the smoky atmosphere, she could be weighed in the portable, sit- on scales. Later, her involuntary movements, writhing and spasms became too extreme and, although it was highly unscientific, estimates had to be made on the basis of how well, or not, her clothes fitted. The fact that her weight, although not ideal, was kept reasonably stable was entirely due to the devotion of her carers, who offered her supplement drinks constantly. They all became very fond of her and would take her on outings and holidays. In spite of Debbie's condition, the atmosphere in her little flat was always upbeat and jocular. Cups of tea and cigarettes were always on offer and occasionally I would join in with the former, watching and learning. After each visit, the mandatory letters had to be written to the GP. These were copied to at least seven agencies, illustrating the intensive care that such a patient requires.

"Hi Mary! This is your friendly health visitor!"

I smiled down the 'phone. I was always happy to have a call from Hazel. She was a salt-of-the-earth, practical type, slightly Bohemian in dress, vivacious and friendly, with a lovely smile and sense of humour. We got on well.

"Will you come with me to see Mrs la Grave?"

"OK then…what's her trouble?"

"She's diabetic and is a double amputee. I don't think she's been keeping to her diet!"

"Right – shall I pick you up?" We arranged a time and a place.

"Wow!" said Hazel. "I've never been driven lying down before!"

This was a reference to my new little sports car. It was rather different from the mini-traveller that I had sold on!

What Hazel hadn't told me was that Mrs la Grave was a true Romany gypsy and lived in a caravan on a designated gypsy site that seemed to be on the hard shoulder of the main "A" road through Woodlandshire. As we entered the site, it was obvious that Hazel knew several of the residents, who returned her friendly greetings. Like many travellers, these families made their living by dealing in scrap metal; broken down cars, tractors, metal drums and various kinds of effete machinery littered the area. I confess to being inwardly concerned about my pretty, bright red Triumph Spitfire and was wondering if I would see it again all in one piece!

As soon as we entered Mrs la Grave's van, I was forced to swallow my fears; it was pleasantly furnished and spotlessly clean and tidy. Everything was in its place. Brass hangings shone with energetic polishing. Brilliant, white net curtains gave privacy. Rugs and chairs had been hoovered and the bed, with its ornate cushions and quilt, could have been photographed for

Homes and Garden. Mrs la Grave, large as life, sat grandly in the middle of it.

"What do you think?" she asked me, as if she had read my thoughts.

"It's really lovely," I said sincerely. "You must take great pride in your van."

"Yes…I do," she said simply and approvingly. "Cup of tea?" My eyes flicked across to Hazel. She nodded imperceptibly.

"I'd love one, please." I had no qualms about accepting one in this pristine home.

"I'll call Baptiste. He'll make us a nice cuppa," she said. And we got down to business, discussing her diabetes.

One autumn, the weather had more than a part to play in influencing my visits: the river, which ran through the centre of the city, burst its banks and many roads were flooded. I had a visit planned for the afternoon. The address looked as if it was dangerously near the river. Undaunted, I set off and, in the midst of a flooded road nearby, managed to find one dry patch on which to park. "I can do this I thought – my wellies are in the car!" I reached through from the driving seat to the back and by some exotic contortions, twisting and turning, wriggling and writhing, worthy of a high-earning pole-dancer, I rummaged through the debris that one carries on such occasions, grabbed my wellies, slipped into the passenger seat and managed to change into them, with more complex joint-bending of which I didn't know I was capable. I gingerly opened the car door and tested the depth of the surrounding water. So far, so good. I tucked my notes carefully under my arm and splashed my way towards the block of flats. The water got deeper and deeper as the driveway sloped downwards. As it lapped the top of my wellies, I could see that this intrepid attempt wasn't going to work. Soggy feet for the rest of the afternoon wasn't worth it. Returning to the car, I used my mobile to telephone my patient.

There was no answer. I found out later that she had gone away and not thought to let us know!

I returned to the office through the flooded roads to do the usual follow-up letters, 'phone calls and enter my stats. Bridget came through from the reception area with a steaming cup of tea.

"You look as if you could do with this," she said, as she put it on my overflowing desk. "Don't stay too late with that lot," she indicated to the pile of papers, some of which I had "filed" on the floor. I grinned. There's nothing like a good British cuppa! And now science has proved what we have always known – that a "nice cup of tea" really does reduce stress and anxiety. Never mind the antioxidants and all that stuff! Warmth and comfort are the main ingredients that soothe ruffled feathers.

"You're a star, Bridget! Thanks." And I drained the lot, while it was still piping hot!

EPILOGUE

Jack Sprat could eat no fat,
His wife could eat no lean;
And so between them both, you see,
They licked the platter clean.
Nursery Rhyme

John Clarke, "In Paroemiologia Anglo Latina"

This is not a book about slimming BUT...I cannot let the opportunity pass without making a few observations.

When I first qualified in the late 1960s, statistics suggested that one-third of the UK population was overweight. 30 years later, it is more than half and predictions suggest that by 2020 it will be 75 per cent. This in itself is bad enough but the "add-ons" are deadly serious.

Everyone has heard of the attendant horrors that accompany being overly fat: diabetes, painful joints and heart disease to name a few. Imagine the extra miles of blood vessels needed to nourish the additional adipose tissue and the load that that places on the pump, namely, the heart. One's body really can be thought of in terms of plumbing, hydraulics and construction. To say nothing of the spin-offs that being overweight has in the shape of excess fares on aircraft; specialised larger beds and expensive tracking hoists in hospitals; strengthened chassis and longer seat-belts in cars; even larger coffins and extra-strong ambulances with special lifting gear, which have been specially adapted for obese patients and can take patients weighing up to 70 stone (444.5kg). Very large hospital gowns have been purchased, which measure two metres in width, in order to give dignity to obese patients. And...there is the effect on crematoriums, where larger furnaces have had to be built in order to deal with larger coffins and the extra fat content of the bodies. Worse, is the possibility that the bereaved families may have to face a "fat tax" of around £40.00 from their local council, which would go towards modernising crematoria in order to cope with the extra demands of the deceased obese.

Hospital admissions for obesity have tripled and surgery for weight loss on the NHS has doubled in two years. Further, obese people need higher doses of antibiotics and are now more at risk of cancer and Alzheimer's disease – scans of the obese suggest that their brains age more quickly. Deaths of middle-aged people from obesity have doubled in a decade. Some local hospitals have banned mothers who are too big to give birth safely and urged them to go to their better-equipped county hospital.

Depression and obesity are linked and even some slimming diets, such as the Atkins diet, appear to lower mood. The list could go on. There is the discomfort experienced by others, as they sit in a train, bus, aircraft or theatre, with their neighbour's flesh unknowingly pressing against them. Even more disturbing is the finding that there are websites in which women can "meet" men who encourage them to overeat. These sites work as dating agencies and explicit fat fantasies are shared. As for rising obesity levels amongst the young...well, just don't get me started on that one!

A health visitor or school nurse often asked me to visit and give advice to the parent of an overweight child. The door would open and Mum stood there filling the frame. My heart would sink: what chance does the child have?

It is an observable fact that children of fat parents tend to be overfed and under-exercised. Suffice it to say that, as I write, there has been a suggestion that obese children should be taken into care. Discussing this possibility a while ago, a dietitian friend of mine pointed out that if a child was three stone *under*weight, social services would be down on the family like a ton of bricks. Three stone *over*weight and we paddle feebly, act over-cautiously, tippy-toeing through the muddied fields of political correctness, scared to get our feet wet and dirty, afraid to take action in case we are sued for not being PC, or for upsetting families or the authorities. Childless couples have found that their requests to adopt children have been refused because they are too fat. I cannot help but agree. It is felt by the agencies that the parents' lifespan could be cut short but, my concern would be for the child's diet, nutrition and welfare. What example is that? How would this couple manage to feed the child a healthy diet?

Health and nutrition messages have never been more ubiquitous. They are everywhere from adverts on television to articles in magazines. There are government health department initiatives, labels on foods, health books and programmes on radio and TV galore pointing out the errors of our food choices.

Something somewhere has gone horribly wrong, especially in the area of taking personal responsibility for our health. Many were the times in the dietetic clinic when I would want to say to patients: "I would love to lose weight for you! But you – and only you – can do this for yourself."

If one looks more closely at what has gone on in the past with seriously overweight patients, there may be a history of non-coping, low self-esteem and all the rest of it. The resulting self-abuse may take over in the form of alcoholism, over-eating, under-eating, self-harming, drug taking and so on, making lives even more miserable in the long-term.

We do seem to be losing structure in our lives, especially during childhood and this seems to go through the generations. One of the funny things about the vagaries of human nature appears to be that the more advice and information that we have, especially with regard to health, the greater we seem to be determined to ignore it.

Reflecting on the obesity balloon, I considered the number and types of different slimming diets that have been popular since I qualified.

Professor John Yudkin (whose car registration was "NUT 1"), was our esteemed Professor of Nutrition at London University (now deceased), who wrote his definitive book, *Pure, White and Deadly*, (Viking, 1972) while we were under his tutelage and devoted his life to proving that sugar was the root of all health evils. In retrospect, his message was the precursor to the Atkins diet.

There has always been calorie-counting for a low-calorie diet and many dietetic hours have been spent assessing a patient's caloric needs and matching the foods accordingly. Then, we had The F-Plan; The Pritkin Diet; The Mayo Clinic Diet; The G.I. Diet; The Grapefruit Diet; The Apple Diet; The Cabbage Soup Diet; The Milk and Banana Diet; Five-Oranges-a Day-Diet; Beverly Hills Diet; Weight Watchers; Slimmers' World; Scarsdale Diet; Rosemary Conley Low Fat Diet; Low Carbohydrate Diet; *Slimming Magazine* Diet; The Dr Hay Diet (*Don't Mix Foods That Fight*); Richard Mackarness' *Eat Fat and Grow Slim*; The Atkins Diet; The Blood Group Diet; Very Low Calorie Diets; The Sacred Heart Diet and then entering the realms of eating and psychology, Think Yourself Thin and so on. I am sure that I have left some out. All have their pros and cons. Not all would suit everyone.

As I write, Ann Diamond, the writer and broadcaster, thinks she has cracked it. Her book explores the problem worldwide and why people, like her, "Yo-Yo" diet, with disastrous consequences.[1] Experts have told her: "It's not your fault but it

[1] Diamond, A. 2008. *Winning the Fat War: Expert Ways to Lose Weight in a Fat World.* Capstone.

is your problem." She argues that government, health services, the food industry, the leisure industry, town planning and architects all need to come on board and indulge in "joined up thinking" to help.

The former Head of the US Food and Drug Administration, a Dr David Kessler, thinks that the blame should rest with food manufacturers for making snacks, cereals and ready-meals of a particular mix of fats, sugars and salt. The pleasure centre in the brain is thus tricked into making us eat more. Our "bliss point" is activated. *"It is time to stop blaming individuals for being overweight or obese"*, he is quoted as saying in his new book.[2] He suggests that we have made a world where food is always available. Not only that, it is designed so that we *want* to eat more.

Hmm...looking back to my childhood meals (admittedly home-cooked) and even into early adulthood, it seems to me that these were loaded with fat and sugar. We had pudding, pastry and/or cake every day. Suet and steamed puddings, meat pies, bread and dripping and sugar sandwiches were our staples. I was about to say that we gorged on butter and, when we could get it, cream. (My mother spent some of her teenage years in Devon, where she discovered the delights of spooning clotted cream, sprinkled with sugar, straight from the pan!) But our perception of "gorged" in those days was moderate in the extreme by today's comparisons. And, I can still remember rationing! We did NOT overeat or get fat. We MOVED more! I respect the fact that Dr David Kessler is an eminent scientist but I feel that there is more to the obesity epidemic than ready-meals and chocolates stirring up a few neurones.

There are cost implications too: in response to the obesity enigma, manufacturers of "slimming aids" and "slimming

[2] Kessler, D. 2009.*The End of Overeating: Taking Control of the Insatiable American Appetite.* Rodale Press.

foods" have made billions out of people's inability to reduce their girth. In 2006, the market value for low fat, low calorie foods was around £2 billion. The slimming foods market as a whole has actually reduced over the last five years to a mere £81 million: manufacturers are responding to this by re-naming their foods as "health foods", based on "natural ingredients", which have an overall health benefit, rather than being specifically for slimming. Add to that the number of slimming clubs and magazines, pharmaceutical and university research, advertisements via the Internet, to say nothing of the increase in bariatric surgery (the number of stomach-stapling operations and similar went up by 50 per cent in 2008), liposuction and the like and we are looking at a multi-billion pound-a-year business, which so far has produced, overall not a thinner nation but a fatter one.

There is worse. It is suggested that Britons "are too fat to work". As of August 2008, over 2000 Brits were receiving incapacity benefit after being diagnosed as obese. They could be costing the tax-payer up to £9.4 million a year in welfare payments.

The National Audit Office reports for 1998 showed that obesity accounted for 30,000 premature deaths and 18 million days of sickness leave.

Bus drivers for some companies have been warned that they must not exceed 23 stone (146kg) on the grounds of health and safety, the driving seats not being able to withstand more than this weight. Until they slim down, they will be re-deployed.

Even the Scotland Yard Police Force is taking measures: it seems that five per cent of our pedestrian plods are overweight. They have been encouraged to sign up to a new fitness drive and join "fat clubs". The canteen, appropriately named "Peelers", will offer suitable foods. Let's hope "Peelers" will take on a whole new meaning in "peeling" fruit and vegetables, or better still, "peeling" off the excess poundage.

There are those for whom maintaining a plumper shape is an indicator of good health. A colleague I met had had cancer but had recovered: she had lost a huge amount of weight when ill, but by the time that I met her she was visibly rotund.

"I'm scared," she told me, "that if I lose weight, that could mean that the cancer is coming back."

This book is not intended to explore why Britain is a ticking obesity time-bomb; rather, I leave you, dear reader, to figure it out for yourself. Suffice it to say, it is a complex subject – a veritable witches' cauldron – a bubbling mix of genetic tendencies; the availability, growth and sales of the food and drinks market; pressures on people through family relationships, work and the media; loss of self-respect and self-esteem; changing lifestyles resulting in the reduction of physical activity and eating patterns; lack of knowledge concerning food values and cooking (in spite of being bombarded daily by this kind of information through the media). There is an overall perception that it "doesn't matter", that external factors are the culprits and an incomprehensible, tangled and bewildering attitude to food has developed.

All I will say is that the plethora of diets (some of which have been tried and not always tested in the true spirit of science), television programmes, articles in magazines, slimming advice and diet books aplenty, simply reflect the ever increasing problem of people getting fatter.

So, you might be tempted to ask, "What about dietitians? Are all of them saints and inveterate healthy eaters? Do they actually practise what they preach? And do they do any good? If there is so much nutrition and slimming information out there, do people need to see a dietitian?"

Of course, I am biased, but I can vouch for the fact that many people do actually find that talking to an expert in nutrition and dietetics not only answers their immediate questions but also gives essential background information about their condition, such as how their medications and lifestyles might affect their diet. Or, how dietary changes alone can actively cure their condition, such as food allergies and intolerances. Dietitians help to dispel the many "foodie" myths and mysteries that abound and offer counselling to help patients improve their eating habits. The snag is that at the end of the day, after being given the necessary information, individuals have to make the right choices. No one can do this for them. Overweight patients are brilliant at putting up barriers to changing their lifestyles. Have they no idea that if they don't make changes, they are leaving themselves open to the serious medical conditions associated with being fat?

Would even the promise of a financial reward be enough? An advisory group for National Institute for Clinical Excellence (NICE) has published a report suggesting that the NHS should pay people to rectify their unhealthy lifestyles.[3] Critics question whether the public purse should be used for "quick fixes" such as these.

Some dietitians have been brave enough to question their role in treating the obese. How refreshing this is! They feel that it is wrong to classify obesity as a medical condition that requires "treatment". Dietetic clinics and waiting lists are overflowing with people who have been referred for "weight-loss advice". There are not enough dietitians: "They are thin on the ground", remember? Should the dietitians in the NHS be using up so much of their precious time on these people and trying to double as psychologists to help people change their behaviour? Shouldn't they use their knowledge, training and expertise in

---

[3] National Institute for Clinical Excellence. 2010. *Should incentives be used to help people quit unhealthy habits? NICE's Citizens Council reveals its view.* Press Release Online. September 27th. Available at: www.nice.org.uk/ newsroom/ pressreleases/ CitizensCouncilIncentives.jsp

concentrating on the associations between diet and health, which affect everyone? More time could be spent concentrating on nutrition education in schools, diet and mental health, malnutrition in the elderly and the intelligent use of nutrition supplements.

The costs to the NHS due to obesity alone are phenomenal. In 1998, this was £½ billion.[4] Estimates for 2001 and 2010 were £2 billion and £3.6 billion respectively. If things continue to escalate at the present rate, this cost can only rise with a considerable knock-on effect to the UK economy as a whole. In 1998, GPs were writing 20,000 prescriptions for fat-busting drugs, costing the NHS £38 million a year. In 2005 these rose dramatically to 880,000. Ideally, we want to cultivate personal responsibility – not encourage the NHS to dish out drugs for weight control.

We hear so much about Britain being a fat nation but in sharp and acute contrast to these statistics, we should remember the costs of malnutrition, especially in the elderly. It is widely and constantly reported that between 25–40 per cent of elderly residents admitted to care homes or hospital are already undernourished. This gets worse after admission and in 2006 the NHS paid out £7.3 billion as a result. This figure has now nearly doubled to £13 billion a year. [5] One cannot put a monetary cost on debility, suffering and pain.

Makes you sit and think, doesn't it?

[4] National Audit Office Online. 2001. *Tackling Obesity in England.* Report by the Comptroller and Auditor General. February 15th 2001. Available online from: www.nao.gov.uk/publications/0001/tackling_obesity_in_england.aspx
[5] BAPEN, 2009. *£13 billion cost of malnutrition must be tackled.* Press Release. February 6th. Available at: http://www.bapen.org.uk/res_press_rel142.html

ACKNOWLEDGEMENTS AND THANKS TO:

Jeremy Thompson and Terry Compton of *Matador*, who patiently answered my many queries.

Patients and staff, with whom I have worked and without whom there would be no stories.

Elsevier, for allowing me to use an Editorial from *The Lancet* (circa 1972), "Everyman Speaks to His Doctor".

The British Dietetic Association for allowing me to use an article, a version of which first appeared in their in-house Magazine, *Adviser* (2001), "Palliative Care and Dogs".

The editor of *AGILITY* (The Journal for Physiotherapists Working with Older People) for kindly allowing me to use material, versions of which first appeared in the journal, *AGILITY*, (Issues: Spring/Summer, 2008 and Autumn, 2008) for the Chapters on Dementia, Malnutrition, Nutrition Screening and the story, "Hip-Hop Knickers".

Dr Max Pemberton for permission to quote from his columns, "Finger on the Pulse", in *The Daily Telegraph*.

Christopher Howse, The Letters Editor of *The Daily Telegraph*, for permission to reproduce relevant extracts.

The Reverend George Pitcher, former Religious Editor of *The Daily Telegraph*, for permission to reproduce an extract from his column.

Tamsin Oglesby for permission to reproduce an extract from her article in *The Daily Telegraph*.

The Warrington Guardian for permission to reproduce a report of the St. James' Church Women's Fellowship meeting.

The Shrewsbury Chronicle for permission to reproduce their report of the Shropshire WI meeting.

My neighbour, Graham Rouse who, through some I.T. wizardry, rescued my document when it disappeared off my computer into the blue beyond. Phew! I am forever indebted!

John Rose for designing a brilliant cover.

Glynis Henville and Sarah Rouse for proof-reading the final draft and for helpful comments.

Stephanie Crossley who gave sound advice on choosing a publisher.

Iain Connor who guided me through the legal language of publishing contracts.

Family and friends who have given encouragement, support and advice:

My brother and his family – John, Sue, Lucy and Tom.

Sue Ely, Hester Holden, Trevor Southey and Ann Thornton, who were the first to read the first scrappy draft and took the trouble to make helpful and kindly comments.

Marilyn Cohda, Hazel Crane, Lesley Curr, Penny David,

ACKNOWLEDGEMENTS

Philippa Jackson-Cox, Jonty Kinsella, Jim and Chri Muir, Sally Parsonage, and Alex Shand, who were all tickled pink at the idea, made useful comments, as well as complimentary and encouraging noises.

A Big "Thank You" to all.